# The Season

# of the Hedge Gypsy

# The Season

# of the

# Hedge Gypsy

by

## Patricia Young

Verrington
Books

Copyright © Patricia Young 2003
First published in 2003 by Verrington Books
Sunnybank, Old Hill
Whitehall, Wincanton, BA9 8BE

Distributed by Gazelle Book Services Limited
Falcon House, Queen Square
Lancaster, England LA1 1RN

British Library Cataloguing in Publication Data
A catalogue record for this book is available from the British Library

ISBN 0-9542344-0-5

Typeset by Amolibros, Watchet, Somerset
This book production has been managed by Amolibros
Printed and bound by T J International Ltd, Padstow, Cornwall

# The Season

## of the Pheasant

*S*omething in the hedgerow stirred. A spider's web, stretched between stanchions of thorn, shivered and shed a fragile pattern of dew. Something in the hedgerow sighed intimately as if associating with a sudden huff of wind. Had her wellington boots not sucked at the mud, Louise could have been taken for a heap of discarded clothes. The splayed threads of an old brown coat that played host to a colony of parasitic trinkets, a child's broken watch, an inch of silver chain, gave the impression of something swept to one side of the road. Beneath a dimpled beret sporting a badge of plastic holly, her weather-etched face and wooden expression revealed neither age nor experience. Even the brown pigmentation dotting her temples could have been the freckles of youth or the liver spots of ageing. Perfectly still and vacantly staring, her grey eyes reflected no more than the windows of a deserted building, as if the personality that had once looked out of them had fled, leaving behind only a shabby anonymity. An hour ago she had stomped across the wet field, ducked under the spider's web, halted abruptly, folded her arms and remained there like a dusty moth, while time passed unheeded. It was a bolt of sunlight that sent her into ragged flight, pursuing the thought of food along the lane that led to Amwell.

Louise could not be bothered bussing into town. A timetable was no use without a watch and it was a palaver to go delving for change in the stretched womb of her coat pocket. It was more convenient to step into the path of an oncoming vehicle, arms flapping. Arrested by such dishevelled anxiety, motorists would brake, cursing or concerned, to a screeching standstill. 'Amwell,' she would demand.

They might expect payment, the social worker warned darkly but sweetly. Do you understand what I'm saying? Of course she understood. Asylums are trading posts. Sex, chocolate, cheap jewellery and illicit penknives are bartered equally. Undeterred by warnings and driven by the memory of fingers dipping into a newspaper cone of chips she proceeded in her rapid, wooden-limbed way of walking. Salted, vinegared, succulent chips.

A red Range Rover, space-hogging, arrogant, came bumping along the lane. It passed Louise, causing no more than a temporary deflection from the thought of food. Its engine faded, leaving her conscious of diesel fumes and the pattern of its tyres heavily embossed in the mud. She too intruded only minimally on the driver's lofty line of vision, leaving no greater impression than a sudden branch or some other small obstruction in the road. He was briefly aware of an unkempt person scruffily camouflaged against the hedgerow. He had beside him on the front seat a bottle of twelve-year-old single malt. It was there because George was coming to lunch. He had never asked whether it was George's preferred tipple, watching him gulp it down he assumed it was, although that wasn't the reason for buying it. Whisky not only matched his irascible nature, it conjured up grouse moors, beaters, rutting stags and the man's eagle beak of a nose. It was a nose that gave Nye the impression of being overlooked from a craggy height. It implied rarity, breeding and a reminder that he, Richard

3

Nye merely resided at Ebury Hall and certainly didn't own it, not by a long chalk.

Ebury Hall. A sun-splashed June evening, dinner-jacketed gentry, the 'warf, warf' sound of county chat. Matilda Wentworth in her dead mother's pearls, plump and pink like one of the drawing-room cushions, himself bowing and offering a crooked arm. Twenty years later he could still recall how she had looped her arm through his and wafted a perfume toward him that smelt of marshmallow. After twenty years the grandeur of the Victorian mansion had turned to pomposity, gentility to mediocrity. Languid evenings on a croquet lawn were illusory and outnumbered by winter days. Draughts from warped window frames now translated into the cost of having promoted himself, via marriage, to a second-rate estate in the country.

'Amwell!' Louise stood in the middle of the lane flapping her arms. The van braked and skidded, the back skewed by the weight of its load. There had been an accident perhaps? The driver got out, concerned, just as Louise settled herself audaciously in the passenger seat. 'Amwell!' A rancid smell rode on her breath.

'Amwell, you want to go to Amwell? There's a bus due. I don't give lifts, the company don't allow it, see.'

'Amwell,' she insisted, her steel grey eyes cutting through his objection. Her mental condition was evident and he did not trouble to argue. Already a milk tanker blocked the lane behind, the impatient throb of its engine nudging him forward. The driver pulled away with Louise bolt upright beside him.

'I'm not supposed to take passengers,' he grumbled. She

found it convenient to ignore the complaint and stared ahead. They proceeded, she intensely silent and he somewhat discomfited by her presence. It was, he thought, as if a painted puppet rested on the seat beside him. 'You shouldn't go hitching lifts on your own,' he ventured after two miles. "Tisn't safe, me dear—' he meant for somebody like her. He did not speak again until they reached the outskirts of Amwell. He had business in Bishopsgate and wanted to drop her there.

'Dean Street,' she ordered imperiously without taking her eyes from the road ahead. When he told her that he wasn't going any further than Bishopsgate she flung herself back against the seat and screwed her fists in frustration. Not wanting to provoke the frenetic jerking that had halted his van in the lane—somebody might think he was attacking the woman—he drove toward Dean Street. It had the effect of returning Louise instantly to her bolt upright, rigid pose. Her fists, still tightly screwed, rested in her lap. It was, the driver observed, as if a puppet master had suddenly let go the strings that made her work. Halfway along Dean Street he was forced to do another emergency stop when she thudded on the dashboard with the palm of her hand. She flung open the passenger door and left without bothering to close it or to thank him.

Louise had walked three miles out of Amwell overlooking the chips which had sent her there in the first place. It was not until she neared the outskirts of Sandpits that she thought about them again. She halted, drooled, then scoffed rapidly. The last chip slithered down her throat with the grace of a fish down a pelican's gullet when Sir George came round a bend, belching behind the wheel of a Mercedes. The dyspepsia which had inflamed his guts since breakfast was about to be anaesthetised by Nye's fine old malt. Today he was lunching at the Hall.

'You stupid bitch!' he bawled at the woman who leapt, seemingly out of the hedge, into the middle of the lane where she stood flapping her arms like a demented crow. She crossed to the passenger door, tried it and, finding it locked, took to mouthing strenuously through the window. He lowered it.

'Sandpits, I want to go to Sandpits.' Her demand entered the car in a gas of grease and vinegar.

'I'm going to the Hall,' he boomed back exhaling on his own breath the smell of antacid. 'It's only half a mile to the village, you can walk.'

'It's me legs.'

'There's nothing wrong with your legs.' He pressed a button and the electric window sealed out the rest of her curse. He thought he heard 'cunt' and stared straight ahead over his aristocratic beak of a nose. Enraged, Louise curled her fists and rained blows on the bonnet of the car.

'Sandpits, Sandpits, Sandpits,' she drummed in a ferocious rhythm. Sir George sounded his horn and accelerated away with the expression of an irate bird of prey. Louise continued in the direction of the village muttering to herself.

'It's Uncle George, darling.' The ebullient squeal hovered like an irritating insect at the top of the grand staircase whilst Matilda descended heavily. Nye remained aloof on the landing where he could best observe the spectacle of a forty-five-year-old woman hurling her full weight into greeting the guest.

'Uncle George is here, darling.' The mimicry left the corner of Nye's lopsided sneer unheard by anybody below. He often indulged his desire for a little covert sniping at Matilda. Occasionally he got caught out, typically by a female dinner guest. Women, he noticed, were so adept at spotting nuances in marital exchanges. Sometimes recognition took the form of a frown but more often an expression of aroused sexual curiosity. He would smile charmingly and incline his head toward whoever had been clever enough to spot it. If anybody had questioned his compulsive need to bait his wife he would have promptly admitted, I do it for sport. It was a sport that had all the advantages of indulging his distaste for the fetters of marriage whilst maintaining its benefits. Even so he had to be very careful, should she be allowed so much as a peek at his true intentions then the gravy train halted abruptly—the uncle would kick him off the board and the niece boot him out of Ebury Hall. He had accordingly developed the technique of whining around her subconscious with the persistence of a midge on a warm summer evening; move in for the blood and be off before she even started to scratch—if, indeed, she noticed the barb in the first place. Typically, she did not.

Sir George, he noticed, was looking even more dyspeptic than usual. His red cheeks, with their fractured capillaries, were working like bellows as if to relieve the pressure on his heart.

Matilda linked her arm through his and led him enthusiastically to the drawing room where she showered him with superlatives about her new mare. 'She's absolutely super—lots of spirit—' drifted back to Nye loitering on the landing. 'Oh do come down, Richard, Uncle George is here.'

He had already decided to remain obstinately aloft then descend in his own good time. Unlike Matilda's new mare he would deliberately balk at the first hurdle, in order to throw the rider. The ploy was one of a collection that he had added to over twenty years of married life and served to demonstrate who was Grand Master of the interactive game. Five measured minutes elapsed before he entered the drawing room with his hand extended.

'George!'

'Dickie!' Their ritual hand pumping was superfluous since they had been together in a board meeting the previous evening. 'Bloody woman!' Sir George exploded.

'There was this dreadful woman in our lane...' Matilda barged into the narrative.

'She had a screw loose,' Sir George elaborated. 'They shouldn't be allowed out. Cheeky bitch wanted to be taken to Sandpits. I told her I was going to the Hall, she could walk half a mile into the village. Put a dent in the bonnet of the car.'

Loose folds of flesh quivered beneath the man's chin reminding Nye of the flabby jowls of a Boxer dog. There had been a time when Nye found George's bullish habit of hunching his shoulders and craning his neck extremely intimidating. These days, with his place on the board assured and his marriage drearily secure, he found the square-chinned belligerence rather reassuring. It was a solid milestone marking how far he had come in life.

'You had better pour your poor uncle another drink.' Nye regarded Matilda through a whisky tumbler, its undulating surface magnified and distorted her wonderfully. Subliminally conscious of his surveillance her hand patted at her hair. Otherwise she was ignorant of his subversive game. It was only one means of distorting her image. Another, more amusing since it was achieved publicly, was a simple entertainment that involved mimicking her vocabulary. Her lexicon which had hardly been added to since her hockey-playing boarding-school days, provided him with a stock of silly exclamations and tired superlatives which he returned with barbs attached.

What do you think of my new togs?

Gosh, stunning, absolutely fabulous, were often cited at her frequently inappropriate and ill-fitting choice. Why, he wondered, had she succumbed so easily to this entrapment in his nasty little hall of mirrors without finding the realities of their relationship reflected there? She was like a hen with its head poking through chicken wire brainlessly assuming that where its thoughts went its body was sure to follow. Why didn't she stop heaving her bulk into his life and recognise that there was no room for her there? His gaze fell on a glass showcase in the corner of the room. It contained a ghastly Victorian tableau of a stuffed fox with glistening glass eyes. Its lip curled in contempt at a cornered pheasant whose outstretched wings were about to embrace flight. A fox and a pheasant, how analogous it was to their marriage—two characters trapped in a suspended narrative.

'Oh I love this time of the year, the beginning of the season. Don't you remember, Uncle… Mummy, Daddy, you and Auntie Beth? Mummy used to look absolutely stunning on a horse.'

Nye stared out of the drawing-room window noting the way autumn leaves glued themselves wetly to the sodden croquet lawn. The November afternoon, pregnant with grey moisture, wrapped itself around his mood.

'You love the beginning of the season too, don't you?' There she went again, peck-pecking at his likes and preferences, trying to find something to please him. He did not reply, but confessed to himself that indeed he did—the field was the only place where he and his wife's uncle met on equal terms.

'Bloody woman!' The old boy was still massaging his indignation over the incident in the lane. He had not even been lured away from the topic by evocations of hunt seasons past. 'I told her straight, "You can walk, it's only half a mile. There's nothing wrong with your legs." They shouldn't be allowed to pester the public like that.'

Matilda had started to feed herself hungrily from a plate of canapés. Nye observed her, amused now by the gluttony that used to disgust him. 'Help yourself, George, before they disappear. Matilda appears to have requisitioned the canapés.'

Louise slept in an old caravan that rested on four pillars of crumbling brick in a ramshackle corner of the field. Tear-stained by algae, embraced by barbed arms of bramble, it was little more than an outgrowth of its surroundings. A key to the lopsided dwelling was left unused and rusting under an upturned flowerpot. With no property to steal, what was the point of locking the door? The five-bar gate guarding the entrance to the field, however, was left locked. Infrequently the farmer would apply oil to the padlock that secured a rusty chain and commit a piece of irreparable farm equipment, corpse-like, to its final resting place.

Across this burial ground metal teeth and protruding limbs were beginning to take on the historic and sombre presence of museum pieces. Louise came and went through a gap in the hedge, her exits and entrances hidden from public view as was her Spartan shelter. She did not undertake any housework, being content to tread in liberal amounts of dirt. Leaves and cobwebs became artefacts by proxy since no personal possessions were to be found indoors that might indicate who she was and where she had been. Even the three jam jars on a shelf, two of them containing a little money and each labelled with a letter, had not been put there by herself.

Money for gas, money for food and money for fares. Remember, GFF. Her social worker had attempted to impose order on her vagrant lifestyle, an order which Louise promptly sabotaged by removing the money from the jar marked G and distributing it randomly between the other two. She did not intend using the calor gas because it ignited with a small explosion that she found intimidating. On cold nights she would sit hunched outside on an upturned milk crate next to her bonfire. With her thin arms hugging her skinny knees she would mutter at the dancing flames, addressing the illusions that pricked her fears and taunted her with accusations. Only when the flames were reduced to embers, would she retreat indoors to curl beneath a pile of ragged blankets like an animal in a leaf-lined burrow.

Waking at dawn she would set off, walking briskly through the half-light to follow a circuit of rich resources— yogurts left on a doorstep by the milkman, a pint of milk or a carton of fresh fruit juice snatched from the back of his float as he reversed in the yard at Harmers Farm. As long as her social security money lasted she would buy chips from Amwell. When it ran out she would loiter in the car park at the back of The Plume of Feathers, keeping an eye on the kitchen. As soon as Chef's back was turned she would nip in and help herself. An empty plate, Chef's irate face at the window, Louise with her plastic bag walking rapidly along the village street were the ingredients of a tale told frequently.

'It's theft, Louise,' pointed out Clare Bracey, the most recent in a long line of social workers dealing with her case. She had smoothed out the evidential wrappers from chocolate bars and shook the contents of a cigarette packet. Louise denied the charge by vigorously shaking her head. 'Well, then, is this what you're spending your social security money on?'

'Found 'em,' came the terse defence, truth darting out of reach like a lizard under a rock. It was useless to try enticing it out.

'You must accept, whether you like it or not, that removing goods either from the shop, the pub or somebody's house without permission is stealing, not finding.... You need something to occupy your time. The Day Centre, why don't you try joining us at the Day Centre?'

'My day don't need no centre.' Louise produced the same pout she wore when periodically rounded up, like a sheep for dipping, to be taken for a shower and de-lousing. Naked under a coarse white bathrobe she would wait grumbling in a line, together with all the homeless people of the district, whilst her clothes were sent for fumigation, to be returned in exchange for an agreement to take a disinfected shower. She would shuffle off in the direction of the cubicle as if being ordered into a gas chamber.

'If you don't keep yourself clean nobody will want to know you.'

'They'd best keep away then, hadn't 'em?'

They came and went, these social workers, each adding their thoughts to her copious case notes before concluding resignedly that their caring art was ill-defended against their client's philistine logic. They could not force her to take her drugs, eat a proper diet, keep herself clean, so they withdrew, contenting themselves with maintenance doses of human contact.

As for Louise, her day needed no centre since its pattern was determined by survival. Her needs were simple—chips, tobacco and chocolate, to which she was heavily addicted. They were needs that were met by foraging. If they left a social security cheque for her then she would snatch it and be off without thanks. Wherever she went she would return to her territory to sit hunched in contemplation of those things that she loved the best and aggravated her the least. As for other people, they drifted inconsequentially past the bubble within which her thoughts floated. They occasionally tried to communicate, but they might just as well mouth at a goldfish in a bowl for all she cared. A robin's piping song she would listen to, a blackbird excavating amongst the ashes of the night's fire she would watch for hours, indifferent to cold, damp and the passing of time. Only when sleet pock-marked her cheeks would she be driven indoors, or her craving for chocolate lead her to uncover an Aladdin's cache beneath her bed.

Nye was observing the unbridled and compulsive intensity with which his wife ate lunch. The steak had long since disappeared, fat and all. Now the sauce in which it had been presented spread across her plate in a pool of reddish brown. She tore up a chunk of fluffy white baguette then skated it expertly through the liquid creating an S-shaped runnel. She said, apropos of the sauce, 'My one claim to fame.'

'Eating, you mean?' Nye chipped in, wearing an innocent expression. Mid-morning she had been in the kitchen, elbowing Mrs Deeks away from the cooker. She threw shallots into melted butter then sweated them, sweating herself over the rituals of her eating habit. Oh yes, he had the measure of her addiction all right.

'I'm off to the health farm next week,' she continued with her mouth full. Sir George was not impressed and munched on through his own lunch, diverting only briefly to give his opinion of such places.

'Smother them with cucumber and feed them on watercress then charge them the earth. Quite a lucrative business, eh, Dickie?'

'My objective is to lose half a stone.'

'Try eating less, it's cheaper.' Nye placed his knife and fork on his plate with neat deliberation. A third of his own steak remained and the sauce was untouched, so too the bread on his side plate. The message read self control. With uninhibited enjoyment of food, Sir George raised the glass dome over the cheese board—he was going for the Stilton, and the cheese knife fell with the accuracy of a guillotine.

'Fat runs in the family.' A solid portion of blue-veined cholesterol landed on his plate.

'Not on her mother's side.' Nye inclined his head in the direction of the hall where an oil painting of the late Caroline Wentworth portrayed her seated elegantly on a chestnut mare. Tall, slender with her brown eyes as demure as a doe. The resurrected beauty of the dead mother was guaranteed to send the daughter on a bout of compensatory eating. She gulped half a glass of claret then reached for the cheese board.

'I don't know why she bothers,' Sir George continued as if his niece were absent, then dabbed at his mouth with a napkin. His own lunch was over, bar the brandy. 'She is as she is, it's genetic.'

'It's the hunt ball at the end of the month, I assume you'll be coming, George.' Nye's invitation was not a kindly diversion from the subject of his wife's obesity, on the contrary he entertained himself with the thought of it being pummelled like dough at a health farm before being stuffed into an haute couture sausage skin selected for the occasion.

'We've decided to have an animal masquerade this year. I shall be coming as a butterfly.'

'Metamorphosis,' offered Nye cruelly.

'Oh gosh, yes, metamorphosis.' Matilda pounced on the notion, greedy for compliments. Her eyes sparkled brightly in piggy pink folds of flesh.

Sir George stared at the tablecloth and frowned over Nye's gratuitous sarcasm. It was made all the more poignant by his niece's sublime ignorance of it. Granted, he thought, she was not the best of breed when it came to looks, but she was good old county stock and in marrying her Nye had landed at rainbow's end. He had no background to speak of, no money either. He had sprung up from nowhere, using his wits and his ambition to get him where he wanted to be. There was nothing wrong with that of course, but he should recognise that his marriage had secured a decent

career for himself and the estate for his heirs. Marriage to
Matilda could hardly be described as a prison; if it was, it
was a very luxurious internment. If he wasn't happy, then
he should content himself, like a lot of men, with discreet
compensations elsewhere. Personally he didn't give a damn
what Nye did, provided private discord did not reverberate
publicly. As for his niece he just wished she would stop
behaving like a fatuous teenager by throwing herself at a
man's feet for him to walk all over her. She should rely less
on his opinions and try developing a few ideas of her own.
Granted she was not overly blessed with brains, but she had
her talents—she was an excellent horsewoman.

'What do you think you'll go as, Uncle?'

'Good Lord, I've no idea, haven't had much time to think
about it. What about you, Dickie?'

'As it's the beginning of the season I think I'll go as a
foxhound,' Nye smiled a crooked little smile of satisfaction.
Indeed it was the beginning of the season. It was that time
of the year when Foxy put on her rural clothes and rented a
cottage on Milestone Terrace. The field was not the only place
where he and Sir George rode neck and neck. How gratifying
it was to share another man's pleasure behind his back.

'And here's to it,' Sir George toasted, unaware of his
unwitting endorsement.

Just as a brandy glass tilted in the dining room at Ebury
Hall, Louise nipped into the kitchen at The Plume of
Feathers to snatch a hasty lunch—two chicken portions
from plated salads. Having eaten her fill by the time she
passed through the gap in the hedge she threw the leftovers
on the ground.

By supper time, in that same corner of the field, moonlight transformed the cutting edge of a ploughshare into a guillotine and under its ghoulish shadow Old Rogue and Paintbrush met in vulpine combat over Louise's discarded chicken bones. She had just started to gather kindling along the hedgerow when she heard their contact calls, firstly from the direction of Ebury Hall, followed shortly by a reply from Pike's Wood.

Wow, wow, wow! bounced back and forth through the dusk as the two foxes located each other, moving closer together on the perimeters of their respective territories.

I'm here, where are you?

Here, where are you?

Wow, wow, wow! Their sharp barks came closer until they materialised suddenly as elongated shadows, gliding into view under the moon as if into a blue-lit arena. Louise watched them with the fascination of a child at a magic show. On meeting, Paintbrush offered his superior opponent a high-pitched whine which shortly after converted to an eerie shriek of submission. Their vocalisations cut into the frosty night, seeming to sculpt it and fix the stark black outlines of the abandoned farm equipment so that sound and shadow became one. In spite of his submission Paintbrush was still tempted by the smell of the chicken bone with an ample portion of meat still clinging to it. He slunk forward, lusting after it and was instantly met with a rapid cuck, cuck, cuck warning from Old Rogue. Then, as if to a pre-arranged signal, the two foxes locked in a barging contest. Shoulder to shoulder and haunch to haunch they pushed their combined weights backwards, forwards, side to side, partners in a primordial dance, until Old Rogue's greater bulk sent his rival teetering. He took his prize deftly and trotted off into the night.

Arm in arm, cheek by jowl, back, side together, the dancing partners described aitches while moving in a circle around the ballroom to the genteel rhythms of a palm court sextet. A press photographer looked down on the annual event from the mezzanine to capture the portly and the important. He assigned a caption from the top of his head and left. From the same position Nye focussed on the scene through his own lens. Round and round went the hunt ball, the movement of bodies belying the immobility of their masks behind which they gossiped and flirted. A bunny, The Mad March Hare, Taurus, Reynard and Jaws. Sir George sweltered inside an eagle's head which gave him the appearance of a truculent turkey.

'Ya hoo!' Matilda's strapless gown had squeezed her body upward like a tube of toothpaste under pressure. White bosoms spilled generously over the top of a wired bodice. The wobbling flesh at the top of her arm was caught spitefully in the sudden light of a flash bulb fired deliberately from the mezzanine. Metamorphosis had not been achieved by the health farm nor by the butterfly mask. A black plastic proboscis tap-tapped periodically on the head of her donkey partner.

'He haw, he haw,' It must have been Holbrook-Jones laughing through the elongated muzzle of a donkey's head. Nye was particularly amused by the way a suspended carrot appeared to dip into Matilda's cleavage so he recorded that too for his album of the absurd. Sir George's eagle beak was similarly trapped on film. Reynard, Taurus, Jaws, unlikely partners in an unlikely dance. Fingers grasped fingers, sweat mingled with greasy deposits from the buffet. A slender unicorn hovered by the tasty delicacies, its ivory horn and silver mane blending with the smoke-grey silk shift that reached to the ground. Nye kept an eye on a slit at the back of her gown, fancying that at any moment a pretty hoof in a silver sling-back would stamp impatiently, except such fabled rarity did not quite match Suzanne Blinney's reason for being there—Sir George.

Wherever her sugar daddy went 'Foxy' was sure to follow, shunned by the county women and admired by their menfolk, albeit out of the corners of their mouths. She would chat to them politely and, amiably aware of their intentions, would melt away on the appearance of their female partners. She was elegant, stylish and as common as muck. Her fingers glided as if over a keyboard, descending every now and again on appetising choices— she was a cautious gourmet. Deeks filled her champagne flute and grinned wryly. Perhaps she had said something risqué. She left the ballroom and headed toward the conservatory with the champagne balanced on her plate, her unicorn horn pointing the way forward. Nye's own foxhound mask lay abandoned at the bottom of the stairs with a foppish felt ear over its brows. A spiky stiletto heel descended precisely in the socket where his eye should rightly be. Matilda went sailing by with her donkey partner, dragging the mask after her with its felt ears flying behind like two exclamation marks. She discovered the accident with a whoops! and a gosh! Holbrook-Jones stooped like a farrier to lift her foot and pull it free without having made sufficient allowance for his donkey head which butted ignominiously beneath an ample buttock. The sextet played on and the dancing couples flowed like traffic round the obstruction.

Nye retrieved his foxhound mask, checked on the whereabouts of Sir George, and gave chase. In the conservatory his nose led him along a cigarette smoke trail to a dragon tree that grew from a florid Victorian pot. 'Foxy,' he called softly and put on his mask. A narrow, bony foot in a pointed silver shoe twitched with irritation.

'Gawd,' said Sir George's escort.

'Guess who?' Nye's dented plastic muzzle squashed his voice lending it a sinister corner-of-the-mouth tone. Welcome or unwelcome he presented himself and sat opposite to her in a cane chair. In a corner of the room an old black Labrador woke, rose from its basket and turned in a circle, before flopping back to sleep with a disgruntled sigh. Nye studied Suzanne's face, advantaged by the fact that his own remained hidden. Her cupid lips held his attention for a while, they had been traced with bright red lipstick and kissed cigarette smoke goodbye as it left them in little rings that lounged on the air before fading. The gesture gave her a bygone, whimsical look much appreciated, no doubt, by Sir George's generation. Her unicorn mask lay at her feet like a shed skin, although its removal revealed nothing since another identity lay beneath the painted persona she wore to the hunt ball.

'Had your eyeful, have you?' she asked.

'Not quite,' he continued with his studies, noting how tight dark curls, released from the mask, framed her face like sculpted black grapes which emphasised her pert and petite features. Her broad vulpine brow creased lightly in a frown above green elongated eyes which signalled both disapproval and wariness. Positioned by the dragon tree, she left Nye with the disconcerting, yet arousing, impression of being observed from behind a bush. 'Mind if I join you?' Nye removed his mask as if to introduce himself.

Suzanne didn't give a damn whether he stayed or left. She stubbed out her cigarette and selected a biscuit which supported a little pyramid of red caviar. 'It's your house.' She bit into it.

'You look like a million dollars tonight.' He indicated the gown. 'A present from Uncle?'

She did not bother to reply, but continued feeding herself with luxurious morsels, eating with evident relish.

'A little reticent, aren't we?' he persisted.

'Gentlemen don't usually come to me for conversation.' She made the words sound as if they had been spoken by a Lyons Corner House cashier; there was something eminently respectable about her kind of prostitution. Fashions ebbed and flowed, yet somehow she had become stranded in Sir George's generation. She was a thoroughly modern woman and could afford Chanel, yet whenever she wafted past Nye he thought he could smell Paris Soir and face powder. He guffawed loudly, his pretentious baying causing the old black gun dog to grunt grumpily in his sleep. His laughter ceased abruptly leaving behind a theatrical silence.

'One day, Foxy, I'm coming to get you.'

Suzanne lit another cigarette and stared neutrally at the conservatory window that held the black night at bay and reflected the bright lights of the room. When the image of Matilda appeared there she rose to her feet instantly and, with her unicorn mask dangling loosely from her hand, she drifted back to the ball. 'Good evening, Mrs Nye.'

She was acknowledged only vaguely with the same taken-for-granted gesture reserved for staff at the Hall. Matilda's agitation at Nye's absconding from the events in the ballroom was transmitted to the quivering proboscis.

'Ah, Madam Butterfly,' he said.

In a chilly shadow under the hedge the Fox Man sat hunched and listening.

Wow, wow, wow...I'm here, but where are you?

Wow, wow, wow...Here, and you? Closer and closer they came until two vulpine silhouettes met in brief contest then left, delivering parting shots of sound over their shoulders. Cuck, cuck, cuck—came out of the night like ricocheting bullets, their exchanges magnified by the cold atmosphere. A cease-fire came fifteen minutes later after the combatants had returned to their respective territories.

Terence put on his earphones and set off in their wake to eavesdrop electronically on the night-time activities of his radio-tagged subjects. At the beginning of the study they had been merely foxes, but now their individual differences he translated as personalities and those personalities acquired names. Old Rogue, so named because he had aristocratically established himself in the select territory of the Ebury Hall estate. There was something about the audacious creature that evoked picture-book illustrations of vulpine intelligence. One sunset, the sinking gold light splashed vividly on the red brick of the Victorian mansion, offering excellent camouflage for Old Rogue's burnished coat. Above the creature's head a giant variety of blackberry trailed out of his reach along wires. Terence observed through his field glasses how Old Rogue had balanced on his hind legs with an almond-shaped fore paw placed neatly against the brickwork then craned his neck upward towards the juicy berries above his nose. On another occasion he had seen him remove an egg from a pheasant's nest within yards of the gamekeeper and on another take a young pheasant without causing a squawk.

Old Rogue was a mellow gentleman-about-town sort of fox that lived well on the rich pickings of the estate. In his fourth year he was quite elderly by wild fox standards. His lifestyle contrasted sharply with that of his younger rival, Paintbrush, whose strenuous, albeit athletic, attempts to pounce on rodents scored high on style but low on achievement. He had a habit of throwing himself in the air then dive-bombing his prey, the white tip of his tail flashing characteristically. Their territories, Ebury Hall and Pikes Wood, overlapped and aggressive encounters were common.

Terence guessed, from their increasing clicketing vocalisations, that their rivalry was intensifying because of the mating season. The subjects of his study had been having an exceptionally fidgety night which sent him from one co-ordinate to another in order to fix their locations. They must have exhausted themselves because towards dawn, a normally active time, they had decided to retire, which left him shivering on his camp stool whilst waiting for them to wake again. Once the blips and bleeps of their transmissions indicated that neither was moving, Terence attended to his numbed feet and aching joints which had been ignored by the need to concentrate.

His circulation restored, he felt in his pocket for a bar of chocolate when the ragged tenant of the caravan in the adjacent field came bursting through a gap in the hedge, her body tense with fury. She headed toward him so rapidly he instinctively held up his palms in surrender. Only feet away she stopped suddenly as if a power source had been switched off. Although her manic irritation had been triggered by his presence it was not being directed toward him but the sky at which she shook a clenched fist as if at some Olympian presence in the stratosphere. Perhaps she regarded the field as her own and his presence there as trespass.

'I'm sorry…I was just leaving, really,' he offered, since he had no desire to stoke her extraordinary and uncalled-for anger to boiling point. He turned to collect his receiver which was balanced on the campstool. Too late: with amazing dexterity Louise snatched it and held it above her head as if about to smash it to smithereens. Suspended thus the innocent equipment took on the appearance of a sacrifice offered up to the gods. 'Please—be careful…it's delicate.' His appeal in the face of such hostility sounded limp and inappropriate. 'I use it for my work—I need it to track the foxes.' A wave of his hand indicated both Ebury Hall and Pikes Wood.

'Cunt, cunt, cunt!'

Terence wasn't sure which disturbed him more, the cackled obscenity or the shaking of his receiver. Nonplussed he speculated that she might have thought he intended harming the foxes.

'They wear special collars, it doesn't hurt them, they have tiny radio transmitters.' He might just as well have been a witchdoctor offering mumbo jumbo. 'My work helps to save foxes.'

His final appeal put a finger on the right button and seconds later her arm relaxed. She lowered the receiver to waist height, but kept it at arm's length. Terence, still holding the headphones attached to it offered them to her. 'You can listen to them if you like, it's very interesting.'

Louise's previously unfocussed gaze settled on them with an animal wariness. She backed away forcing him to follow at the end of the connecting lead. She in turn took another step away from him. If he took another step forward, they would proceed around the field like this indefinitely. He felt in his pocket for some loose change hoping to offer money in exchange for the receiver, but found none so he held out a chocolate bar instead. Louise's eyes alighted on it with greedy interest and her free hand shot out to snatch it. Terence prudently withdrew the reward out of reach while holding out his other hand ready to take back his property. Louise obstinately clung on to it while attempting to snatch the chocolate from him. Their respective efforts to regain equipment on his part and to win chocolate on hers continued until practicality resolved the issue. Louise, faster in her responses than Terence had judged, succeeded in grabbing the coveted fruit and nut bar. Finding that it was not possible to remove the wrapper and hold on to the receiver at the same time, she thrust it back at him like a child who had lost interest in a toy. While she chewed the confectionary he quickly packed both receiver and earphones into his rucksack and slung it over his back, thinking that if it was out of sight it would be out of mind.

'What's your name?' he asked, sensing that a too rapid departure might be mistaken for escape and encourage her to hurl herself after him. She ignored him and, with a frown of concentration, rolled the silver wrapper from the chocolate bar into a thin cylinder. Her fingers then began to fiddle away at it until it resembled a knot that she then pinned to her coat amongst the numerous other keepsakes. The garment was so cluttered that bits of sewing cotton and safety pins had become as much part of its weft and warp as the original fabric.

'What's your name?' he asked again. Magpie, what else? he answered himself. She had heard the question, comprehended it, yet obstinately attended to the silver paper ornament rather than answer. Nearby a flash of red in the grey dawn light caught her attention.

'Robin Red Breast, that's what I'm called.' There was a little twitch at the corner of her mouth suggesting sly humour. She had snatched at the idea childishly in the same way she snatched at the chocolate.

'It's a lovely name,' Terence flattered. He too had seen the little bird that had been piping shrilly from a hawthorn twig. 'My name's Terence, you can call me the Fox Man if you want.' The title sounded silly, but he felt he could relax his inhibitions in front of this odd little woman. He held out his hand, but she didn't feel inclined to shake it.

'Do you smoke?' The sudden coherence and sociability was as startling as her former hostility.

'Yes...I'm afraid I do, I did try to give up but...'

Louise wasn't overly interested in his efforts to kick the habit so she turned on her heel.

'Come,' she ordered and retreated across the field with a walk reminiscent of a clockwork toy.

As he tramped over the fields in pursuit of his foxes Terence had often glimpsed Louise, although it was always at a distance. Occasionally he succumbed to curiosity and spied on her through his field glasses, focussing on her activities in the way he might focus on one of his vulpine subjects. It was no coincidence that she had called herself

Robin Red Breast since he could plainly see how she would dip and dive along the hedgerow amassing bundles of twigs with the patience of a bird making its nest. She always seemed to be busy and intent on her purposes, her energy consumed by the daily chore. Like her chosen namesake she was defensive about her territory, evidenced by the way she had descended on his intrusion all of a shrill piping and flutter, as if to ward him off and send him packing. He wasn't conscious of holding a particular opinion about her lifestyle, he just assumed that it had been chosen rather than inflicted upon her.

Quite often, when his studies took him to the top of Long Coombe, he would look back and see the blazing light of her camp fire with her beside it, her arms around her knees in a posture that signalled a stubborn self-sufficiency. Don't you go interfering with me, she seemed to be saying. She eschewed convention, stuck two fingers up at the material world which she represented with the worthless ornaments stitched and pinned to her coat. It was as if the normal world still pursued her but in a miniaturised, less threatening way. I will get married by stitching a ring to my coat, I will have authority by stitching a badge of plastic holly to my beret. She was so much at home with the hedge and the field and her camp-fire that he had never thought of her as homeless. Vagrant, unconventional, a little loopy, nomadic, call it what you will, but he had not thought of her as deprived until he stepped through the doorway of her meagre home. It was then that he perceived the extent of her poverty. Although the caravan possessed all the usual domestic amenities—there was even a small WC, taps for running water and a gas fire—it was all decrepit and decaying. The layer of black dust and cobwebs across the surface of a calor cooker had not been disturbed for years. On a shelf he saw caddies for tea, coffee, sugar. There was also a teapot and a whistling kettle, but they were only the unused symbols of somebody else's worthy design.

Without giving much thought to it he reached out and turned on a tap over the stainless steel sink, but no water came.

'Where do you get your water from?' he asked.

Louise's arm shot up stiffly pointing to a standpipe outside that leaned sideways for support against a plank of rotting wood. How many times had he passed the gap in the hedge on winter evenings and felt drawn to the cheerful idea of sitting by her camp-fire? By a camp-fire one could keep reasonably warm. Inside the caravan one could easily freeze to death in the squalid cold. He looked with disgust at a pile of filthy blankets seething with fleas; under these, he assumed, she crawled each night. Out in the field, sitting by her fire, she did not evoke pity. In stepping out of a natural environment into the caravan he had entered the world of human values, expectations about possessions and standards of living. Measured by such yardsticks he found her a poverty-stricken outcast. Indoors, amidst such indescribable squalor she could perish. Terence recognised that whenever he had seen her outdoors he had been judging her by animal standards. Inside, human standards judged her to be disadvantaged, inadequate, unable to cope. Above the all-pervasive smell of a dirty body he caught briefly the smell of tobacco and chocolate as she lifted the lid of a bunk bed and dipped into a cache beneath.

Shivering, he stooped to inspect the calor fire. The gas valve turned freely and seemed to be the only thing left in working order. Even before his match flared, Louise dropped the lid of the bunk bed and rushed past him like a rabbit flushed from cover. When he looked up he found that she had taken off across the field with her hands over her ears. Her flight left him with a feeling that he should not have meddled, it would have been better just to have accepted the offer of a cigarette, smoked it and left. There seemed little point in remaining so he started for home, cold and glad to be on his way. He tried to put his finger on what it was about her condition that dismayed him the most. It was not the dirty caravan which, with a little help, she could have cleaned and repaired, it had been the way she had fled in terror.

'Foxy!' Nye's voice plunged into the cold afternoon, unwelcome. It was as unnecessary as a stone thrown into a placid pond for the pleasure of disturbing its ecology. He sat in a hayloft with his feet swinging idly over the edge and narrowed his eyes through the sights of a shotgun. He saw something move out of the corner of his eye; it was Suzanne in a red tracksuit that glowed briefly then disappeared from a watery pool of sunlight. He aimed at the point where she had appeared, shattered a flowerpot then peppered a metal watering can with lead shot. Rainwater spurted surrogate blood.

'Do you mind!?' A voice, male, middle-class and retired spoke from a potting shed that belonged to a neatly renovated cottage next door.

'Rats, I'm afraid.'

'Try the Environmental Health people, they're quieter.'

Nye placed the gun in the straw beside him but not before sighting it in the direction of the complaint. He waited for Suzanne to come to him. She knew what he was there for, his need was as obvious and protuberant as a bandaged thumb. Beneath him he heard the click of a cigarette lighter, a cloud of tobacco smoke rose up.

'I didn't hear you come.'

'Light on me tootsies, aren't I?' By way of demonstration Suzanne put the lighted cigarette between her cupid lips, faced the loft like a poised athlete then leapt, alighting easily beside him.

'Your talents are unlimited,' he noted dryly although he was duly impressed.

'Not bad for a forty-year-old.' She looked him up and down noting his wax jacket and wellington boots. 'Dressed and ready for sex, are we?' She had a habit of making him feel like a patient at a VD clinic. He searched his repertoire for a quick quip, but found none before she grabbed the edge of the loft and somersaulted expertly over the top to land neatly on the floor below.

'And where did you learn that little trick?'

'I was with a circus—trapeze artiste,' artiste being pronounced in a respectable Essex French.

'And...?'

'And what?' She was going to make him feel obliged for every bit of information he could wring out of her—her biographical details came extra.

'One retired, did one?' he mimicked her accent.

'One left,' she mimicked his. 'My partner had an accident as a matter of fact.' She was as parsimonious with information about herself as she was with her body. Equally aggravating was the way she stood at ease propped against the barn doorframe smoking. Her body was relaxed, her silence was rigid.

'Not very forthcoming, are we?'

'No.'

'It would do you good to talk about it,' he said shallowly.

'It would do you more good to hear about it.'

'So, your partner came down to earth with a bump?'

'She was paralysed from the waist down—now see if you can find something funny to say about that.'

'Oh dear.' Nye dismissed his insensitivity with unconvincing sounds of sympathy. 'And after that?' He pursued the one subject that really excited his curiosity—the history of Suzanne's prostitution.

'They put her in a wheelchair.' She still had her back to him smoking so he couldn't tell from her expression what was on her mind.

'Ah, but what about you?' He tested the limits of her tolerance.

'Mind your own bleeding business.'

'That's what I like about you, Foxy, even your accent sounds as if it's slunk out of an alley.' He felt in the straw for his gun, he wasn't ready for sex. There was something that hung in the afternoon air undissolved, in suspension; it needed shaking up.

Suzanne looked pointedly at her watch. 'Spinning out the foreplay today, aren't we?' She borrowed his idioms in the same way he took the piss out of hers. A tortoiseshell cat presented itself at her feet and began to smooch around her calves. It had appeared as if summoned out of the atmosphere like a witch's familiar. Amused, Nye raised his gun ready to put a pot shot across its bows. 'Meow!' he rehearsed the creature's ignominious flight.

'Put that bloody thing down, can't you?' she snapped.

He ignored her and continued to target her feline companion.

'Tell me about Uncle,' he said as if threatening to shoot it if she didn't.

'No.'

'Does he know what you are?'

'Does he know what you are?'

'Oh yes, that's why he made me finance director.'

'Shush!' The cat fled at a tangent as Suzanne stepped back into the shadow of the barn putting her finger to her lips for silence. From his perch above her head Nye peered irritably through the open barn door that exposed a strange and ragged woman who had halted there. She inspected the dark interior quickly before disappearing. It was as if a magpie had landed there wearing an expression of pert curiosity.

'What the bloody hell!?'

'Shush.' He was silenced again. A minute or so later the same woman paused again by the barn door to nibble on a bar of chocolate. Having disposed of the confectionery with the efficiency of a hungry shrew she then peeled a banana. Her coat pockets bulged with consumable items—fruit, biscuits. She remained long enough to polish off the banana with an irritating squelch before passing on her way without so much as a by-your-leave or thank you.

'Oi!' Nye bawled after her.

'Leave her.'

'Cheeky cow.'

'I don't mind.'

'You don't mind! She's just broken into your premises and stolen your property.'

'Give it a rest, the door was open anyway. She often

comes down here and helps herself. Poor old rag-bag. They call her Loopy Lou down the village.'

'She should be locked up.'

'Why?'

'Because she's a sodding menace. She's the one who attacked George's car.'

'As long as she doesn't attack people, dear, that's the main thing.' Suzanne succeeded in sounding like a school matron applying ointment.

'Try telling that to George.' She merely shrugged her shoulders and went indoors leaving Nye to feel peeved over her amiable dismissal of the crime. Generous and warm-hearted she could afford to be, with Sir George's money. He remained in the loft swinging his legs. He had been thwarted by her shrugging shoulders that said up yours to the world of property and ownership, thereby conveying an irksome moral authority, to say nothing of her indifference to his opinions. Nye wasn't getting very far with Sir George's woman. He pursued her down a series of dead ends, the same dead ends every time they met. A moderately intelligent creature, such as a rat searching for its food in a maze, would quickly construct a mental map of the journeys it had taken, striking off the unrewarding culs-de-sac. Not so Nye, who had persistently undertaken the same journey only to meet each time with Suzanne's indifference. It was not love he sought; the rewards were not amorous. It was all about pride, personal male pride. He had never met with female indifference before, that take-it-or-leave-it attitude. He had never become involved with a woman who was not passionately affected by him. Even when affairs ended messily after a few short months, Nye was always able to tell himself that if the discarded object of his lust hated him forever, so much the better. That way he would always be in their thoughts. As for Suzanne…well, who cared for the opinion of a whore anyway? What really concerned him was the way she always succeeded in gaining a bit of interpersonal ground and Nye was not the sort of man to tolerate the surrender of territory, however small.

When he thought the time right, he left the loft and sauntered into the kitchen at the back of her rented cottage to find her feeding the tortoiseshell tom, presumably with the same spirit of generosity that she fed Loopy Lou. The creature produced a low obsequious purr before dissolving, tail aloft, into the grey afternoon.

The Nyes' only daughter hunched herself over a music score and penned in a phrase which she had snatched out of the air the moment she heard Matilda shouting for Mrs Deeks. 'Mrs Deeks, Mrs Deeks! Where's Mr Nye?'

How did a woman, as compliant as jelly in the presence of her husband, manage to sound like Boadicea when addressing the staff?

'He went shooting, Mrs Nye.'

'…And Caroline, where is she?'

'She was in the drawing room the last time I saw her.' The other side of the drawing-room door, the piano-player's fingers spread like startled talons and descended to sprint away over the octaves.

Where is Daddy? The question ascended in her mind accompanied by a rapid progression of chords.

I don't know.

When did he leave?

I don't know. Two hours previously her father had left with a game bag slung over his shoulder and a shotgun in his hand.

Cry-baby bunting, Daddy's gone a hunting—ostensibly. She was not a cry-baby bunting, she had given up crying years ago over her father's assignations, the public knowledge of which had caused her intense embarrassment, the private experience intense grief, grieving as much for the loss of her childish belief in fidelity.

Mrs Deeks knew, her husband Eddie Deeks knew and everybody in the village knew, so why didn't Mrs Deeks simply add ostensibly? She should say, He's gone shooting—ostensibly. Everybody knew that because Nye slung a gun over his shoulder it didn't mean to say that he was going hunting. Quite where he went nobody knew, although everybody speculated whilst Matilda sniffed around like a dog in a wood missing the one scent that instinct alone should urge her to pursue. She would sit at home and wait, doleful and pining for his return.

'Where's Daddy?'

'Hmm…not sure,' came the reply from one ostensibly concentrating on their music. Daddy's gone a hunting…Daddy's gone a shagging—some woman in the village. Sometimes she was tempted to lance her mother's festering naïveté with truth-telling and get rid of that pustular growth of infidelity at one fell swoop. It would hurt for a while whilst it was healing, it might even leave behind a little scar tissue, but at least it would be gone.

Matilda closed the door and left in a bit of a fret over Nye's whereabouts. He wasn't normally this late when he went shooting so she headed off for the kitchen. It was the memory of her mother's footsteps in the hall outside rather than the actual sound of them that hooked at Caroline's conscience. The possibility that her own knowledge might be a form of complicity sent her to follow. On entering the kitchen she did not find a woman betrayed, only a sad and silly wife stuffing her face with a slice of gateau. It was an infuriating act of self-betrayal that eroded pity. She stared at her mother's hunched shoulders which she felt like shaking until all the podge and gullibility wobbled away and what remained were the bare bones of a new person, a woman with pride. 'Really! You're going to a health farm next week, what's the point?'

'Quite right, Caroline.' Nye had entered the kitchen from the garden and stood in the doorway with a game bag swinging from his fingers. The hind legs of a dead rabbit dangled over the edge, the white flash of its soft tail giving the impression that it had conveniently bolted under cover of the canvas. A small yellow price tag, overlooked by the putative huntsman, told the story as surely as a wagging tongue.

Deflected from further gateau-eating by the sight of game and her husband's return, Matilda jumped to her feet. 'Gosh! I forgot, Uncle's coming to lunch.' She wiped crumbs from her mouth and relayed to the pantry, 'Venison stew with wild mushrooms, Mrs Deeks.' Shortly after Nye's rabbit landed with a bony thump on a pantry shelf. He did not trouble removing the price tag since he could rely on Mrs Deeks' silence.

'A successful morning, Mr Nye,' she noted and with a deliberate air snipped off the plastic tag.

'Indeed it was.' He produced his crooked smile that said and wouldn't you love to hear about it.

'...and don't stint on the burgundy.' Matilda's further instruction was muffled by another slice of gateau. 'Lunch is at one-thirty,' she told Caroline who had been listening to the morbid sound of a hacksaw severing frozen meat in the pantry.

Carcasses plucked, skinned, beheaded, gutted, twisted into odd postures, marinated in wine then savoured by tongues that knighted them with culinary accolades that avoided the realities of meat-eating. It was abhorrent to Caroline whose mouth had shut firmly against all but vegetables, eggs and cheese from the age of four. 'Do you mind if I have a snack in my room, I've got a seminar Monday morning to prepare for?'

'But Uncle George is coming.' It sounded like a papal decree.

It was that time of the year when Sir George returned south from the grouse moors and the conversation was what Caroline termed as all bag and beaters. She sat at the table inventing the alternative sport of throwing cushions into the air since it appeared to her to make as much sense as blasting the feathers off wild birds. Sir George tucked into the venison stew with his face close to the plate, his loose jowls seeming to engulf it. It was that time of the year when he traditionally returned to the shires with an entourage of fellow sportsmen, an assured bag of wealthy businessmen and an ever-diminishing circle of aristocrats. It was approaching the fox hunting season, time for him to don his hunting pink and take up his role as Master of the Amwell Hounds. He chomped and sucked at his food, careless about the noise he made, yet showing pernickety concern for the symmetry of his eating as he cut meat into neat chunks and coiled threads of noodle around them. Caroline's eyes remained fixed on her own empty plate—all the time his tongue was thus employed it was not free to criticise. It seemed a suitable time to slip away, but Sir George had taken it upon himself to examine her plate. Pointing his knife at an inoffensive stain of chilli sauce that had covered beans and rice, he said, 'Not going to get fat on that, are you?'

'No.' The reply was polite, but short enough to remind him that it wasn't his place to comment.

Nye sipped his wine, alerted by the developing conflict between his daughter and her great uncle.

'Diet fad.' Sir George's diagnosis left his mouth at the same time as a belch. 'Beans and gravy, no nutrition in that. You should watch the girl's diet,' he directed Matilda, who seemed about to rush off to the kitchen in order to deal with the matter. Since her eating habits had been called to the witness stand Caroline promptly defended them.

'Beans and wild rice provide all the minerals, fibre and proteins needed for a healthy diet.'

'If anything, Caroline is very diet conscious.' Her father had selected the word diet precisely; he always drew his words from a scabbard and tested their cutting edge. Her attention was caught unexpectedly by the fastidious way he had attended to his nails which were clipped short, antiseptically clean and manicured. There was something very cold and self-obsessed about the way he presented himself to the world. With the recognition of that physical fact came another, more shocking understanding, that her father was a provocateur.

'Not dieting like her mother, is she, Dickie?'

Reduced to the third person and handed over to her father for comment Caroline decided it was time to excuse herself.

'She eats with a clear conscience, George,' she heard her father say as she left the dining room.

'What's beans and gravy got to do with a clear conscience?'

'It's what's known as political correctness.'

'She'd better not try preaching political correctness to me!'

How many times had Nye pushed his daughter into the arena armed with only a sling and stone to face her uncle's Goliath conservatism. Although his trouble-making had more to do with a will and a codicil, Caroline sensed his sadistic pleasure in watching the uneven contest. Why did he blame her so? She had no more control over Uncle George's will than he did. On her eighteenth birthday she had been told that, apart from inheriting Ebury Hall from her mother, she would also inherit a substantial amount from her great uncle, subject to an understanding that the Hall would be kept as it was, including fishing, shooting and the continuing right of the Amwell Hounds to meet there.

What had her father to be so jealous about? She had no interest in the draughty old inheritance. Ebury Hall and its traditions was already an anachronism and, by the time she got around to inheriting it, its odd culture would be ancient history. She certainly had no intention of rearing pheasants for the gun nor fish for sport. As for the Amwell Hounds, with luck, they would shortly be voted out of existence. She would dearly have liked to clear the air and discuss the issue with her uncle, but, whatever she did, whether she defended herself against his bigotry or bowed her head to criticism in saintly self-abrogation she would still find herself tripped up by her father's polite malice. It was so subtle that to confront it would be like slicing a shadow with a sabre.

In the drawing room she sat at the piano, dwelling again on her father's fingernails and the way he presented himself. Everything he did was seamless and precise, whether buttering a roll or raising his gun to shoot a rabbit. He had a cat-like grace and a cool, feline concentration would often set his expression to signal he was about to pounce. That was it, that was why her attention had been held by his sharpened nails. His good looks, which she had found admirable as a teenager, now disturbed her. They were so ill-matched with her mother's stocky and bullish appearance, a contrast which her father went out of his way to emphasise. If Matilda overate, he controlled his diet. If Matilda looked a bit matronly, he contrived to look younger and if her clothes appeared a little old-fashioned he would promptly order the latest designs for himself. These days, it seemed, her father troubled less and less to hide his disdain for her. Far from helping to allay her mother's constant anxiety about her appearance and the menopause he deliberately set out to give them a good stir. Such were the eddies and implications behind everything he did, Caroline's visits to Ebury Hall were frequent enough to please her mother and brief enough to avoid a confrontation with her father.

Before lunch Caroline had been composing a nocturne. She had intended to evoke the moonlight and shadows that haunted the Hall after the tensions and the hidden items on the marital agenda had put themselves to bed. It was then that peace became President of the Hall, elected by the hoot of an owl in the park, the bark of a fox, the homely snuffling of a hedgehog beneath the drawing-room window. As a child she had always thought of the notes on the stave as small birds assembled on a telegraph wire, unable to take flight until her fingers touched the keys. Now the intended nocturne struck her as equally whimsical. Beans and gravy, no nutrition in that. She wasn't a child any longer, why the hell should she be forced to defend her own eating habits? Stuff Uncle George's will and sod her father's petty machinations! The nocturne was shredded to ribbons and lay on the floor. A page was turned and on it appeared the title, 'Requiem for Uncle George'; in brackets had been added 'who died from cholesterol and refined starch'. The resultant score was thoroughly modern, discordant and played loud enough to reach the dining room where Sir George had dismissed vegetarianism as faddish nonsense. He had just selected the hunt saboteurs as a suitable subject to go with the port and Stilton when his cheese course was interrupted by a violent crescendo. 'Is that what passes for music these days?'

After a few excruciating chords, Nye heard Caroline's quick steps and the slamming of the front door. The knowledge that it had been his behaviour that sent her pedalling furiously along the drive made him feel only mildly guilty. There wasn't much point in pledging himself to reform because, like an addict, he knew that he would return habitually to the issue of Caroline's inheritance. If Sir George left his money to Matilda, unencumbered by the terms of a trust, all would be well. Five million pounds, together with more capital raised by a consortium, would create a sound business out of Ebury Hall. There would be a golf club, country club and hotel with conference facilities. As it was the place was falling apart and needed an injection of capital now, not when Sir George decided to pop his clogs. There was little point counselling the old boy, he had made up his mind. How a man who had spearheaded a major electronics company could indulge in such financial tomfoolery was beyond him. The only way forward was to make it plain to Sir George that the future of Ebury Hall was not going to be secured by Caroline who was more likely to turn the place into a music centre for vegan asylum seekers or some equally worthy project.

His imprisonment by marriage and the fact that his life was in the custody of his wife's uncle, to whom he owed his job and a place amongst the lesser gentry, also contributed to his urge to bait his own daughter. If only they had produced a boy, a red-blooded rugby-playing male, life would have been more fun, his internment more tolerable riding to the hounds with a youth streaks ahead of the field. First to the kill he would have initiated the boy by ritually daubing his cheeks with fox blood. What had he got instead? A vegetable-eating female, a passive resister, a pale-faced nun of a girl drifting about the place, wearing her silent condemnation of his values like a wimple.

Peter Deeks entered the kitchen and wiped his shoes on the mat with the same measured pace he tackled any task. He placed a basket of free-range eggs on the long deal table. They came from a flock of Old English Game which strutted handsomely around the grounds during the day and were ushered into the coop in the evening. Largely bred for the table they nonetheless produced enough eggs to supply the Hall. The eggs nestled in straw, looking pleasantly natural. Mrs Deeks separated six for themselves and committed the rest to the larder. Her easy retention of what she regarded as her perks made him feel a little uneasy. He never helped himself to anything from the grounds without bringing it to the kitchen first as if by crossing the threshold he registered what he had taken and of what quantity. Although he had been told often enough to help himself to produce from the estate, as part of his remuneration, he did not share his wife's rustic socialism which claimed a right to take as much as would be necessary to make up the shortfall in her wages—a pittance for the hours she put in.

She sat down again heavily and rubbed at her ankles which seemed unusually swollen. 'Give my feet a nice rub, Pete.' She kicked off the black court shoes which Mrs Nye insisted she wore as part of her uniform when serving at table. She groaned with relief as his fingers dug into the soles of her feet. 'That woman's kept me on my feet all morning.' She glared at the traditional servants' bell above the kitchen door. Polite hints had been dropped that it would be so much kinder on her feet if she were not required to walk the length of the house to collect an order then back to the kitchen to fulfil it. It could be achieved simply by installing a telephone extension. The suggestion was not taken up because bell pulls and servants were the way things had always been done. Mrs Deeks had ventured to experiment by not answering the bell, only to find that Mrs Nye picked up a small hand bell which she kept ringing all the way from the dining room to the kitchen, accompanied by a clarion call, Mrs Deeks, Mrs Deeks, climbing the octaves and coming to an anxious finale at the kitchen door. Mrs Deeks did not repeat the experiment.

The foot massage had not reduced the swelling around her ankles so Deeks dutifully filled a bowl with cold water into which Mrs Deeks plunged her feet. 'You should say something,' he suggested.

'Like what?'

'Ask if you can wear more comfortable shoes.' It was a conversation they held regularly that normally ended with Mrs Deeks mimicking the way Mrs Nye's hands tended to rotate inconclusively whenever she was confronted with a problem. Problems would precipitate anxiety symptoms such as nail-biting and gateau-eating and were therefore best avoided. Being something of an amateur psychologist, Mrs Deeks would leave a suitable interval before presenting her own solutions as Mrs Nye's *fait accompli.*

'Did you see Caroline go off after lunch?' she asked.

Indeed Deeks had seen Caroline pedal off, looking very tight-lipped.

'What's got up her nose this time?'

'Well...' She leaned forward as if to address a fellow conspirator. The gossip, which had no direct bearing on Caroline's angry departure, began at mid morning with Mr Nye's return from shooting. Relishing every moment, no detail was spared. Her account began with the way she had deliberately snipped the price tag from the rabbit's foot and concluded with 'A successful morning, Mr Nye?'

'And what did he have to say to that?'

'Indeed it was.' He savoured these snippets as much as his wife. Neither of them cared much for Nye. Not that they had a specific reason to grumble. If anything he showed them more consideration than Mrs Nye, but they simply didn't trust him. He hadn't married for love but to get his hands on a family fortune. When he recognised that it was going to be difficult to wrest it from Sir George's plans for the future of the Hall he set about causing a rift between his daughter and her ageing benefactor. Mr Nye's self-interest was blatantly obvious to all, except to his wife, who remained foolishly convinced of his love for her and his indifference to Wentworth wealth. Moreover the Deeks's speculation found support from the gossip of a stockman from a neighbouring farm who had overheard a confidential conversation between the farmer and Mr Nye about planning permission for a golf course. If Mr Nye ever got his hands on Sir George's bequest then goodbye Ebury Hall, and the park's unique ecology. In would come the so-called march of progress with a battalion of yuppies, golf buggies and squash players. Yes, Mr and Mrs Deeks knew exactly what Mr Nye wanted for the old place and it certainly wouldn't include them any more. Mr Nye would be sunning himself in the Bahamas on the proceeds and they would be out of work.

Mrs Nye they recalled from their own childhoods in Sandpits as the girl from the Hall, a plump Maisy Perisher, shunned by the other children in the village on account of her bossiness and a tendency to burst into tears when it seemed nobody liked her any more. She had not changed a great deal in thirty-five years. Nevertheless, she could be relied upon to stick to her word, her word being that Peter and Brenda Deeks could live in Cartwrights cottage, rent-free, for the rest of their lives and augment their incomes with produce from the estate. In spite of her self-obsessed anxieties, upon which she dwelled without noticing others around her, they felt a kind of loyalty toward her and a pity on account of the way Mr Nye made her look such an idiot.

As for Sir George, they trusted him unreservedly. Granted he could be a bit of an ill-tempered old bigot on occasions, but nonetheless had a passion for the old Hall which had been his childhood home. The Wentworth estate had been divided between two sons. His brother had inherited the Hall and George Wentworth the family investments. It was largely due to him, as Mrs Nye's guardian, following the premature death of her parents, that the Hall was kept as it always had been, providing some of the best pheasant shooting in the county.

Having done with basting his wife's feet with cold water he ditched it outside and returned to finish his cup of tea and catch the end of the lunchtime news, hot from the dining room. 'Well, after that off she trots to play the piano. Thump, thump, thump. "Is that what passes for music these days?" says the old boy.'

In the twisting lane that led away from Ebury Hall cycle tyres made a mind-calming swish on the wet tarmac. Furious pedalling slowed to a steadier rhythm, summoning back the musical notes that Caroline's frustration had put to flight. Anger was such a barren thing, it created nothing, only recreated itself as one hot and resentful thought led to another. It was best suppressed. After all, in eight short months she would be graduating and no longer dependent on any of them. She would be packing her bags and heading for a future that would have nothing to do with Ebury Hall. The future was foreign territory to be travelled with music as her passport. Work, practice, accomplishment would buy her all the meals and accommodation she needed.

Summer after summer through her teenage years, she had grown up watching the massing of swallows over the park, tuning into the swirling sound of their practice flights before they headed south for the winter, and clung to the thought that one September she too would migrate. She had longed for the autumn morning when she would pack her bags and leave for university, turning her back on the appalling memory of her father in the woods shagging a woman whom she recognised as somebody living in the village.

It had been one June morning when her father had set off with his shotgun and she felt an urge to track him along the trail of hints and innuendoes that had been coming to her from a number of sources—not least the eavesdropped information gleaned from the kitchen when the Deekses thought nobody was listening. Initially she had found the idea of stalking her father rather exciting. It was no more than a schoolgirl prank. She was just fifteen and at a stage of subliminal recognition of her father's sexuality. The desire for fuss and attention from him vied with an instinctive standoffishness which arose from an awareness of her own sexuality. She had simply wanted to put the gossip to the test and had not really expected to find anything at the end of the trail, other than a man shooting rabbits.

Had she not heard a woman's voice, local and high-pitched, she would not have frozen, as she had, the other side of a hawthorn bush. Even now the sight of its bridal veil of white blossom in spring brought back feelings of anguish. The muttered greeting was little more than a quick preamble before getting down to the business that had brought them to the wood in the first place. She wanted to creep away but found herself more appalled by the thought of her father knowing she was there than witnessing the indecency. There was no art, no romance, no skill, no pretence even. Her father's trousers dropped to the ground leaving his buttocks exposed beneath a T-shirt. Without further ado his anonymous paramour climbed aboard, her legs wrapped around his waist. The lasting and most disturbing memory of their bizarre gymnastics was the way the woman's bright blue trainers danced on the end of her thin white legs to the rhythm of his jerking groins.

With hindsight she could probably have crept away undetected since her light-footed retreat could never have been heard above the sound of her father going about his pleasure, groaning like a rutting stag.

The months and years passed, ticked off in a diary, a diary that recorded only her personal achievements from GCSE passes to 'A' level results and finally the journey of a fresher bound for university. None of those diarised events, however, had succeeded in diminishing the memory of that bright June morning, nor did any entry refer to it. She tried hard to like him again and took to leafing back through her life to earlier days, to a part of the narrative dealing with the days when she'd learned to wobble around on her first infant two-wheeler, with him in pursuit applauding her success. She tried to recall how he'd taught her to swim, play a decent game of tennis, but the man who'd done that was dead as far as she was concerned and there would be no reconstructing of him in the present. These days, when she came home, it was with a more philosophical frame of mind. People are short-lived, their projects impermanent, their sins and virtues brief, so did any of it really matter? She returned to the Hall with this question in mind and invariably left earlier than planned with it unanswered.

Deeks raked at the fallen leaves covering the feed ride before laying fresh straw for the pheasants. It was a regular autumn task to ensure the stock remained on the estate. If the pernickety birds were forced to search for their grain in a gooey mass of wet leaf mould they would look for better feeding sights elsewhere. He was so preoccupied by the arrangements for the first shoot of the season, that he wasn't aware of Sir George's approach. When he looked up to find the man regarding him at work he had the impression that Sir George had chosen to remain undetected for a moment or two. 'Afternoon, sir.'

'Good afternoon, Deeks.' Mrs Deeks condemned the forelock-touching sir, this and sir, that. She had it on good authority that Sir George was knighted simply because he'd been in industry long enough to be automatically recommended for some sort of honour. She personally saw no good reason for calling him anything other than Mr Wentworth. Since three generations of male Deekses had worked as gamekeepers for three generations of Wentworths, Deeks asserted that good afternoon, sir and good afternoon, Deeks meant no more than affirmation of their respective roles. As far as he was concerned the Wentworths owned and ran the Hall whilst he managed the estate. Deeks took pride in the fact that Sir George and Mrs Nye often sought his opinion and, during a shoot, placed themselves entirely in his hands when it came to the organisation and discipline of the guns once a drive was underway.

Quite often, when Sir George visited the Hall he would take a stroll with Deeks, congratulating him on the condition of the poults, or remarking on how successful he'd been in keeping ground vermin from chewing at the shoots of young trees.Occasionally he would don his plus-twos and a shooting jacket to stroll with him around the traps. Bound by a mutual interest in natural history they would share their observations. Sir George might halt by some pigeon feathers on the ground and point out, 'There's a hen sparrow hawk about.' Deeks often left rabbit carcasses around to see what took them. If the eyes were missing, he would note, 'Some corbies have visited us I think.' If the whole carcass disappeared they would agree a fox was in the wood. Of late they'd been puzzled by the way a rabbit carcass had been eaten but the skin and some bones had been left. Their joint researches led them to a feral cat.

Deeks rested on his rake and both men stood in contemplation of the exposed ride. Sir George, he thought, looked out of sorts. He was a sprightly seventy-two-year-old, well able to ride neck and neck in the field with a man half his age. Today the chin, usually thrust interrogatively forward, appeared to have sunk towards his chest.

'Only a week to go before the first shoot.' Deeks felt inclined to cheer him up.

'It's a busy time of the year for you.'

'I enjoy it, I always look forward to the first shoot, seeing the birds fly high and strong the way they should.'

'Let's hope we'll see a few more.' His tone struck Deeks as oddly fatalistic, particularly as the estate had worked towards building up a stock of wild birds to improve the shooting for the future. 'Well, I must be off.' Sir George straightened his shoulders as if having inadvertently allowed his body to sag with his thoughts.

Deeks returned to laying straw then whistled up the birds as he scattered grain on it from a huge leather satchel. Although the birds had been conditioned to feed when he whistled, which kept them on Ebury territory, they emerged from the wood cautiously, in twos and threes, dominant cocks first. It was a good sign, their instincts were becoming wilder. Tame pheasants didn't make good sport nor hand-reared hens good mothers able to protect their chicks. He left the ride to attend to another, with concern for what Sir George had said pecking at the back of his mind. He asked himself, if push came to shove, would the seemingly benign old captain of industry show as much concern for the conservation of the Ebury Hall gamekeeper as he might for the natural history of the estate? He attended to the next ride assuring himself that the future of the place wasn't entirely in Sir George's hands anyway and that Mrs Nye's enthusiasm for the shooting guaranteed its continuity. Perhaps the insecurity he seemed to be expressing was no more than a shudder at the thought of his own mortality, which must surely beset an ageing man from time to time.

'Tanya!'

'What?'

'It's Caroline.' The arrival was announced from the bottom of the stairs at the front of the house and acknowledged from an upstairs window at the back. There was something operatic about the Tunstalls' communication system, they always delivered their falsetto messages from balconies—the landing, a bedroom window, occasionally the lavatory. Caroline wiped her feet on the mat and excused her way round Tanya's mother who was still blocking the narrow stairway. She found Tanya in a haze of tobacco smoke, examining some incomprehensible samples of rock under a microscope.

'Honeybun!' Tanya leapt to her feet, the microscope rocked perilously, and flung her arms around the visitor. 'It's been ages.' In fact it had only been five weeks since they'd last seen each other. 'Find a pew if you can.'

'I'll do my best.' Caroline shifted the careless deposits of clothing on a sofa bed.

'Won't be a mo.' Tanya focussed the microscope and jotted down some observations in a copperplate hand on a notepad which stood out as an island of neatness in the chaotic room. Tanya's cluttered bedroom, with its strata of bric-a-brac, clothes, second-hand records and study notes hadn't changed since her school days. It occurred to her that Tanya's tendency to pile her possessions on top of one another then proceed to remove them all again was in some way an expression of her desire to study geology. Tanya had come tumbling exuberantly one day into the coffee-stained, smoky milieu of the sixth-form common room at Amwell High. Essentially shy, Caroline latched on to the extrovert teenager, glad to be taken by the arm and dragged around car boot sales, charity shops, gigs and parties. Tanya rummaged through life as if it were a bargain box, ideas, opinions, aspirations flying off in all directions until she settled on *the very thing*. Caroline watched the cigarette in the ashtray continue to burn like a slow taper leaving a snake of pale ash. The room had been a bolt hole during her late teens, somewhere to flee, as far as she could reach, culturally and socially distant from Ebury Hall.

'So, what's new?' she asked.

'Right.' Tanya promptly retrieved the cigarette now reduced to a dog end. 'Some good news. I might, and I stress might, be going to the States as a research assistant—Fargo. I'm going to study fossilised beetles and get paid for it.'

'Is Caroline stopping for supper?'

The enquiry could have come from either the bottom of the stairs or the open kitchen door beneath the bedroom window. Tanya put her finger to her lips.

'Mum doesn't know about Fargo yet. I won't say anything until it's all firmed up, okay?' She flung open the window and yelled. 'Me and Denis will get something up the pub—there's a meeting.'

'It's about time you came in for your wash, Ivor.' A different message was loud-hailed in the direction of the garden where a four-year-old pedalled a tricycle with wheels as wobbly as an ox cart. He followed a dirt track that he had made for himself, skilfully avoiding a glass cloche and inadvertently knocking against some brussels sprouts.

'Mind those sprouts or Dad'll be after you!' A male voice came from behind the garage followed shortly after by the clanging of a wrench on concrete. The child hunched over his handlebars with such frowning intensity it was as if concentration alone would motor him along. On hearing his mother's voice he abandoned his tricycle and de-materialised so his mother re-directed her orders upward instead.

'Tanya!' With the expression of one whose life is beleaguered by the rest of their family, Tanya threw open the bedroom window again.

'What now?'

'Find our Ivor, love, I'm in the midst of cooking.'

'It's all right, I'll go,' Caroline offered, since she could see where the child had hidden himself. She found him work-shadowing his elder brother who stooped over engine parts that had been assembled like ingredients. Some marinaded in cleaning fluid, other bits had been basted with oil. She hovered in the dusk for a while, watching. She couldn't remember Tanya's brother doing anything other than dismantle and reassemble engines and when he went to Manchester to study engineering it seemed a natural extension of what he'd always done. As a teenager she'd been in awe of Tanya's older brother. His colloquial humour had a way of cutting through pretensions which made him so unlike the boys presented to her by her mother as eligible—typically polished, guffawing bores.

'Pass us thik spanner,' he ordered his little brother briskly, then looked up to find his sister's pale-faced friend from the Hall. 'I thought it was our Ivor standing there.' He wiped his hands on a greasy rag and for one uncomfortable moment she thought he was going to shake her hand. 'Long time no see,' he observed, a little embarrassed.

'How do you like Australia?' She referred to his recent holiday following graduation.

'Brilliant, loved it.'

'The tan's worn off.' She felt a bit foolish for saying it.

'In that case I'll have to go back and top it up, won't I?'

'How long have you been back?'

'About a month.'

'What are you doing?'

'Right this moment patching up a Citroën Light 15.'

'I meant workwise.'

'I'm with Starkeys in Amwell, designing bearings.'

'Do you like it?' Again Caroline felt the same necessity to fill the awkward silence.

'It helps to pay off the debts and keep my little brother in Lego, doesn't it, our Ivor?' The child nodded slowly whilst taking covert glances at his sister's friend.

'Ivor...' His mother's voice came searching from the kitchen door.

'I've come to collect Ivor, his mother wants him to wash.'

'Ivor!' Denis relayed the message to the garage over his shoulder and was answered by a giggle. He finished wiping his hands and strode inside to return with his little brother suspended by collar and trouser seat, the child giggled rapturously. Having been set down to wobble unsteadily, he curled his small fists and began laying into his big brother like a punch bag. Recognising that he was showing off for the benefit of the visitor Denis tucked him under his arm. 'You've got to go indoors for your wash, Mum said so.'

'No 'er never,'

'Yes 'er did.' Ivor wriggled and giggled so much Denis was forced to set him down and lead him firmly to the kitchen door. The child turned round to stare with coy curiosity at the pale female who loitered in the dusk behind them. He was, Caroline thought, like a little cloth teddy with a grin on its face—cuddled, thrown over shoulders, dragged bumping through a happy humdrum family life, loved. Denis and his little brother stood side by side silhouetted by the kitchen's homely light. 'Are you coming in or are you gonner bide out there for the rest of the night?'

When Caroline had left the Hall it had been with the aim

of cycling round for a while to discharge the frustration that had built up over lunch. She'd intended putting in an appearance later, for the sake of her mother, before returning to the haven of university and the house she shared with fellow students. Going to see Tanya hadn't occurred to her until she reached the outskirts of Sandpits and felt the same old urge to take cover in the Tunstalls' house. Following the devastating exposure of her father's infidelity, she had become an intensely private person, wrapping reticence around herself like a magic mantle, making herself invisible to those likely to harm her. Having determined never to reveal her friendship with Tanya she was enabled to slip away from the Hall and reappear in the midst of the Tunstall family as if one of them, more than happy to blend in with whatever was going on. When Tanya had suggested she joined her and Denis at The Feathers for a meeting she drifted along as she had done in the past. It had not occurred to her to ask what sort of meeting they had in mind.

They left the house for The Plume of Feathers with Tanya effervescing, bombarding her brother's ears with gossip. She lit a cigarette and created a huge head of steam that seemed to take on its own exuberant character. Denis loped beside her, more interested in the quiet girl who walked on his sister's other side, as if hiding in the shadows of her personality. He looked furtively at her whenever he could, noting the way her hair parted like dark curtains either side of her neck.

The first time Tanya had brought her back to the house she'd been sixteen and painfully thin. She looked on the world with huge brown eyes, wearing the expression of somebody who bore a deep and wounding knowledge. She had always given him the discomfiting feeling that he was being observed, weighed up, which put him in mind of a roe deer camouflaged by the dappled light of a woodland edge—should he move too quickly she would take flight.

When he'd looked up to find her watching him at work in the garage, it was no longer a shy sixteen-year-old observing him but a woman standing there making an open and confident appraisal of him—now it was he who felt like taking flight. Borne on the surprisingly warm October air, from time to time, he caught a painfully delicate perfume, painful because it was recognised briefly then lost, like honeysuckle on a summer hedge.

Deeks smelt the fox long before he caught sight of it, its rank, burnt-toast odour was unmistakable. At first he had put the pheasants' unusual timidity down to the fact that Sir George had been around during feeding. Whereas they would come to him for food, they fought shy of strangers. Sir George, however, had been well out of the woods when he reached the second ride; clearly the birds had sensed danger from another quarter. He could hear the wild stock beginning to roost in the wood, their coughing chatter cutting sharply through the moist autumn air. One of his tasks before returning home for his evening meal was to ensure that none of the hand-reared poults were left wandering outside their release pen. The young birds were now mature enough to take off and roost in the taller hazels within their enclosure. In so doing they would frequently miss their perches and flutter down on the wrong side of the wire. Not overly gifted with brains they would wander round fruitlessly trying to rejoin their comrades on the other side rather than re-launch themselves and return the way they had come. He had found only one or two stranded in this way and ushered them back to safety. It had been sheer luck they had not been snatched by the fox.

Anticipating that it would come sniffing round again he decided to keep the pen under surveillance for a while, and despatch the intruder.

There was a deer seat close by, one of a number he had constructed for culling the small herd of roe deer. They were set well off the ground to avoid the animals getting wind of the marksman when they came to feed and also for safety reasons. High-powered rifles, capable of sending a bullet three miles, are best fired downwards. If the fox did return, he would be able to despatch it by aiming down on it without risk to the poults. Deeks climbed to his own roost where he perched like a king of all the pheasants and waited. Although dark there was sufficient light left to make out the silhouette of a large dog fox emerging tentatively from behind some brambles. 'You cunning bugger,' Deeks whispered to himself. 'You were tucked up in those brambles just waiting for me to go. Well, hard luck, me son because I'm still here.' ''E sees I and I sees 'e and 'e knows I'll be after 'e'—the humorous refrain ran through his mind as he raised his gun.

Somebody else had also raised a gun, Deeks heard the distinctive click of a barrel being cocked. He was surprised the fox hadn't been alerted too. He focussed his field glasses on the woodland to find Mr Nye outlined under an old chestnut tree about to fire. Without further thought Deeks produced the sound of a squealing rabbit. Enticed by the prospect of finding more instant fodder than that supplied by a well-guarded pen, the fox took up a course which led it beneath Deeks's deer seat. Nye lowered his gun and strolled towards the elevated gamekeeper.

'You make an excellent rabbit in distress, Deeks.'

'Sorry about that, Mr Nye. I was a bit concerned that the poults might catch some stray pellets.'

'Were you?' Nye's tone was acid. 'It occurs to me, that since Mrs Nye and myself own this estate, I think we can afford to take the loss of a few poults.' Deeks had no answer, he had been firmly put in his place. 'Good evening, Deeks, enjoy the rest of your vigil.' Nye concluded the brief exchange, not unpleasantly. Mr Nye was never unpleasant, he didn't have to be since everything he said had a sub-text anyway.

Deeks returned to his surveillance of the release pen troubled by the encounter. He had known full well that the angle at which Mr Nye had sighted his gun was such that there was little chance of a pellet straying near the birds, most of which had gone to roost above ground height anyway, he also knew that Mr Nye was an excellent shot. He couldn't quite explain it to himself but he simply hadn't wanted Mr Nye to bag that fox, hadn't wanted him to come muscling in on his and Sir George's domain.

When he got round to relating the story to Brenda over their supper she would probably tick him off and point out that Mr Nye had every right to muscle in. Granted, Mr Nye didn't own the estate but his wife did and a considerable amount of his income went into its costly upkeep. Perhaps he wouldn't relay this particular event to Brenda which, after all, had more to do with his own feelings of insecurity.

He remained perched above the ground thinking that although Sir George had a considerable influence at the Hall, it seemed to him that, as Mrs Nye's uncle grew older, and at times a little frailer, Mr Nye asserted himself more fully. Deeks had no good reason to suppose this had any bearing on the future of the estate, no reason at all beyond a crude animal instinct.

Wrapped in contemplation, Deeks wasn't aware of the return of the fox, which took an investigative circuit of the pen. Finding the birds secure and safely at roost it turned to smaller prey. A wood mouse had come to feed on some grain left on the ride. The fox tensed, made ready to pounce, when a tawny owl dropped silently from the sky. The mouse left the earth with an indignant squeak. The fox sat promptly on its haunches and took to staring, not at the spot from where its food had been snatched, but at those secure and well-fed pheasants roosting above its head. Only yards away from where Deeks had nodded off into a light doze, the fox remained seated like a dog waiting for food to drop under its nose.

Deeks surfaced suddenly from a dream conversation with Mr Nye in which the latter was laying his cards on the table. Not once in his life had he ever done anything so stupid as to nod off to sleep with his finger on the trigger of a shotgun. As he jerked awake to find himself still perched at tree height his trigger finger flexed. The gun went off with a resounding blast of pellets into the ground below.

Pandemonium broke amongst the birds in the pen, one of which took flight and landed awkwardly outside the fence, more or less beneath the nose of the waiting fox which snatched it and disappeared into the woodland shadows. 'Shit!' said Deeks. 'Shit, shit, shit!'

As they ate their way through their bar snacks Caroline became acutely aware of Denis Tunstall's presence. He seemed to her to radiate a confident physicality, both exciting and reassuring. When he'd placed drinks on the table she had to confess to herself that the coy crush she'd had on her friend's brother during her early teens had matured to blatant sexual interest. She was also aware that he too had been indulging in a clandestine appraisal whenever he thought she wasn't looking. When she looked up he looked down and vice versa until their mutual interest in each other took on the choreography of two billing and cooing doves, orchestrated by Tanya's jokes at which they both laughed a little too strenuously. Somebody selected 'Love Letters' on the juke box. Seated in the middle of the more or less empty lounge bar, his groins stirred by the insipid potency of the tune, Denis Tunstall could not have felt more self-conscious than had he been asked to waltz naked in public.

The man responsible for selecting it wandered through from the public bar, his biker's leathers not quite at ease with the romantic thrust of its lyrics. In his early thirties, broad shouldered and a good six-foot-five he dominated the room, his jeans tight enough to suggest the accoutrement of a rampant ram. He gave the young women a brazen appraisal, then greeted Denis. 'How be on, Titch?' He ruffled the latter's hair.

'All right, Bouncer. How's yourself?' Denis replied in the same deliberate colloquial code.

'I expect you've heard about my promotion.' Bouncer turned a chair around and sat astride it like a cowboy in a saloon bar.

'No,' Denis told him. 'I can't say I have.'

'You haven't heard about how they did give I the Sandpits beat?!'

'They never did!'

'The Chief Constable he got on the phone to I and he says, Bouncer, me son, I've heard such good reports about your contribution to the work of the county constabulary that I've decided to award you the Sandpits beat.'

'It couldn't have gone to a more deserving case. Close to home, a decent pub within staggering distance.' Denis grinned.

'It's a gem, it's a gem. There in't a police officer in the country who don't covet the Sandpits beat. One crime per annum and a clear-up rate of fifty per cent.'

''Tisn't bad, me son, 'tisn't bad,' agreed Denis. 'Mustn't grumble.' The genial giant got to his feet, caught Denis by the collar and drew him forward.

'What am I?'

'A fascist thug,' Denis replied promptly.

'And don't you forget it.' Bouncer left to rejoin a billiard game in the public bar singing 'A policeman's lot is not a happy one. Not a happy one,' in a magnificent baritone, breaking off to remind Denis about the next rugby club meeting.

'Honeybun!' Tanya rushed across the bar, arms outspread, to envelop a newcomer. Spikey Longfellow emerged from her voluptuous welcome, blinking in the light of the bar like a hedgehog, his close-cropped hair and John Lennon glasses adding to the impression of a creature that had just emerged from hibernation. Sighting Denis along his snout of a nose, he headed straight for his table causing a strong desire on Caroline's part to escape unnoticed. She had recognised the slight figure and deceptively meek posture of Phillip Longfellow as soon as he walked in. As a former student at Amwell High, some three years younger, she recalled his inveterate zeal for campaigning. The beneficiaries of Spikey's crusades were as diverse as Amazonian tribes whose existence was threatened by illegal logging to the denuded rights of sixth-formers to better facilities in the common room. Whatever the cause, he had always managed to attract a bobbing flotilla of earnest supporters. Having seated himself, tapped some leaflets and notes on the table like a pack of disorderly cards, he focussed on Caroline.

'I spy strangers,' he announced. Having seen the logo on his T-shirt, a huntsman chased by a pack of foxes, Caroline looked at Tanya as if to implore her friend's discretion but it was too late.

'Carrie Nye,' she told Spikey, 'you remember she was in my year.' Spikey put his chin in his hands, an intimidating characteristic of his, and looked into Caroline's face. She imagined his brain whirring like a busy computer searching for the file that linked the name Nye with Ebury Hall. An older man who had entered with him had been beaming on the group members with chubby geniality as if in parental charge.

'Terence.' He held out his hand to Caroline then indicated a tall, lanky hunt saboteur next to him as 'Ned'. Ned had settled on a chair like a puppet with its strings relaxed, one arm over the back. 'Hi,' he gestured vaguely at Caroline. Spikey seemed to have come to some sort of conclusion about the stranger and selected an application form from amongst his papers which he pushed towards her. It was followed by a biro. For one disquieting moment she thought the truth was about to come blushing onto her cheeks and identify her as great niece of the Master of the Amwell Hounds and a resident of Ebury Hall, one of the county's most famous pheasant shoots.

'I'm sorry, Spikey, I only came in for a drink with Tanya. I'm in Bristol most of the time so I don't think I'd be much help. I've got to get back to uni first thing in the morning. Bye, Tanya, speak to you soon.'

Tanya, rebuffed by the sudden exit, was about to protest but was silenced by her brother's foot nudging at her shin under the table.

'Right, the Ebury Hall shoot. Any comments?' Spikey opened the meeting. Everyone around the table had compelling reasons for either supporting or opposing Spikey's proposal to sabotage the debut shoot on the first of October. Denis's were entirely emotional since he wouldn't want to do anything to embarrass the woman in whom he had become increasingly interested. Sabotaging a foxhunt was one thing, trespassing on territory belonging to the family of a woman he fancied was quite another, so Denis Tunstall formulated a seemingly rational argument against the proposal. Pheasants were shot to be eaten so pheasant rearing could be regarded as farming. The birds died quicker and with less stress than chickens reared in poultry factories and were certainly freer than most so-called free-range chickens.

'Numbers in some holding pens are equivalent to factory farms and disease is rife,' Spikey quoted from a leaflet. 'We're talking sport, not farming and that's what the Hunt Saboteurs oppose,' he reminded the newly formed group.

Terence, who knew Peter Deeks to be a good game-keeper, with a genuine concern for wildlife, put down his own marker to the effect that Peter Deeks did everything he possibly could to ensure the welfare of the birds and certainly didn't harass them.

'Of course he harasses them!' Spikey snapped. 'His beaters drive them onto the guns. Most of them aren't killed outright and try to fly on injured.'

'Okay,' Terence agreed, 'but that's not comparable to setting up and hounding a fox to its death.'

Suddenly Ned, one hand drooping over the back of his chair whilst the other played drum majorettes with his pen, dropping it occasionally, came to life. 'Yeah, but.'

The group became silent. Ned vocalisations were rare and often had such an obscure connection with the thrust of the argument they felt they were being invited to search for enlightenment.

'Okay, right,' he continued. 'Welfare. You're looking after the pheasants, right. You build them up to make good shooting, right. Isn't that like saying, okay join the army, meet people then shoot them.'

Terence gave his point polite consideration, nodded wisely and decided not to tease out the strands of tenuous connection between the two ideas.

'I should think a pheasant shoot would be quite difficult to sabotage,' Tanya suggested.

'Nothing simpler,' Spikey told her.

'Yeah, right,' Ned piped up again. 'You put yourself in with the guns, it's what a lot of sabs do.'

'Literally, put ourselves between the guns and the beaters?' Tanya looked horrified.

'The point is,' Terence explained, 'if anybody other than

an approved gun is present at a marked spot at the end of the drive the shooters are ordered to unload their guns for safety reasons.'

'So the shoot would be suspended until the sabs left?' Tanya asked.

'That's the general idea,' Spikey confirmed adding, 'which wouldn't be before the police arrived and went through the formalities. Bouncer!' he called through to the public bar. Bouncer ambled in, chalking the end of his billiard cue. 'How long would it take a patrol car to come out and answer a call, say for aggravated trespass?'

'Not intending sabotage are you, sir?' Spikey shook his head comically. 'In that case,' continued Bouncer, 'it would depend what else was on. On an average quiet day, say from the station, about half an hour.'

'And how long would you have to allow for due legal processes.'

'Due legal processes? Well, it all depends. There are choices, see. I've got long cautions, that's where I speak slowly, and short cautions, that's where I speed up a bit. Charges come in varying lengths, it's all down to consumer choice.'

'Have you got a choice of colours for speeding tickets?' somebody called through from the bar.

'What kind of car have you got, sir?'

'A Porsche,' answered the humorist.

'They come in midnight blue with a smart alloy grey trim.' Bouncer returned amiably to his game.

'Yeah, right, so we could hold up the shoot for maybe two hours,' Ned suggested but nobody else, except for Spikey, looked happy about the proposal. He looked from face to face as if to inject their flaccid reluctance with guts.

'Sorry, Spikey, count me out.' Terence put his palms on the table. 'When you asked me to join the group I was quite clear about my motives. I'll support the sabs against fox hunting to protect the subjects of the Fox Project but don't expect me to headbutt with Pete Deeks. He's given me a lot of invaluable information and even collected samples for analysis. I can't be expected to take on one hand and stick two fingers up on the other. Whatever the rights and wrongs of pheasant shooting, he's a good gamekeeper, one of the best.'

'Yeah, okay, right,' Ned looked as if he wanted to broker peace whilst maintaining an alliance with his principles. 'Shooting for sport, right, we're against it.'

'I'm not convinced.' Terence stuck to his guns. 'I'm inclined to regard pheasant rearing as farming for food and if we want to encourage best possible practice then I'd like to see more Peter Deekses in the trade. That's my position, the rest of you might think differently.'

'Can't we just concentrate on the Amwell hunt?' Tanya suggested. 'If we're going to sab it effectively we need time to prepare. The Ebury shoot's only a week away. Denis is working, I'm back at uni. It's a weekday so Anne and Bob will be working as well. That only leaves you and Ned.'

'Yeah, right, we're not going to do a lot with just two sabs.' Ned came to life again. 'Maybe we could put down some grain, lure the birds off the estate by creating new feeding sites.' Like many of Ned's proposed strategies there was a logic in it somewhere. Terence thought it likely that the birds would return to their established feeding sites in the wood where they would feel safer. It was Tanya who brought the debate to a close by proposing that they suspend any action on the shoots until after the Ebury Hall meet and a vote of three to two settled the matter.

'Right.' Spikey moved to the next item on the agenda. 'Deploying resources on the day of the meet. There'll only be seven of us. Any ideas?'

A single cycle light flitted along the hedgerow. Briefly a hedgehog was caught like a performer in the small circle of limelight then left to forage in darkness and peace. The creature's spines recalled Spikey's prickly obduracy and his ability to focus so single-mindedly on a cause. He had challenged her to join the sabs as if playing a trump card. He knew damned well who Caroline Nye was and where she came from. His underlining of the Ebury Hall shoot in the first item on the agenda had not been idle doodling. What a bonus for the campaign if it had a spy in the enemy's camp. His unspoken message had been, if you're not with us then you're against us.

Phillip Longfellow hadn't changed a bit since his Amwell High School days. He was a politico and saboteur by nature, the charismatic pull of his campaigns having as much to do with a rather manipulative streak in his nature. Nevertheless she embraced his cause wholeheartedly. However much she admired Peter Deeks, indeed he was a gifted amateur naturalist and she had learned a lot about wildlife through him, she still couldn't condone shooting pheasants for sport. The poor things were not that well adapted for flight and they only took to the air when they had to—either to flee danger or to roost at night. Since it was their instinct to seek cover when threatened they had to be flushed out and put to flight over the guns. However good the gun, there was never any guarantee that a bird would be killed outright. She'd seen it for herself, birds grounded and bloody, unable to take flight again, waiting to be despatched. No, she simply couldn't support it, however admirable Deeks might be as a keeper.

As for fox hunting it was abhorrent and nobody could persuade her otherwise. Usually the act of pedalling drew out all the anxieties and frustrations like a poultice, leaving her calm and able to reason, but the frustration discharged by the cycle ride to Sandpits was now building up again on her return—thanks to Spikey. She felt ashamed at not having had the courage to challenge Ebury Hall and all it stood for by filling in the form. Unlike Spikey, she was a placid peace-keeper and always had been. Silence had prevailed over her father's disgusting infidelities. Silence had prevailed over his deliberately public mounting of her mother's submissive intellect in order to peck at it like an arrogant cockerel. She had kept the peace too over her uncle's undue influence at the Hall.

There were times Caroline stood outside of herself, regarding the doe-eyed peace-keeper and despised her. It was consideration of this that almost made her turn around, pedal back to The Plume of Feathers and snatch up Spikey's application form, signing it with such ferocity that her signature would remain ingrained on the pub table. Another more cautious self counselled wait, wait until you're self-supporting and then you can do what the hell you like.

There was music to prepare for a public performance, a performance that if it received a good adjudication would contribute substantially to her CV for the future. Music had to be her priority, not Spikey's campaign. Caroline opened a french window that led onto a small terrace at the back of the old Hall and let in the autumn night. She often composed and rehearsed this way and had done so since childhood. It was as if the open door extended her stage and invited in the hidden listeners in the park to act as her audience.

Nye and Matilda, as she often dubbed her parents, were out for the evening and wouldn't be back until late. She liked the house best when there was nobody there, it was as if the building sank gratefully into slumber. Even the creaks and groans struck her as no more disturbing than the snores of an ageing person at rest. They were known sounds, explicable, now to be caught up in the sonata which juxtaposed nocturnal peace with domestic hostilities. 'Sounds of the House', as she had entitled the piece, had returned to its thematic starting point when car head-lights flickered through the trees along the drive, the Deekses, she assumed, en route to Cartwrights Cottage.

Calm chords, prolonged and controlled, left the drawing room and wandered into the garden where somebody loitered listening. Somebody on the lawn was watching Caroline's body move and sway as if the music were an extension of her innermost and intimate desires. Somebody on the lawn felt enthralled but refrained from approaching, preferring to remain hidden beyond the light cast by the open window and listen from an admiring distance. It was a social distance, too, that held Denis Tunstall at bay and from the midst of the beauty of it all came unexpected feelings of unworthiness. Here was this attractive, hugely talented young woman living on this opulent estate. Here

70

stood Denis Tunstall from a council estate, Denis from a whole line of male Tunstalls who smelled of carbolic and cutting oil. It would take him years to afford such a piano, let alone the lifestyle that surrounded it. If he had any designs on Caroline Nye perhaps he'd better forget it.

He was about to return the way he'd come when the music halted suddenly and a peal of giggles took its place. 'Are you going to come in, Denis Tunstall, or are you going to bide out there for the rest of the night?' Caroline had seen his reflection in the half-open french window. Denis could not have been more startled than had the deer, with which he'd always compared her, emerged from its dappled camouflage and spoken to him.

'I'm sorry, I tried the front door but I couldn't make anybody hear,' he lied. In truth it had been the music which lured him to the back of the house. 'You left this at the pub,' he held up the hunt saboteurs' leaflet.

'I thought you'd come to hear me play.' She pouted like a mademoiselle. Her eyes danced in complicity with his intentions as she sat with her hands in her lap on the piano stool.

'You're brilliant,' he said.

'What did you think of the piece?' she asked.

'Beautiful. It seemed to fill up the whole of the garden.' He hadn't intended saying anything quite so adventurous but it seemed to please her.

'Good, it was meant too. I composed it.'

'Tanya always said you were very gifted.'

'I hope the judges think so, I'm writing it for a competition.'

'Good luck. You deserve to win.' He crossed his fingers feeling a little foolish.

She bowed slightly as if to an audience then said, 'Do you want a drink?'

'I'm driving.'

'Did you bring the Citroën you were telling me about? Can I see it?' Before he had time to reply she was racing across the lawn in the direction of the drive. He caught her up and explained that the poor old thing was looking a bit sorry for herself. Indeed the Light Fifteen looked every inch the survivor of a battle against ageing, with daubs of rust-proofing and filler evidence of her body's need for first aid.

'It's a Maigret car.' Caroline flung out her arms then assumed a suitable character part to match its era. 'Take me for a spin.' Denis willingly opened the passenger door and she stepped inside like a lady. The interior of the vehicle had been beautifully cared for, leather seats in perfect condition and the wood on the dash polished like a mirror.

Denis and Caroline returned through the french windows, Denis chattering enthusiastically about the Citroën, which he was about to spray black to retain its classic looks. Originally he'd thought of selling her but, after all the work he'd put in, he couldn't bear to let her go.

'You mustn't,' agreed Caroline. They hadn't expected to find Mrs Deeks in the drawing room looking at the hunt saboteurs' leaflet with the briefly scribbled message from Denis asking whether she still wanted to join. She appeared somewhat put out.

'Good evening, Mr Tunstall,' she addressed him with ridiculous formality—Denis's father often drank with her husband. Even Caroline, used to the quirky traditions adhered to by the housekeeper, felt there was an icy disapproval behind it.

'Evening,' Denis returned.

'I saw the light on and the french window left open with nobody in, so I popped across to make sure everything was secure,' Mrs Deeks explained. Caroline, who had been looking forward to the rest of the evening in the company of Denis Tunstall, felt like telling her, Now you've assured yourself, you can go. Mrs Deeks, however, didn't look as if she was prepared to leave. Denis, whose own ardour had been shrivelled by his chilly reception, decided to excuse himself. He looked at his watch.

'It's an early start for me in the morning,' he told Caroline. 'Let us know how you get on at the competition, Carrie. See you around.' Mrs Deeks barely looked up to acknowledge his departure then returned to reading some blurb on the back of the application form.

'Thinking of joining?' Caroline asked pointedly, then held out her hand for its return.

'Your uncle isn't going to like it, is he?' Sometimes one small event, be it an expression on someone's face, a gesture, a nuance, can bring personal experience into sharp and shocking focus. Out with the peace-maker and in with the rebel.

'It's none of Uncle George's sodding business, is it?' Caroline snatched the leaflet. Mrs Deeks's mouth pursed into the shape of a cat's arse, thus annoying her even more. 'Nor yours either,' she added, since one might as well be hung for the sheep as well as the lamb.

'I don't need to remind you,' said Mrs Deeks, 'that I don't wish to be spoken to like that. You forget, I've been at Ebury Hall for quite some years.'

'So's the woodworm,' Caroline slapped the leaflet on top of the piano and made as if ready to commence playing. Mrs Deeks exited through the french windows.

Uninterrupted sleep never came easily before the first shoot and Brenda's rapid-fire report on Caroline's impudence inflamed further the sensation of a rash forming on Deeks's already restless brain. He lay awake scratching at the perverse irritation. Usually he was amused by her reportage based on the Hall, her words weaving a rich tapestry of figures frozen into well-known characters. The sheer detail with which she described a sly look in Mr Nye's eyes or a frown on Sir George's brow was an art in its own right. Of late, however, her reports from the house bore so much hint and speculation he was inclined to study them more closely for those items that had a direct bearing on their futures at Ebury Hall.

Brenda had no right to challenge Caroline's interest in the hunt saboteurs and had received a mouthful in response, rightly so. On the other hand the thought of the daughter of the house aligning herself with a group who would happily see himself and the shoot out of business he saw as disloyalty.

He recalled a touching picture of a young girl standing on the ride watching him feed the birds and if he went off around the estate to attend to tasks a concerned, piping voice would call out, Can I come, Deeks? He'd never taken offence at her calling him Deeks, it was simply what everybody else called him, as they called his wife Mrs Deeks. She had never behaved as the daughter of the house nor spoken down to him. On the contrary she would come to the rides and pens like a timid visitor hoping to be invited into his world.

Caroline was now a young woman with ideas and interests of her own which were quite alien to the stubborn and ingrained practices of the Hall; perhaps he understood this better than Brenda did at times. No, it wasn't Caroline's interest in the hunt saboteurs that haunted the sleep-starved night but something more spectral—the future.

The following morning Caroline's fingers descended on the piano keys to scatter the crochets and quavers that had settled far too compliantly into the gentle nocturne composed the night before. Her notes resettled into a quarrelsome and moody phase of the sonata. It swung from the notion of a world asleep under a coverlet of blue moonlight, preferably with Denis Tunstall, to one at war under a blazing complaint from Mrs Deeks.

She sat, fingers poised, ready to compose the next phrase, when she heard the housekeeper's rapid footsteps pass the drawing room en route for the study. Her pace suggested an urgent mission—the reporting of a misdemeanour. Caroline accompanied her with a frenzied arpeggio and added it to the score, thinking perhaps the change from peaceful moonlit night to hostile morning was too abrupt. The piece required some linking passage—what better sound to preamble warfare than tale-telling. She heard knocking on the study door followed by a distant response from Matilda.

Mrs Deeks had served breakfast at nine in a miffed silence designed to pave the way for the complaint that would be served with coffee at eleven. Just as the fluttering arpeggio had been penned, Deeks himself passed by at a leather-squeaking pace. Quite often, when Mrs Deeks wanted to register a complaint it would be done in the company of her husband, since they were jointly employed by the estate and what affected one affected the other. Deeks was never at ease in the house and would move about it like a funeral director. Caroline escorted him to the study with a cuff-straightening funeral march since her reputation, she rather fancied, was about to be lowered into the grave.

Her mother would predictably avoid broaching the subject directly. She would fret for an hour, eat gateau, drink coffee and prepare a speech. Music can be very subversive, she wrote at the bottom of the score.

Caroline had been right. It was at least another hour before Matilda flung open the drawing-room door and presented herself like an agitated prima donna. 'Thornton Holbrook-Jones,' she announced, waving a blank invitation card. She had spent the previous hour alternately fussing with a pile of them and fretting over a lecture on how to speak to the staff. Conflict and confusion rippled over her expression brought about by the problems of attending to the priorities of one issue whilst considering the minutia of the other. The tensions of issue management left her in a no-man's-land of indecision where the brain refuses to resolve anything at all. 'I thought you might like to ask Thornton to the dinner.'

'What dinner?'

'The Ebury Hall Meet dinner, silly.' The dinner referred to was customarily held each year on the eve of the meet. To call it a dinner was to misname it. It was a feast attended by fifty leading lights amongst the hunt supporters who came to gorge on goose stuffed with poultry and game birds, organised in descending size order, the last being the diminutive quail, itself pregnant with stuffing. The guests would eat their way through course after course in grotesque celebration of protein.

'Sorry, I don't think I'll be able to make it this year. I've got to be back at uni the day after Boxing Day for rehearsals.'

'But you must, you must,' Matilda's hands rotated. 'It's the start of the season.'

'I don't want to celebrate the start of the season. I don't agree with it, you know I don't.'

'That doesn't mean you can't come to the dinner. All your old friends will be there. It's going to be super this year. Uncle George wants us to make a special effort in support of the Countryside Alliance. I'll get Mrs Deeks to make you a tasty vegetarian dinner and Daddy can drive you back to your rehearsal after.' Since refusal would only bring on distress and another bout of gateau-eating Caroline relented.

'Okay, but I'm not inviting Thornton Holbrook-Jones, no way.'

'Why ever not? He's so suitable, Uncle George thinks he's very eligible.'

'He can go with Uncle George then. The last time I saw Thornton Holbrook-Jones he'd been eligibly dressed in an ass's head.' Caroline saw a twitch of a smile on her mother's lips. 'I don't think we've got much in common.'

'But...but...you've got lots in common. Uncle George is going to be terribly disappointed.'

Caroline considered a picture of Uncle George's omnipotent opinion rising from an inflated arse to preside over everything that went on at the Hall. She took a pin, pricked it and away it went, air escaping with a satisfying fart.

'Stop snickering and concentrate.'

'Concentrate on what?'

'On inviting Thornton to the dinner. You've got an awful lot to offer one another.' The hint of marriage was infuriating.

'Thornton Holbrook-Jones is ignorant, stupid and boring and when I do decide to marry it won't be to somebody who spends their time poncing around trying to be something in the city.'

'Well, who do you intend inviting?'

'Nobody.' Matilda looked as if about to protest again. 'Mummy, I'm sorry, I'll put in an appearance but I'll have to go back to uni that night.' The truth was she didn't want to be anywhere within the vicinity of the Ebury Meet which Spikey and his sabs intended disrupting.

'Mrs Deeks,' Matilda moved to the matter she had been postponing.

'Yes, I'll apologise to her,' Caroline looked suitably contrite.

'You were rather rude.'

'I know and I promise I'll make it up to her.'

'Were you drunk or something?'

'Sober at the time of the offence.'

'Mrs Deeks felt that the remark about the woodworm was most uncalled for.' Caroline's efforts to bite her lip to suppress a grin failed. 'Who's Denis Tunstall?' Matilda asked suddenly.

'Denis Tunstall is himself,' Caroline replied facetiously to the question which really meant who is this nobody from the village.

It was Stella, one of a pair of Labrador bitches who woke first. She hurled herself at the kitchen door snarling and whining alternately. Her frantic efforts to get out brought Deeks downstairs. Bleary-eyed and dressed in pyjamas, he stuffed his arms into an overcoat and pulled on his boots. He went out into the night with a torch in one hand whilst the other held tight onto the dog's lead. The disturbance seemed to be coming from the direction of the grain bins. Grain for the birds was stored in two huge plastic vats raised above the ground to make it impossible for rats, notoriously strong nibblers, to get a purchase on them and gnaw their way through. The tops were firmly secured by strong metal clips. No other security was necessary since the only grain thieves Deeks knew of were rodents.

The lid of the first bin had been removed and was now lying in the grass. Clearly the intruder must be human. Stella strained at the end of her leash and hurled herself forward as if in extreme frustration at being so restrained. Nonetheless Deeks would not unleash her until sure of the situation. Silencing her, he listened intently until he picked up the sound of light, rapid footsteps retreating through the wood. Whoever it was knew his way around the estate, otherwise he would be stumbling about in the dark, tripping over fallen branches and snaring himself on bramble.

With his torch searching from side to side, Deeks followed the dog along a narrow track carved out by the constant passage of deer, badgers and foxes. It led to a stock fence which had been lifted to allow the intruder to pass under. Whoever it was had disappeared into the pastureland beyond the perimeter of the wood. Since the land belonged to an adjacent farm there seemed little point in pursuing him further. The dog, thinking she had done a good job in seeing him off, now trotted at Deeks's side, nudging at his hand with her nose to seek a pat and approval.

Deeks secured the lid of the grain bin, speculating that the culprit might have been a poacher, but when he gave it further thought concluded it was most unlikely. A pheasant wouldn't be enticed from the safety of its roost in a tree to feed at night. Besides an experienced poacher had merely to pick a sleeping bird off a branch like a ripe fruit, and ring its neck without causing so much as a squawk. Puzzled by the incident, he remained by the bin for a while, just in case, whilst Stella propped herself fondly against his knees. Why on earth would anybody want to pinch grain? There was one far-fetched idea that occurred to him, that it could have been a form of sabotage.

If the incident of the night before had bothered Deeks a little, the behaviour of the pheasants the following morning troubled him deeply. They didn't seem quite themselves when he whistled them up. They straggled onto the ride in ones and twos to peck at their food in a desultory fashion. Such behaviour would normally be associated with a parasitic worm the birds were prone to but no symptoms were evident, if anything they were in pristine condition. A telephone call to Ben Dutton, head keeper on a much larger estate, did not confirm his suspicion that sabotage was involved. The sabs only had to get in with the guns to create havoc, why go to such elaborate lengths as trying to lure the pheasants away from their feeding sites? Granted the tactic might work to a limited degree with pheasants hatched in the wild, but it would almost certainly fail with hand-reared birds, particularly those newly released. Had it occurred to Deeks that if the sabs were behind it they might be employing a psychological tactic?

He must have been scowling because Brenda asked, 'Are you going to share it or spare it?' Deeks decided to share it and told her about his conversation with Ben Dutton. It was her opinion that if this was sabotage, actual or psychological, then it was best countered by putting padlocked chains through the clips securing the bin lids and thus get a good night's sleep.

What Deeks did not share with her was a piece of additional worry, the feeling that he was being watched. As he fed the pheasants he was convinced that somebody in the wood was keeping an eye on him. After thirty years of working in the same environment, he knew what was normal. Sounds that might spook somebody else were as comforting as a lullaby, be it a branch creaking in the wind or a rat making its way towards the grain on the feed rides. Feral cats, he found, were the most elusive watchers. Expert hunters they inched their way undetected towards their prey as silent as stealthy ghosts but they didn't always succeed in passing the corner of Deeks's eye. If he'd been losing chicks to a feral cat he showed it no mercy and if he didn't have his shotgun handy they were evicted from the wood with undignified haste. No, it wasn't a feral cat keeping an eye on him, but something more human. Whenever he looked up, however, he saw nothing but the dappled presence of autumn leaves or a blackbird tenaciously turning the woodland debris for bugs.

A delicious steak and kidney pie enticed his attention from the issue and he tucked in, the first open fire of the autumn dancing in the grate behind him. It was a good time of the year, a fecund time of fruit and nuts and for him the opening of another season, the season of the pheasant. Feeling replete after his steak and kidney pie and a glass of beer, Deeks retired to the fireside with a newspaper. Brenda was on her way to the Hall to make sure it was all locked up since the Nyes were out for the evening. 'Take Stella with you,' he advised.

'Stop fussing. I shall be all right.'

Brenda cut through the woods for the first hundred yards separating Cartwrights Cottage from the Hall, then across the lawn to the back. It was as well she decided to check since the french windows of the drawing room had been left unlocked, yet again. She selected the right key from a huge bunch which serviced the house, stables and other outbuildings when she noticed light falling across the hall floor; evidently someone was in. She had understood that Mr Nye was playing snooker and Mrs Nye had intended joining a meeting of the Countryside Alliance. There were voices coming from the study. Was it blatant nosiness or a sense of responsibility that drew her to creep across the drawing room? She saw Mr Nye on the other side of the hall outlined by a reading light in his study. She had no business to be there. She should have revealed her presence and left him to secure the building for the night but there was somebody else with him and Brenda Deeks had never been one to restrain her curiosity.

She stood breathing quietly and deeply in the dark of

the drawing room, excited by her own subterfuge. She watched Mr Nye pour a generous measure of whisky into a tumbler and hand it across his desk to the visitor who was out of sight behind the open door. He poured another for himself. 'Here's to the shoot,' he toasted.

'Many coming this year?' It was unmistakably their neighbour, Robert Freer who had asked. Freer was a former accountant who had semi-retired into farming on land adjacent to the Hall then discovered it had been an unwise choice—apparently. Local opinion had it that accountants never make unwise choices, being thoroughly circumspect when it came to balancing the books. There was no doubt in anybody's mind that he had bought the land with a view to further development. Whether he would succeed was another matter.

'The usual crowd,' Mr Nye replied.

'Will you keep it going?' Freer asked.

'I doubt it. A pheasant shoot in the middle of a golf course wouldn't be very practical.'

'It would still earn a bob or two,' Freer pointed out.

'Not enough to justify any amendments to our outline plan,' came Mr Nye's opinion. 'I don't think we could afford to give that amount of land to a shoot.'

'What would you do with the pheasants?'

'Oh just let them go wild. Deeks has been building up a wild stock anyway. They would make a charming addition to the golf course.'

'I don't think your gamekeeper would agree with you there. He's been on the estate for thirty years, so I hear.'

'I'm afraid I don't intend to let a gamekeeper stand in the way of the future of the Hall. Have you spoken to any of the others since the last meeting?'

'Not in any detail,' replied Freer. 'I assumed you wouldn't want me to until you felt confident about proceeding.'

'Quite right, Bob. There's a bit of groundwork to be done, not least with the old boy. Which is why we need to be discreet. At this stage I want everything discussed in principle only. Incidentally I haven't even discussed it with Matilda. If George gets wind of any of this we can kiss goodbye to five million. At the moment it's tied up in a trust for the future of the Hall and Caroline.'

'Hardly accessible, is it?' Freer pointed out.

'That depends on my powers of persuasion. He's thinking of stepping down as Chairman to retire. I think he could be persuaded to sell his shares and reinvest the capital in the Ebury project.'

'And you'd be a happy man,' concluded Freer.

'Bob, I would be relieved and delighted if this came off. Caroline would have a sustainable inheritance, Matilda and I could enjoy a prosperous retirement without me having to put my hand in my pocket to keep this bloody place going in the style to which my wife and her uncle have become accustomed. So, all this is still strictly confidential.'

'I accept that but the consortium can't be kept on hold indefinitely, they would want a rough timescale.'

'I can't make any promises,' said Mr Nye, 'but I would hope to get things moving within eighteen months.'

Brenda Deeks's instinct was to confront Mr Nye and tell him what an utter self-seeking bastard he was. Her little bit of domestic espionage had been no more than a petty adventure to provide some juicy gossip to take home for Deeks. Her excitement and curiosity was now replaced by a feeling of utter betrayal. There had been rumours for some years about Freer's interest in developing his land in conjunction with Ebury Hall. The Deekses had only taken it seriously when the issue was stirred up by another so-called overheard conversation. Now the status of that rumour had changed to become as good as fact. She shook so much she was barely able to slip away without being heard.

She left the french window open, as she'd found it, and crept back over the lawn towards the woods. The lights from Cartwrights Cottage glimmered like signals from a safe harbour. In a matter of eighteen months Cartwrights Cottage may no longer be their home. It might be a holiday cottage, or more likely used to house a greenkeeper or golf professional. She swallowed hard against her tears.

A light fell across the lawn and Mr Nye's voice hooked her around. 'Was there something you wanted, Mrs Deeks?'

Normally, when he caught her snooping, it amused him, acknowledging it with a wry grin. Not so this evening. He stood in the drawing room, elevated above the terrace outside, looking like a supercilious Colossus. His tone was icy, so icy that she knew that if he wanted his own way he would get it.

'I came to check the window. I thought everybody was out this evening,' she barely managed to reply.

'You didn't make a very good job of it, did you?' Mr Nye closed and locked the window in a deliberate fashion and drew the curtain across.

Hailed by a text message which began Honeybun, guess what! Caroline left Bristol for Sandpits. Guessing at the content of the good news, she walked into The Plume of Feathers to be greeted by Tanya flinging out her arms and chanting Fargo big apple. Denis stood beside her beaming with pride, and delight at seeing Caroline again. Tanya looked as if a crown jewel had fallen into her lap; what student wouldn't if they'd been offered their sandwich year on full pay in the United States? Denis returned from the bar with a bottle of sparkling wine to celebrate.

'When are you going?' Caroline asked.

'At the end of the month.'

'I'll miss you.' She saw part of the past slipping away with Tanya waving goodbye and recognised that they were all now adults growing into separate roles. She thought sadly of the haven of the Tunstalls' house and made up her mind to pop round whenever she could to see Tanya's parents.

'I'll miss her too,' Denis said.

'You'll just have to keep each other company whilst I'm away then, won't you.' For the first time in his life Denis could have whooped for joy at one of his sister's blunt inferences.

'Only if he lets me drive his Maigret car,' said Caroline. Mary and John Tunstall would be arriving soon to celebrate with an evening meal provided by Denis. He invited Caroline to join them. She put up a token protest to the effect that, since it was a family occasion she should go.

'But you are one of the family,' asserted Tanya, thus firming up the arrangements for what was going to be a good evening.

How do quarrels arise, do they spring from the agendas of the participants, bent on bringing about a confrontation, or from some more random process? Caroline had good cause to favour the latter explanation—it was all down to the hapless juxtaposition of certain events and certain people. The lounge bar door swung open suddenly and all three looked up expecting to see John and Mary Tunstall walk in. Instead Deeks entered looking thunderous and glaze-eyed from alcohol. He could not have failed to notice Caroline and the Tunstalls, yet walked past them, pointedly blanking them out.

'Shit ! What's up with Pete? That's not like him.' Denis got to his feet intending to follow him into the public bar and ask what was wrong. Caroline suggested it would be better to wait and let him calm down. She explained how she had offended Mrs Deeks over the hunt saboteurs' leaflet and although she'd apologise for her sarcasm she wondered whether it had affected Deeks more deeply than it had his wife. Even so, this kind of behaviour was atypical of the gamekeeper who was so good-natured and reasonable.

Deeks sat himself on a bar stool and curtly ordered a pint of strong lager, taking the friendly Liverpudlian licensee by surprise.

Concerned, Irene watched him down it rapidly and order another like a man determined to get himself thoroughly plastered.

'Not your usual self,' she noted.

'No I'm bloody not,' agreed Deeks. 'I've just had some bad news. It looks as if me and Brenda could be flung out of our jobs after thirty years' service, that's if Richard Nye gets his own fucking way.' The explosion of expletives from a normally civil man took her aback.

'Where on earth did you hear that?'

'Brenda heard it being discussed between him and Robert Freer.'

'Oh not that old chestnut. That's been rumbling around

Sandpits for years. Ignore it. Robert Freer can discuss it as much as he likes but there's no way he's going to get planning permission. Take my word for it, I sleep with the Chief Planning Officer.'

Irene's humorous claim at the expense of her reputation brought a smile to Deeks's face.

'Green belt is green belt,' she added reassuringly.

She might well have been successful in calming him and returning him to Cartwrights Cottage a sober man, had not another random event rekindled his aggravation. Terence entered the bar in the company of Spikey and Ned, both of whom were eking out their limited PhD grants by assisting him on the Fox project. Covered in mud and scratched by bramble on account of being led to whatever discomfort their radio-tagged subjects took them, they looked like a bunch of desperadoes. What Deeks instantly saw was a bunch of trouble-making hunt saboteurs.

On hearing Spikey's voice, Caroline cringed. It was the worst possible scenario—the niece of the Master of the Amwell Hounds, the gamekeeper and the chief amongst the local saboteurs. She was on the verge of excusing herself from the meal saying that it really should be a family affair. Besides Mary and John would want to spend as much time as they could with Tanya before she went to the States. Her intentions were pre-empted by the sound of a bar stool being toppled followed by Deeks bawling at the top of his voice.

'You,' he pointed his index finger at Spikey's chest, 'keep away from my bloody shoot. If I see you anywhere near those bins again I'll put some lead shot up your fucking arse if it's the last thing I do.'

Spikey was not the kind to be deterred by threats. A

veteran campaigner and demonstrator, he had learned to deal with violence simply by self-confidently asserting the justice of his cause. Political correctness, morality and the law tripped off Spikey's tongue as fluently as notes from a song thrush. There was something about him that seemed capable of halting a bull in its tracks. Whatever charismatic magic he employed to hold authority figures at bay, it now utterly failed him in the altercation with Deeks. He gaped uncomprehendingly. 'I don't know what you're talking about.'

'Don't you give me that bollocks, you little wanker.' Deeks's forefinger was stabbing repeatedly at Spikey's chest, forcing him to take a number of teetering steps backward. 'You've been up the park helping yourself to grain and luring the pheasants off the shoot and don't try and tell me otherwise.'

Ned and Spikey looked at each other, a flash of comprehension and disbelief crossing Ned's face.

'Right, yeah, okay,' he moved towards Deeks. 'It was discussed but...'

Now it was Terence's turn to badger Spikey.

'Did you?' he asked sharply, remembering the group's unanimous decision to postpone a discussion about sabbing the shoot.

'Of course we didn't.'

'Right, yeah, we agreed, let's just calm down, discuss it, right.' The sight of Ned making peace signals like a Buddhist guru was too much for Deeks.

'Who pulled your chord, jessie?' That did it, Spikey was back on form with a cause to defend.

'So what's this, your evening for bashing gays?'

'I'll tell you what I'm bashing, people like you,' Deeks rounded on him again. 'People like you swanning around at university at the expense of people like me. I'll tell you something else. If you're thinking of putting yourselves in with the guns next week you'll find yourself looking down the barrel of a shotgun—mine. If you think you can put me out of work, you the sabs or Richard Nye, then you can fuck off, the whole sodding lot of you.' Having had his say Deeks came storming into the lounge bar and stood swaying. Dismayed by the sight of him in such a state Caroline got imprudently to her feet to try and talk sense into the situation.

'Deeks, please, listen.'

'Mr,' he growled at her. 'It's Mr Deeks to you. Got it?' He left slamming the door.

Caroline returned to the table pale and stunned. The evening which had started out as a celebration of Tanya's success and friendship had been corrupted by a drunken brawl. She had not heard the earlier conversation between Deeks and Irene only her father's name cursed vehemently.

'I think we'll adjourn to the Lotus House,' Denis offered tactfully. 'I'll give Mum and Dad a ring so they know where to find us, right?'

'It's really kind of you but I think I'd better get back.' It was difficult to muster one's dignity under the circumstances so Caroline withdrew under the old magic mantle which enabled her to slip away quietly and reappear elsewhere. In the student house in Bristol nobody had heard of Ebury Hall.

When the last bus passed the Lotus House, she briefly caught sight of the Tunstalls seated around a table and observed, unsentimentally, that Denis and Tanya belonged to a family whilst she came from a social class. Even the affection she'd held for her mother was gradually fading to recollections of childhood. These days it was habit and duty that drew her back to the Hall. Wherever she went and whatever happened, however, there was just one piece of the old place she would take with her, the memory of the drawing room with the grand piano, her own siren song played as she'd never played before for the lover who stood hidden and listening. She would see Denis again, she had made up her mind. Once tickets were available for the forthcoming performance of her sonata, she would send one to him.

Spikey seemed to have drawn some strength from the incident; he assumed the posture of a party activist and launched into a lecture about the need to stand up to people like Deeks and be less respectful and mealy-mouthed about sabbing the estate. Terence who felt like telling him just to shut up, pointed out that a decision had already been reached about the issue. Ned seemed to be drifting about, perplexed by the question of why it was people couldn't simply chill out and settle their differences peacefully. Irene, even more perplexed by the sudden loss of customers, decided to put the record straight—Deeks had come into the bar already having had a skinful, unusual for him, because he'd heard he was going to lose his job after thirty years' service. Her brusque polishing of the bar suggested she didn't want to hear any more about it.

Deeks couldn't remember much about the walk back to the cottage. From the state of his clothes the next morning he inferred he must have blundered around in the woods before locating the front door and crashing out on the sofa. He came to with his mouth tasting like the bottom of a parrot's cage, to find Brenda tight-lipped, frying breakfast. 'I know we've got problems but drinking isn't going to resolve them,' she told him curtly.

The next few nights before the opening of the first shoot were sleepless, trepidations about the future cutting into their dreams and waking them suddenly. Once one rolled over to rest the other would introduce the topic again until between them they wrung every drop of possibility from the issue. 'Well,' Brenda concluded, 'I can't see the old boy letting five million quid go into some fancy corporate scheme, can you?'

'I suppose not,' he agreed, although not entirely convinced. Suppose the old boy had a stroke or lost his marbles? He'd be entirely at the mercy of Mr Nye, since Mrs Nye didn't seem to have much clout when it came to her husband's opinions. Secretly Brenda had her doubts too. Peter hadn't been exposed in the same way she had to Mr Nye's machinations and expertise in undermining relationships to his own advantage.

'What shall we do, if they do make us redundant?'

'Carry on living here and find work on another estate in the county. Ben Dutton would find something for me. Even if it's just as an assistant keeper, it's better than nothing. What do you think?'

'This is a tied cottage,' came Brenda's gloomy reminder.

'In that case we'll have to hold Mrs Nye to her word, won't we?'

Deeks rolled over again into sleep.

Brenda didn't voice her observation that Mrs Nye's promises had no legal status whatsoever unless signed, sealed and witnessed.

Her eyes snapped open, woken by the sound of chains

rattling. Deeks woke too and immediately stumbled downstairs to put Stella on her lead. The couple and their dog spilled out of the front door together as if pushed into the night by an unseen hand. When they reached the first bin it was as it had been left when Deeks last checked it— firmly secured with a padlocked chain. Stella, however, was not to be appeased. Someone must be quite close for her to set up such a hullabaloo.

When Deeks shone the torch on a point some five feet beyond the grain bin, it lit up two human eyes which remained regarding him only long enough for him to get the impression they were set in a pale and wizened face framed by ragged strands of grey hair. If Deeks, and Brenda agreed with him, was asked to describe what he'd seen in the brief illumination he would have said it was a pheasant that had taken on a human form before disappearing into the wood.

Occasionally a voice would ascend, squeaky on account of nerves, above the politely whispered conversation in the foyer. Performers, relatives and friends gathered together as if to chorus their agreement that this sort of gathering was exacting and everybody would prefer to be in their seats listening to the music. Occasionally a soloist would break free, having found something inspiring to say.

Denis arrived confidently expecting Caroline to be waiting for him. He had entered as if having been discharged by the revolving doors into a chapel, so hushed and reverent was the conversation. He looked around, appearing to be on the brink of returning the way he had come when he saw a young woman seated at a table by herself. She wore a stylish evening gown. Somebody had gone to considerable lengths to pile her dark hair on the top of her head, thus extending her tall, pale-faced elegance. 'Hi.' She waved vigorously at him.

Denis approached, eyebrows raised comically. 'Caroline?' he asked grinning.

'I'm afraid it is.'

If a man had been permitted to indulge his passion in public, Denis Tunstall would have behaved like a caveman.

'I don't believe it! I didn't recognise you.'

'To be honest I feel a bit uncomfortable, but it's statutory gear for the performers. Members of the audience can wear what they like.'

'You look bloody fantastic.'

'I feel dreadful.' Caroline looked as if she were about to wilt.

'Nerves?' Caroline nodded. 'I could murder a large gin and tonic.'

'I'll get you one,' Denis offered.

'Buy me one after the performance.'

Denis held up a carrier bag. 'Presents.' He placed a small box in front of her, beautifully gift-wrapped with a card from America on which Tanya had written 'Wish you were here,' then crossed it out, adding, 'Wish I was there to see you play. Good luck, Honeybun.'

In the small box was a piece of sample rock which had been highly polished except for one area where a fossilized beetle had been skilfully exposed. 'Oh wow. I'm going to have it put on a chain, it'll make a fantastic pendant.' Mention of jewellery sent Denis searching in the carrier bag again. A tannoy announcement called all the competitors back stage.

'Try and open the box from Mum before you go on stage, it's a good luck charm.'

Caroline hastily returned the gifts to the bag and hesitated for a moment or two before leaving. 'I'm really, really glad you came.'

'And I'm really, really glad I came,' he joked whilst suppressing a desire to kiss her passionately and wish her luck. The only problem was if he did she would never get to the performance.

'Good luck, Carrie.'

She nodded, her mind now absorbed by her music. Suddenly she was gone and he thought again of the timid doe withdrawing into the dappled light of the wood. Perhaps it wasn't a good thing to wish somebody luck too much, it made them nervous. Caroline's rapid departure, however, hadn't anything to do with pre-performance tension so much as the arrival of Nye, Matilda and Uncle George through the revolving doors. Matilda was the first to be discharged into the foyer, chattering so animatedly she appeared to be at risk of spinning round in the entrance indefinitely.

The first adjudication of the inter-university music festival had put Caroline forward as a finalist in a competition to select the most promising student. A major UK-wide event, it was an accolade in itself to be included amongst the finalists. Her composition had been described as intriguing, original and daring. It was regarded as an unusual piece that was difficult to perform. The house in 'Sounds of the House' was a metaphor for the sounds within herself that arose from the contrasts and contradictions of experience, shocks and disappointments and longing for reconciliation. The sonata had not been composed solely for the festival but had its core in her early teens, evolving over the years. Now it had come to fruition with maturity and this very public and declaratory expression of her innermost feelings. It was a disingenuous, intensely emotional piece, yet at other points cerebral, then rebellious. The composition shifted between baroque and a defiant jazz, all of it drawn to a conclusion with a gentle nocturne.

A difficulty she would face as a pianist, one that had already been pointed out in the first adjudication, would be in making a convincing transition from one movement to the next.

It was this she had in mind when she stepped onto the stage and looked up to the gods to be greeted by an outburst of whistles and cheers from fellow students who held up a banner with Bristol University painted on it. Their noisy reception as loud as singing on the last night of the Proms, was humorously received by the host for the evening who noted, 'I see you've brought a few supporters with you, Caroline.'

The auditorium finally silenced, Caroline settled at the piano. Tonight she would play for Denis, her friends and the college who had done so much to support her. Her fingers descended, put asunder the notes gathered on the stave and recalled a bright June morning when a young girl's faith in her father had been wrecked.

At the end of a long and exacting evening the panel of judges placed Caroline Nye third in the competition. For Caroline it had been a completely unexpected outcome. If the judges had been judging the composition alone and her ability as a composer they would undoubtedly have placed her first but they felt that the piece demanded a standard of performance which she hadn't quite reached. As it was, Caroline had been delighted to have been selected amongst the finalists, let alone be amongst the first three.

Just before coming on stage for the performance she had managed to open her other gifts. Mary Tunstall had lent her a good luck charm, a family heirloom left to her by a great aunt. It was a Victorian choker with a sprig of heather delicately worked in gold. She put it on and wore it throughout the performance. Denis's gift was a card, on the front he had reproduced a photograph of the Light Fifteen, now complete, with a mock number plate saying good luck. Inside he had written a note inviting her to dinner at the Lotus House, but only on condition that she won, otherwise it would have to be a fish and chip take-away.

She found Denis in the bar having ordered a pint for himself and a large gin and tonic for her. As she arrived he passed his mobile phone to her with a text message, Well done, Caroline, we're very proud of you. All our love Mary, John and Tanya. She remembered Mary's good luck charm and started to remove it for safe return to Sandpits.

'Keep it on, Mum would want you to wear it tonight. You were brilliant.'

Caroline, feeling she couldn't absorb any more emotion without bursting into tears, deflected further congratulations by raising her glass. 'Here's to the Light Fifteen.' She gulped a substantial mouthful, took the clips out of her hair, kicked off her shoes and sat without any vestige of dignity. 'This is the best gin and tonic I've ever tasted.' The rest of the drink disappeared causing an instant rush of alcohol to her brain, followed shortly by a giggle.

She put her chin in her hands and addressed Denis. 'Right, Denis Tunstall, I've come to claim my prize.' She held up the greetings card. Caroline was about to round off what was turning out to be a brilliant evening by putting forward the idea that he might like to come to a party organised for the competitors by the Students Union, and if he was worried about where to stay there was plenty of room for him to crash out at her place.

'Sweetheart, you were stunning.' Nye's voice hailed her from the bar. Heads turned to watch the approach of a handsome, well-tailored gentleman. He kissed her elegantly on both cheeks; his gestures, like his clothes, were always in the best of restrained taste. Matilda followed shortly after looking delighted but sweating profusely in one of her over-the-top outfits.

'We're so pleased for you, darling, so pleased for you. You were absolutely fabulous.' Was it Caroline's imagination or did Denis suppress a grin? She had to confess that if the creators of *Absolutely Fabulous* had found a real-life model for their TV series it must surely have been provided by Mrs Nye. She seemed to be in one of her indecisive, hand-spinning modes, that often happened when she needed a bit of extra social support.

Uncle George looked proud of his great niece and took hold of her hand—he never went in for kissing—and said, 'Well done, Caroline, well done. Your grandmother would have been very proud of you.'

Not for the first time in the last few days Caroline had good cause to ask herself how accidents arise. You look back, telling yourself if only I'd gone somewhere else, made different arrangements, not taken the journey at that particular time it would never have happened. You always take measures to ensure accidents don't happen. In this case she had assumed that because the competition was her territory, her show, that she would have control over events. She had also assumed that when Nye, Matilda and Uncle George were outside the bounds of Ebury Hall their influence would accordingly diminish. 'This is Denis,' she introduced him to them.

'Ah, Denis,' Nye held out his hand. 'Denis from...?' Nye waved his other hand as if offering an assortment of approved residences in the county.

'Sandpits,' Denis replied.

'Where exactly in Sandpits?'

'Church Wood,' Denis told him, which Nye already knew but intended to reveal for the benefit of Uncle George. Uncle George and Matilda, clearly sharing the same Wentworth genes when it came to opinions about council estates, stood side by side like two disapproving Toby jugs.

'A local boy,' Nye concluded. The term boy can simply mean our boy whose team we support, or it could mean somebody of no social consequence, it all depends on who says it. Nye could get away with linguistic murder, always managing to get his point across without any repercussions for himself.

'Of course he's local,' Matilda pointed out, 'he's a Tunstall. You remember, don't you, Uncle, his aunt worked at the Hall for a while.'

'Ah, yes, Tunstall. Perhaps you'd like to join us for supper, Denis,' Nye invited.

Denis, already put on his mettle by the shallow hospitality, felt inclined to refuse since an invitation from Mr

Nye, delivered in that sort of tone, was equivalent to being invited to dinner by a shark. Recognising the gambit Caroline put her foot down.

'We're going to a party. The Students Union have organised a do for the competitors and friends.'

'Perhaps some other occasion,' Nye offered. 'Perhaps you might like to invite Denis to the Ebury meet dinner, Caroline... Do you ride, Denis?'

'Not to the hounds,' Caroline inserted sharply. 'We don't agree with foxhunting.' It was a mistake. She should have shut her mouth and let Denis talk for himself.

'We don't!?' Nye exclaimed. 'Well, Denis, the Ebury meet dinner would be the perfect venue to argue your case. Allow me to introduce you to Caroline's Uncle George. He's Master of the Amwell Hounds.'

Sir George said good evening curtly without shaking hands and returned to frowning.

'Don't be silly, Richard,' Matilda piped up. 'We've invited Thornton to partner Caroline. It's all been arranged.' It had been conveyed to Denis in no uncertain terms that he was not good enough for Caroline, whereas Thornton was; in their eyes he would never rise above his station—a mere boy from the council estate; his unworthiness triple underlined. He looked at his mother's treasured heirloom, the only expensive piece of jewellery she was ever likely to own, around Caroline's neck, his own card inviting her to dinner and the piece of rock bearing a fossil from Fargo and felt like throwing the whole lot in her face. He looked at his watch and excused himself tersely.

'I've got work tomorrow. See you around, Carrie.' He left abruptly. Matilda's eyes, which had been fixed on the choker around Caroline's neck, flickered briefly, noting his departure as if it had been no more significant than a fly brushed off a tablecloth.

'Where did you get that choker?' she demanded.

'Denis's mother. She lent it to me to wish me good luck.' Caroline injected her tone with as much accusation as a public venue would allow.

'Well, I can't see why you found it necessary to borrow jewellery. You should have worn something of mine or your grandmother's.'

Uncle George looked as if he wanted to end the matter and grumbled about losing their table at Selbournes if they didn't get a move on.

'Aren't you going to put your hair up again?' Matilda asked.

'What for? The performance is over.' If Caroline could have spat acid at her mother she would have done so. 'All I want to do is go to bed.'

Nye instantly protested that she should join them for supper. After all, it had been arranged for her benefit, to celebrate her success, champagne, everything, and Selbournes really was the best place to celebrate.

Caroline packed her gifts in the carrier bag ignoring him. She looked at Denis's unfinished pint on the table, the melted ice and slice of lemon in her empty glass. Two drinks for two people who were just on the verge of getting together. She wheeled round brimful with temper that she had never dared express before. 'Mum, I told you I'm not coming to the Ebury Meet dinner with Thornton. If I'm coming at all it will be by myself.' Matilda, flustered, deferred to her uncle, her chicken self submitting to arrangements that he'd insisted upon. The gesture made Caroline feel even more inclined to let forth. 'I don't like

Thornton Holbrooke-Jones, I never have liked him, I'm never likely to go out with him, so will you please stop this bloody silly matchmaking.' She turned abruptly without saying goodbye.

'Can we get you a taxi?' There was a note of victory in her father's offer.

'No,' she snapped without bothering to turn round.

'I suppose that's what passes for good manners these days,' she heard from Uncle George as she left the foyer.

'See you around, Carrie' had sounded very final. The elation of seeing Denis, of performing in a prestigious competition, of winning a place had taken her flying high, full of pride and a sense of personal achievement. For no apparent reason Nye had pulled the trigger and brought her spinning back to earth, at the same time grounding a relationship even before it got airborne. Why? Surely there couldn't be any personal malice towards somebody he had never met, yet he had deliberately belittled Denis.

Usually, on meeting her friends, he was cordially indifferent. It was only when Uncle George was present, or so it seemed, that friends were denigrated or her own ideas presented as unworthy. After a week of exacting practice, her nerves stretched as tight as bowstrings, she simply didn't have the energy to think beyond what appeared to be nastiness to some other motivation. Ready, fire! Ready fire! She and Denis had been set up with about as much concern for them as he might show for a brace of pheasants blasted out of the sky for sport. Ready. Fire! 'Sounds of the House' would never end and certainly not with a gentle nocturne. Ready. Fire! See you around, Denis had severed their relationship abruptly. Back came the syncopated, anarchic rhythms of the introductory movement. Back came that bright June morning with a woman's trainers jerking obscenely above her father's buttocks. Jazz was the original voice of anger and jazz would conclude 'Sounds of the House', if there was a conclusion to such discordance. This time Denis wouldn't be there for the finale, because he wouldn't want to hear her play any more, thanks to Nye.

The soothing regularities of work and the need to focus on preparations for the shoot were beginning to diminish the trauma of the previous few days. If anything, it had given Deeks a new-found determination that all the work he had put into ensuring the development of good wild stock would come to fruition in one of the best shoots the estate had ever held.

Once the guns had drawn lots for their positions, he lined them up repeating the routine safety instructions. He had succeeded in avoiding eye contact with Mr Nye and when addressed by him replied in a crisp but professional tone. It was Sir George he aimed to impress, since it was on his opinion the future of the Hall rested, not this upstart and interloper who'd married his way into it. He rejoined the beaters to give them their instructions for the first drive of the day. He had positioned them to form a half circle that would move forward to drive the birds into the flushing area whilst preventing them from escaping sideways along tracks in the wood. Without this formation they could gain the pastureland beyond the range of the shoot.

Everything was going according to plan with no hint that the day would be sabotaged. As he walked forward with the beaters it struck him that this stage of a drive was like conducting an orchestra. The sticks beat regularly on trees and at undergrowth sounding much like a percussion band. Once in the flushing area the efforts of the beaters would have to be similarly well orchestrated. Pheasants flushed up in a frenzied cloud of escaping birds did not make for good sport. He wanted them up and flying in twos and threes to be either shot cleanly or fly on uninjured.

He watched Mr Nye with his gun tucked into his shoulder ready to take the recoil, every inch the expert shot and so he was, much to Deeks's chagrin. Three birds were suddenly airborne and flying strongly. He watched one go up fast and straight above Mr Nye's gun and concentrated all his psychic energy into wishing the bird a safe getaway. Delighted, he watched it fly on into the hazy autumn sky and felt like cheering. Sir George's bird came down cleanly more or less at his feet and another was unfortunately winged by Robert Freer, yet flew on. He registered the direction of the injured bird and calculated that it would land again within the wood and the safety of cover.

Robert Freer, who got under his skin at the best of times with his clandestine plots and ploys, roughened his patience to extreme irascibility when it came to a shoot. Perhaps he should recommend Freer restricted himself to clay pigeons if he couldn't manage to bring a bird down cleanly. At the end of the first drive he ordered the guns to be placed on the ground whilst the dogs retrieved the fallen birds. Stella, turning out to be an excellent gun dog, was sitting bright and alert, watching him and waiting for her orders. On a command, she set off at an eager trot, Deeks following behind, for a good three hundred yards to a small clearing in the wood. He ordered the dog to stand, intending to despatch Freer's injured bird quickly, but was held back by the most extraordinary and bizarre experience of his thirty years as a gamekeeper.

The bird had a damaged wing; he could see clearly where the lead shot had snapped one of its delicate bones, leaving it to drag awkwardly. The other wing fluttered in an effort to get airborne which only succeeded in sending the creature in futile circles. On her knees, prostrated by empathetic suffering on behalf of the pheasant, was the grain thief, the vagrant woman sometimes seen around the Sandpits area. She held her hand towards the injured bird imploring it to come to her. Seeing it as she might a challenge from another dog, Stella's hackles raised and her lips drew back in an ugly snarl, daring the bedraggled creature on her knees to come closer.

Momentarily, the woman's distress at the plight of the injured bird entered Deeks's own compassion. Now he too couldn't bear the poor creature's suffering any longer. It was a magnificent cock pheasant, its plumage shining brilliantly in the autumn sun. Here was a creature which he had nurtured, protected, no longer an object, something to be shot out of the sky for sport, but an animal with a right to life. Its would-be rescuer was backing away in terror from the snarling dog. Any further delay and there was a risk that Stella would launch an attack. 'Stella!' Deeks yelled 'Heel!' Tugged from her aggressive stance by the sound of her master's voice she came compliantly to his side. 'Down,' he ordered. The woman turned and fled into the wood. Deeks stooped and gathered up the exhausted pheasant and despatched it swiftly from its suffering.

He was rarely sentimental about his pheasants but, as he returned with Stella trotting, head held high and bearing the limp bird between her jaws, he pictured himself laying it to rest at the base of an oak tree. 'Try shooting more cleanly, Mr Freer,' he suggested as he handed over the dead pheasant. There was such concentrated animosity in his tone Robert Freer couldn't have failed to get the message.

# The Season

## of the Fox

At the bottom of the tractor-rutted green lane the gnarled root of a hawthorn protruded from the lip of a three-foot high earth and rock bank. It was here that Pansy had scratched a den for herself and it would be here, at her favoured sleeping site, that she would extend the earthworks and give birth to a litter of fox cubs—given that Old Rogue's amorous hopes were fulfilled. On the first night of courtship, when the confident old bounder had come trotting into view, Pansy did not offer the usual fawning welcome that his status and dominance evoked, but remained audaciously asleep. He approached her den and stared for a while before craning his neck toward her and sniffing the air. Seconds later he trotted away as if called to more urgent olfactory business elsewhere. Some minutes later he returned and with a gentlemanly expression of enquiry, took another investigative sniff after which he disappeared again. There was only one thing that would have summoned him in this way from his comfortable niche at Ebury Hall Park—a receptive vixen.

It was after four in the afternoon when she woke, stretching herself into a luxurious elongation. Then, as if fearful to approach her whilst she slept, Old Rogue appeared miraculously out of the half-light of the winter evening. For the following hour Pansy mooched around her lair making athletic, if unsuccessful, attempts to pounce on small game. In the meantime Old Rogue waited with the courteous air of a butler. Once or twice he raised a tentative paw. His magnificent brush which normally hung in a relaxed curve that seemed to extend his easy-going gait, was now erect and held horizontally to the ground. His body shape seemed to express more anxiety than hope as he pawed at the ground, edging forward. When he did not meet with resistance from Pansy he took the liberty of placing a forepaw on her rump.

Some forty metres away, trussed up to the armpits by a sleeping bag, Terence's ample thighs spilled over the edge of his narrow camp stool. Looking like a quilted voyeur he spied on the vulpine courtship through infrared binoculars that converted Old Rogue's eyes to a ghostly green. Pansy did not tolerate the presumptive paw on her rump and rounded on the suitor with her mouth agape. Cuck—cuck—cuck, she admonished, and trotted off to pursue a zigzag course over her range, visiting larders as diverse as ploughed fields, orchards and a row of cottage gardens. As she moved around she generously sprinkled urine on tufts of grass.

Tail outstretched, Old Rogue followed in her wake, a love-sick shadow. Unbeknown to either of them, Terence slipped out of his sleeping bag and donned his earphones. Antennae erect, he followed behind the pair, electronic blips and bleeps his passport to an environment to which he was as intimately connected as the creatures of his studies.

A thought can become trapped in the brain, scuttling back and forth along the same neural pathway like a mouse in a cage. Thinking about the night of the concert had become a fruitless compulsion, so Caroline distracted herself by re-working the final movement of the sonata. She wanted to give it a more authentic voice, the voice of a more determined Caroline who wasn't going back to Ebury Hall unless she absolutely had to. The finale truly would end the 'Sounds of the House' since she wouldn't be there to hear them any more. The new finale, however, did not have the desired catharsis. If anything its angry jazz morosely recalled the sound of 'See you around, Carrie'.

A close contender for the most persistent sound in her head was Deeks's drunken outburst about her father putting him out of work. His clipped and chilly edict to her to call him Mr Deeks in future seemed to have lassoed her with the same accusation. Unable to focus on anything else, she took Mary Tunstall's choker and laid it reverently in a jewellery case which had once belonged to her own grandmother. The golden sprig of heather looked so delicate against its black velvet lining that she felt drawn to stare at it as if to restore the lucky moments when the judges had awarded her a place amongst the winners. She kept hold of it with a pagan belief that Denis might be charmed into telephoning her. Three weeks had passed without a word from him. She would have to return it soon, or put Mary Tunstall in the embarrassing position of having to ask for it back.

She felt quite confident about taking it back to Sandpits and buying a bouquet of flowers to say thank you for its loan until the Bristol bus pulled into the terminus. She got off filled with extreme apprehension. The old childish notion that she could slip on the magic mantle and enter the Tunstalls' house like one of the family had lost its power. Eleven Church Grove and Ebury Hall had collided after all these years. Surely all the eyes of Sandpits were on her, surely there wasn't a curtain that didn't twitch as she walked along Church Grove with flowers that could never amount to an adequate apology for the way her family had spoken to Denis. Caroline prepared herself for a frosty reception from his mother.

Mary Tunstall was in fact delighted to see Caroline with an armful of flowers. To pre-empt any difficult enquiries about her family Caroline explained that she had popped down for the day to return the jewellery and would be going back on the next bus. 'Aren't you going up to the Hall to see your people?' Mary asked.

'No,' Caroline answered tersely, 'I haven't got time. I just wanted to give you the choker back.'

'You shouldn't have come all the way down from Bristol just for that, it could have waited.' Mary protested further when Caroline insisted she would like her to keep the jewellery case.

'I can't take that. It's your grandmother's. I remember you showing it to Tanya.'

'I never even met her, she died before I was born.'

'Even so.'

'I want you to keep it.' It was as if the open jewellery case had become a Pandora's box of emotion. 'I want you to keep it because you've always been so kind.' The rest of the sentence was drowned in tears. Mary made out that Caroline missed Tanya and wished she was still there. It was an extraordinary outburst which she dealt with in the way nurses do, with equal portions of healing and efficiency. Tissues were offered together with a cup of tea.

'I think it must be the stress of the competition coming out,' she concluded once the rhythmic sobbing had subsided to sniffs.

'Everything's going pear-shaped.'

'With your course you mean?'

Caroline shook her head but did not offer the truth about what had happened the night of the concert. 'There are things going on at the Hall I don't understand.'

'Well, that doesn't surprise me!' Mary said bluntly.

'Did Tanya tell you about Deeks getting drunk and shouting about my father trying to do him out of a job? He had a go at me as well. I don't know what's going on any more, I wish somebody would tell me.' The question hung suspended whilst Mary Tunstall thought through the implications of giving a straight answer.

'Well,' she said, 'Peter told John that Brenda had overheard a conversation between your father and Robert Freer. Apparently she'd gone over to the house to make sure it was all locked up for the night because she thought your parents were out. When she got over there your father was in the study drinking with Robert Freer. They hadn't heard her come in and just carried on with their meeting. Rightly or wrongly Brenda eavesdropped, and as far as she could gather, your father and Robert Freer and some others have got together with the idea of developing Ebury Hall and the farm next to it as a golf course, and the Hall itself as a hotel-cum-conference centre. I think there was some idea as well about sports facilities, saunas, all that sort of thing.'

Mary watched Caroline's large brown eyes widen and brim with tears again, feeling that she'd said too much.

'Ebury Hall's supposed to be my home. Nobody's said anything to me about this. No wonder Deeks was so angry. I hope he didn't think that I knew about it.'

'I'm sure he didn't. Peter knows you don't have any more say in what goes on up there than your mother does. Sorry, I shouldn't have said that.'

'Why not? It's true.'

'Maybe I've said too much. I don't think Brenda and Peter would want me to let the cat out of the bag. Obviously it's a bit difficult because Brenda shouldn't have been there in the first place.'

'She had a right to be, they could lose their jobs.'

'Maybe. Peter's decided that if the worst comes to the worst he'll find work on another estate and ask your mother for a legal agreement over the cottage.'

Caroline, still grappling with the enormity of what her father proposed behind her mother's back, shook her head in disbelief. 'How could he? Ebury Hall doesn't even belong to him, it belongs to my mother.'

When family fortunes are discussed it's better for third parties to remain neutral in case what they have to say is later used in evidence. Mary, therefore, decided to adopt a conciliatory tone.

'Perhaps your mother might agree with the plan. Everybody knows the hall could do with a bit of a make-over and there could be some benefits. A golf course and hotel would bring jobs to the area.'

Caroline was not convinced. 'But he can't just go ahead without telling her.'

'Perhaps he's just keeping quiet about the plan until he knows whether they're likely to get planning permission. Look, don't quote me on any of this because it's all a bit third hand. If I were you I'd talk to Peter and Brenda and find out exactly what was and wasn't said. I think they've calmed down a bit now and they'll give you a clearer picture of things than I can. I know your father's been a bit underhand, but at the end of the day I think he only wants to do what's best for the place.'

Caroline was not prepared to buy in to the idea of her father's altruism and told Mary firmly that she would go and see the Deekses but she certainly didn't intend going home, not after this.

'Oh pop in and see your mother, it's not her fault. Cheer up, Caroline, maybe it's not as bad as it looks. You don't look any happier than our Denis does. He's been moping about for the last few weeks with a face as long as a poker. I don't know what's the matter with you all. He's been talking about going back to Australia and settling there. Perhaps it's the right thing to do. Starkeys pay him peanuts but, degree or no degree, you still have to work your way up. Myself I think he's just feeling a bit down at the moment. I don't get much time to talk to him. He comes in for his tea and he's straight off out again. I don't know,' Mary sighed, 'time flies once you have children. It seems like yesterday when you were all at school, now our Denis is thinking of emigrating and Tanya's in the States for a year.'

Ivor looked up from the Lego car he'd been building on the kitchen table to declare that he was starting at big school in January. Prompted by the thought of flying time Mary looked at her watch. 'I'm afraid I've got to shoot off, I'm on duty this afternoon. Don't forget, you're always welcome to pop in, don't stay away just because Tanya's not here.'

Caroline looked fondly on the child stooping over his Lego project, in profile a miniature version of his brother at work on the Light Fifteen. 'I'll come down one afternoon and take Ivor out.'

Ivor looked up, his face shaping into an exclamation of surprise, again so much like his brother.

'You'd like that, wouldn't you?' Mary ruffled his hair. Ivor nodded coyly and went back to the more significant quest for a steering wheel.

Cuck—cuck—cuck... Pansy wheeled, snirking in Old Rogue's face. She had returned to her lair towards dawn with her forlorn suitor trailing behind, both being followed by the equally ardent naturalist who had spent the night hopping between co-ordinates in order to get a fix on their whereabouts. In the process he had torn his jacket on some barbed wire, ripped the back of his hand painfully on some bramble, then landed on his arse in the mud by Harmers Pond.

The vixen had been unusually active, hunting and visiting caches of food, clearly fortifying her body in preparation for a forthcoming pregnancy. Old Rogue spent the night sniffing moonily around her domain; eschewing food, he had eyes only for her. When light began to streak across the morning sky she returned along the green lane coquettishly sprinkling drops of tantalising urine. She retired to her hawthorn-root bedchamber like a Victorian lady with a headache of convenience. Keeping a respectable distance of some four feet whilst she slept, Old Rogue scratched a shallow depression close to the bank, curled himself around and lay resting, although not sleeping. Through the 'hot eyes' Terence could make out the green piercing stare which did not shift for a moment from the object of his desire.

This poignant expression of an animal's determination to procreate caused him a momentary gloom as he reflected on the fragile possibility of survival, and how perilously close it all was to destruction. Here lay a vixen in her nineteenth month, by canine standards a mere teenager. In captivity she could live as long as a dog; by wild vulpine standards she was elderly—she would be lucky to breed and see her own offspring reach the same age. Her chance of not being run over by a car, snared, poisoned, shot, succumbing to the diseases of domestic pets, ripped to pieces by hounds, were a mere one in five.

He had first caught sight of Pansy when she was six months old. He had been observing the encirclement of Pikes Wood by cub-hunters the previous October. They approached on foot with young hounds which they released into the trees for training, their quarry being four adolescent fox cubs born that season to a vixen he called The Dowager who had been amongst the earliest radio-tagged subjects to join his study. The hunting party spread out spacing themselves evenly around the perimeter of the wood with half a kilometre separating each member. They all carried some means of creating a shindig, one a cycle chain in a metal bucket, another an oil drum and hammer, somebody else, more domestically inclined, a saucepan and rolling pin. It didn't matter what they brought to the cub hunt provided it was percussive and terrifying to a fox's ears. On a whistled signal the hunters began to close in on the wood, each producing their own cacophony and, just in case the unfortunate creatures hadn't got the message that the humans were advancing with their hounds, they added whooping and hollering to their repertoire of silly noises. How ridiculous they had all seemed, descending on the sadly shrinking patch of ancient woodland as if to beat out some lurking spirit which had taken refuge there.

Terence had watched through his binoculars hoping against all the known odds that The Dowager and her four cubs would break free. Those foxes which had the courage to bolt past the terrifying racket were deemed to be the fittest and were allowed to escape, since they would provide some good sport once the season got under way some eight weeks later. Sir George and the Amwell Hounds certainly wouldn't want foxes that just lay down waiting for the end, there would be no sport in that. From the bottom of Long Coombe, Terence could hear the yelping of the young, inexperienced hounds and occasionally a deeper, more directed baying equivalent to the breaking of an adolescent voice. There was nothing he could do to prevent any of it, he could only monitor the story told in crashes, bangs and yelps. He pictured the chaotic scene within the wood of hounds milling around picking up false trails, falling over each other in their anarchistic attempts to pursue individual inclinations.

Pansy had been the first to break free of cover and run the gauntlet of sound. She came streaking toward him, hell for leather, down the length of the valley and flew past mere feet away. 'Oh well done, my beauty, well done!' He remembered her heart-shaped face with its perplexed expression, it made him think of the pretty low-growing flower that was to become her logo. With his binoculars still trained on the wood he waited for another fox to bolt.

For quite some minutes, nothing stirred except for the huntsmen who continued to produce their rhythmic din. He studied their profiles overtaken by curiosity and the desire to observe whatever rationale lay behind their brutality. He was surprised to find a bland normality in their expressions where he had expected to see a devilish, red-faced slavering over the prospect of blood. Indifference, that's what he had been observing—now that really did send a shiver up his spine. It was the same expression worn by soldiers outside internment camps, on duty for some tinpot junta. Not at all concerned about the pain and deprivation of those interned, on the contrary they were bored by it. These volunteer huntsmen were merely doing their job, helping to support the Amwell Hounds. But did it really give them pleasure to impose fear and pain on defenceless animals? Surely not, if they had been able to project their imaginations into the unfortunate creatures suffering they could not have done it. What was worrying, he concluded, was that they were capable of flicking the all too human switch that isolates emotion and permits the disavowal of suffering.

It was a good five minutes before another cub broke free and Terence cheered him on his way. As for the other two, a cry of 'gone away' came to him from the hidden side of the wood indicating that a third must have bolted. The fourth, he guessed, had been taken by the young hounds. As to the fate of The Dowager, it was between gritted teeth that he requested of the Amwell Hounds the prompt return of her radio collar.

The cub hunt had dispersed the family group leaving a vacant niche in Pikes Wood and into it trotted Paintbrush, an itinerant dog fox. Pansy, perhaps from an instinctive aversion to the place, did not return to Pikes Wood to establish herself as the breeding vixen, but forged a banana-shaped wedge of territory which formed a corridor between the wood and Ebury Hall. She lived off her diverse food income comfortably enough. Terence raised his glasses for one last look at Old Rogue's resting form before returning home. Perhaps, guns, poison, hounds, traffic, snares notwithstanding, he would live another day, long enough to procreate.

Did Old Rogue have a notion of the future, or did he just respond to the exigencies of the moment? Terence often defected from his faith in science and tried to imagine life as it is lived by animals, minute by minute, understanding only the contingencies of the moment. Perhaps, by this means, he might then draw a little closer to the ways of the natural world.

As he packed his field-glasses in their carrying case he had a feeling that he was not the only watcher in the green lane. Something, about four metres away, was keeping an eye on him. It breathed heavily, a badger perhaps waiting for him to leave so that it might cross its own highway in safety?

Without warning Louise burst from the hedge and stood staring at him with her arms folded, looking childishly belligerent. The intimidating pose seemed to presage a territorial dispute. Keeping his eye on her, Terence swung his rucksack onto his back, putting the radio receiver out of sight, thus removing the main bone of contention. He took a step or two backwards in order to show willing and said, 'I was just off.'

She was not particularly concerned whether he stayed or went, she didn't even bother to acknowledge him. Her brows were creased in a perplexed frown and she stood as if trying to fathom what, or who, he was, a stance reminding him of the poor old Dowager with her wild and imperious expression. He would not have been at all surprised if she'd suddenly sniffed the wind to get the measure of him. She approached bringing with her an unutterably disgraceful stench, by comparison with which a fox's urine smelt sweet and delicate. It was the worst of animal smells, the odour of somebody completely indifferent to personal hygiene.

'Good morning,' he said and held his palm upward in the hope she wouldn't come any closer. Remembering her love of chocolate he felt in his jacket pocket and produced a wafer biscuit which he offered politely; she snatched it ungraciously before passing on her way, evaporating, it appeared, with the coming of the morning.

Dip and swish, dip and swish. Deeks's hand scooped grain from his satchel and scattered it on the ride with a circular motion to ensure an even distribution. The ride covered to his satisfaction he withdrew into the wood, threw back his head and whistled shrilly. The birds arrived, unaware of their benefactor taking his daily tally of them.

Caroline too remained out of sight, one eye sentimentally on the feeding birds whilst she weighed up Deeks's likely response to a few blunt questions. Dip and swish. That's how she used to accompany the feeding of the pheasants when she was a child. The dip was produced by bringing her outstretched fingers onto the keyboard and the swish was produced by running her thumb backwards over the keys. She remembered how dust from the grain would float in the air for a while, so too its sweet musty smell. Sadly such tactile pleasures were now part of a childhood that didn't seem to belong to her any more.

Knowing that she was likely to get short shift from Deeks

she had decided on a buttery courtesy as the best mode of address. 'Mr Deeks. Sorry to interrupt you but I was wondering if you could spare a moment or two.'

Initially he looked startled, then touchy. He folded his arms deliberately to signal that Mr Nye's daughter was not going to be given an effusive welcome.

'We didn't expect to see you back so soon.' He crisply acknowledged her presence. Both tone and body language made her feel she'd better drop the matter and leave. On the other hand why the hell should she? Why should she feel such trepidations about treading on Deeks's domain to discuss matters which affected them both?

'I've just come to apologise for my father's behaviour.'

Deeks unfolded his arms and shoved his hands in his pockets.

'I've been talking to Mary Tunstall.'

'Oh yes and what did she have to say?'

'She told me that Mrs Deeks had overheard my father talking to Robert Freer.'

'Did she?' came his curt response. The gamekeeper and the daughter of the house stood side by side, watching the pheasants, as if to fill the awkward gulf between them. Caroline had not expected to be stonewalled by silence.

The pheasants' determined pecking and scratching amongst the straw, the impress of their handsome plumage on her senses seemed to be the only friendly thing in the wood. Whatever friendship had been forged by an affection for these creatures was now terminated and there seemed to be little point in staying. The afternoon that had begun with tears seemed likely to end the same way.

'I only came to say sorry, that's all.' Caroline turned away.

'What did Mary tell you?' Deeks relented.

Caroline repeated all that Mary Tunstall had told her about the clandestine plans for Ebury Hall.

'It was the first time I heard about it, it's never been discussed in front of me,' she concluded.

'Well, he wouldn't, would he? He's been keeping it under close wraps.'

'Does my mother know?'

'Apparently not, according to Brenda. He said he wasn't going to say anything to her until he's persuaded your uncle to invest in the project. It seems your father's got designs on the money earmarked for the trust.'

'I thought my uncle had already put money into the trust.'

'Not as far as I'm aware he hasn't. Your uncle's capital is all tied up in the company's shares. As I understand it, the shares would be sold on his death and the capital transferred to a trust to provide an income to keep the Hall going.'

'I see.'

Indeed Caroline did see, only too clearly, as her father's agenda came sharply into focus. Evidently he was out to get his hands on both the Hall and Uncle George's money. It didn't take a genius to work that out. His objective explained why he had worked so cunningly to cause a rift between herself and her uncle. If Uncle George could be persuaded that his great niece was not competent to manage the Hall the way he wanted, what else would he do with his money? Even Caroline, inexperienced as she was when it came to such matters, had the answer. He would naturally leave it all to Matilda. Once he left it to Matilda it was as good as leaving it to Nye. 'How much?' she asked bluntly.

Deeks, wisely, did not quote the amount Mr Nye hoped to persuade Sir George to invest.

'Oh a goodish amount I should think.'

Deeks had a number of techniques for avoiding awkward questions. Caroline recalled one in particular from her childhood. If she ever asked why, Deeks would tell her, 'Because why's got a long tale that's why.'

'How much?' she insisted.

'I couldn't be absolutely sure but Brenda thought she heard five million.'

'The bastard!' Caroline succeeded in setting up two or three pheasants giving a comical tinge to her indignation. Deeks, similarly startled, wobbled on the shooting stick which he had just set up to perch his backside upon.

'Well, maybe, but he's still your father.'

'He doesn't behave like it.'

'I don't want you to think, just on the basis of a conversation with Robert Freer, that he's trying to do anybody out of their inheritance. In fact Brenda heard him say that he wanted something sustainable to hand on to you. I suppose I can see it from his point of view. He's not prepared to keep funding the place out of his own pocket, particularly once he's retired.'

'I don't care, he can't just put you and Mrs Deeks out of work.'

'No,' agreed Deeks, 'but, there again, economic changes come about for better and for worse. You just have to accept it these days, nobody's got a job for life. If your father wants to change this into a golf course, or whatever, and your uncle is prepared to invest in it, there's not a lot I can do about it. Maybe it's right for the place, I don't know. Who knows? Maybe your father will take me on as a green keeper,' Deeks concluded with grim humour. He took a packet of Old Holborne and some Rizlas from his pocket. Caroline watched him working the tobacco.

'What about the cottage?' she asked.

'I'm hoping your mother will keep her word and let us stay on there.'

'Do you want me to talk to her?' Caroline offered.

'No, don't do that. It's a kind thought but I'd rather keep this conversation to ourselves. Brenda's not supposed to know anything about the meeting and we've both agreed it would be better not to say anything, just wait and see what happens next. I wouldn't have said anything about it if you hadn't already spoken to Mary. Looking on the bright side, none of it may happen anyway.'

Deeks had succeeded in rolling his cigarette. He lit up, releasing Old Holborne fumes into the air like incense. It was a comforting smell, like grain and the straw on the ride, all of it blending into the smell of the wood she remembered so keenly from childhood days. Deeks had turned reflective. 'Personally I don't think your uncle would ever invest in that sort of project. He doesn't want this place touched. He wants it kept exactly as it was the day your grandfather shot himself.'

Caroline sat on a log; silence fell, a gap in Deeks's tale, filled for a while by the sound of the pheasants scratching aside the straw to get at their feed. Here was another lie unearthed. Caroline did not question Deeks, she wanted the tale to unfold unhindered, fearing that an interruption might cause Deeks to fold up his shooting stick and be off, then she would never learn the truth. Her grandfather, she had been told, had died in a shooting accident.

'My father found him in the saddle room. I don't think

Dad ever quite got over it. I'm afraid your grandfather made a bit of a mess of himself. He'd left a note for his brother, your uncle, but I'll tell you one thing, that note wasn't read at the inquest. Sir George put it in his pocket and it was all covered up to look like an accident. Apparently your grandfather got very low after your grandmother died from cancer.'

'What was he like?'

'A quiet sort of man but, like your uncle, he loved the country ways. He liked his shooting and hunting. That's what they'd been brought up to, the Wentworths. Dad reckoned that your uncle wanted time to stand still after that, as if he could put the old place in mothballs. Mind, it hasn't changed a lot since I was a kid. Still, that's the way it is.' Deeks had finished the account. Having no more to say he stubbed out the cigarette then, as if unable to bear the sight of any debris left in the wood, stooped to pick it up. 'You had a bit of good luck at the concert I hear,' he said cheerfully. Caroline, however, didn't feel very cheered. None of what she'd heard so far gave her cause to.

'My father managed to sod that up as well,' she told him gloomily.

'Oh, how did he manage that then?'

'I asked Denis Tunstall to the concert and my father made it clear he didn't approve of me going out with somebody from a council estate. We were going to a party but Denis went off in a huff and I haven't heard anything from him since.'

'He's like his father, stubborn. He'll come round.'

'You think so? I mean it's a bit terminal isn't it, telling somebody they're not good enough to go out with your daughter?'

'Young Denis knows who he is and what he's worth. Go

up and see him. He's palled up with Terry, you know the fox man. Denis has been lending him a hand with the radio tracking. He does two or three nights a week for him. You know the green lane up by the old Harmers' tenancy? You'll find one or other of them up there. Whatever you do, don't look interested in foxes or Terry'll have you up to your armpits in mud and brambles chasing after them.' Deeks got off his shooting stick stiffly. 'So, I suppose we'll be seeing you at the Ebury meet dinner. Brenda's roped me in to serve the wine.'

'I don't really want to go. My mother's partnered me with Thornton Holbrooke-Jones.'

'You don't care for Thornton, then?' Deeks asked humorously.

'He's a pretentious Wally.'

'He's too used to money. He starts up one so-called dot com company, it goes bust and his father finds another quarter-million to set him up in another.'

'Try telling that to Uncle George.'

'I don't tell your uncle anything, other than in a very roundabout way. Caroline,' he added seriously, bringing the conversation back to its starting point, 'forget about this business with Robert Freer. By the time any of this affects you financially I'll be six feet under and you'll be a grandmother. Just get on and live your life the way you want it. Don't let them organise it for you.' He jerked his head to indicate the Hall. 'By the way, it's Peter to you, these days.'

Terence spent another night in pursuit of Old Rogue who in turn spent his in pursuit of Pansy who had rebuffed his diligent courtship with tail lashing and snirking. At dusk she set out with a purposeful gait to forage and hunt at the eastern end of her territory which terminated in some cottage gardens. She did not settle there for long, appearing to be moody and erratic, her attention shifting in a desultory fashion. She did not follow her usual route, which took her through an orchard and across pasture land, because the insistent presence of her paramour sent her zigzagging instead around the area of Harmers Pond. From Terence's point of view it was difficult terrain at the best of times. Marshy, dotted with sedge and heavily fortified with bramble, it provided ideal cover beneath which a fox could easily slip and he was not prepared to follow. If the pair coupled there he was unlikely to know of it.

When spectral fingers of light began to streak the sky he returned to his base in the green lane that housed Pansy's lair. With the sleeping bag pulled up to his armpits he sat on his camp stool contemplating the *raison d'être* behind Pansy's movements that night. All his tired mind could recall was a game of triangles played over her province with the sole aim of keeping him on his toes plotting co-ordinates.

As he waited for the vixen's return his chin fell on his chest in an irresistible doze. Close by an owl hooted its supremacy over a rival; the brief challenge wove itself into the fabric of his dreams to become a critical commentary on his own failings. Inadequately prepared lecture notes blew away in the wind and his irate students forced him to flee through a toffee mire that held him back. He woke suddenly with a shudder, craving for hot sweet coffee. It was likely to have been Pansy's return that jolted him into consciousness; he had developed a sixth sense when it

127

came to a question of her whereabouts. He focussed the hot eyes on her lair expecting to find the vixen curled asleep, but saw instead a white plastic pudding basin containing what appeared to be a mush of bread and milk. The food, placed like a libation, had certainly not been there before he nodded off. The tenant of the caravan, he assumed, had crept past him with it. He imagined her giving a pert curtsy before setting down the food at the feeding site. He smiled over the quaint offering until he recognised that the woman's gesture had as much purpose and meaning as his own nightly vigils.

He poured coffee from his thermos and felt in his jacket pocket for some chocolate, needing to fortify himself with fat and sugar against the cold. When his finger encountered the smooth wrapper he felt a pang of guilt as he was reminded of the mechanistic ease with which he could feed himself, satisfy his wants. Granted the dawn found him chilled and a little uncomfortable, but such minor discomforts were more than offset by his interest in the project. He had as fluent a command over resources as he had over the language of his trade, a trade he had freely chosen. The lifestyle of the caravan tenant was not chosen, her discomforts were not self-inflicted. He recalled her fear of the calor gas, a fear that prevented her from making herself a hot drink or, if she was ill, from keeping herself warm. He replaced the unwrapped chocolate in his pocket and took off over the dew-drenched field.

Balanced on his toes, Terence peered through the verdigris stains on the caravan window to be instantly reprimanded by a guttural snore from inside, an animal snarl of a snore. Somewhere in her dingy burrow beneath a pile of dirty blankets the tenant muttered her way through her dreams. Did she too dream of failing, of frustrating flight from threats through toffee mires? He took out his notebook and on a spare sheet wrote, For Robin Redbreast from the Fox Man. He put it on her milk-crate doorstep and anchored it with his small offering of chocolate which, in its own sentimental way, acknowledged the gift of bread and milk that had been left for Pansy.

By the time he had returned to his post in the green lane he found that the vixen had come home, having cut short her hunting trip. Through the hot eyes he picked out Old Rogue trailing three metres behind her, his eyes gliding like green fairy lights just above the ground. Pansy made preparations for sleep, curling herself round and round under the protecting hawthorn roots, then mysteriously changed her mind.

She emerged from her bedchamber and, sensing a break in her defences, Old Rogue advanced confidently with his neck craned in order to take a cautious sniff at her. The move was a serious misjudgement since his ardent concern for the balance of her hormones appeared unbearably irritating to her. She rounded on him, snirking furiously with her tail lashing and her ears flat against her head. He backed away respectfully. Satisfied that the correct protocol for such occasions had been followed, Pansy took to mooching about here and there without much interest. She pounced on small prey a number of times but was rewarded with only a beetle. She broke off from these activities to sprinkle on surrounding vegetation. Without taking his eyes off her, Old Rogue began to edge closer again.

For a full hour Terence observed the attraction and repulsion preamble to mating which formed itself into a shuffling dance. To say that Pansy eventually succumbed would be to put a human interpretation on the act. Survival was the maypole around which these creatures had danced, genetic survival. To procreate is to perpetuate and was in both their interests. Quite suddenly, as if on receipt of a scent signal, Pansy consented and Old Rogue mounted. By the following spring there would be a litter of fine healthy cubs. As the animals were still locked and would remain so for another thirty minutes, Terence did not disturb them by packing away his equipment; instead he returned to dozing, chin on chest, feeling that the vulpine couple had entered into a most satisfactory partnership. Soon he would have a third generation of foxes to add to his group of subjects.

He woke to hear Pansy lapping up the gift of milk and bread left by Louise. By the time Terence had packed away his equipment and departed the green lane a last look through the hot eyes showed her to be curled in luxurious sleep.

It is ambitious in the extreme for a woman to negotiate her way along a green lane in the pitch dark with the hope of finding a man she fancies. This, however, struck Caroline as the least problematic aspect of her mission to rekindle a relationship with Tanya's brother. The most challenging was to explain what she was doing there in the first place. A number of options presented themselves: the first, that she had come to apologise for her parents' behaviour the night of the concert, was roundly rejected—there was a strong risk that he would protest that he hadn't been insulted and he'd left early because he had to be up early for work. Thus Denis's pride would be rescued but how would the conversation develop from there? The second ostensible reason, she had come to thank him for supporting her at the concert, was fatuous—she had already thanked him three weeks ago. This left her with the third, a blunt and direct explanation, I've come to claim my prize, namely a dinner at the Lotus House. It sounded quirky without being blatantly sexy.

Her limited knowledge of radio tracking told her that it required one stationary observer and one mobile. There was always the risk that the man at the end of the green lane, on stationary duty, might be Terence rather than Denis, so she rehearsed for this outcome too. She would tell him that she'd come to talk to him about sabbing the Ebury Meet, that she'd like to help in whatever way she could but it was difficult under the circumstances. Perhaps she could help keep an eye on the Fox Project subjects by assisting with the radio tracking. She could then hang around chatting to Terence in the hope that Denis might show up.

Rehearsing a performance on a well lit stage, mindful of props and set, is one thing, but acting it out in complete darkness is quite another. She heard a number of electronic bleeps close by and a man's low tones repeating locations and compass points. It was difficult to gauge the identity of the speaker. Besides, sound travels at night so he could be further away than judged. Never mind, she had re-hearsed for all outcomes and confidently made her way towards him. Caroline, however, had not accounted for con-tingencies such as a sturdy arm of bramble hooking into her fleece and stabbing her thigh at the same time. Its dag-ger thorns can be both destructive and quite painful. 'Shit!'

she let forth, setting in motion those uncontrollable events normally described as an accident. A torch snapped on behind her, helpfully illuminating her efforts to disengage with the bramble which required a number of backward steps. Caroline never did deliver the well rehearsed line, largely on account of a rucksack left by the camp stool where Denis sat with his torch. Caroline tripped backwards over the rucksack into Denis's lap, knocking him sideways off his stool in the mud, herself landing on top of him.

There is no way, under such circumstances, that a woman could deliver the line, 'I've come to claim my prize.'

The Ebury Meet dinner guests had assembled for aperitifs in the drawing room. The men in their dinner jackets formed a colony of what appeared to be Emperor penguins at one end of the room where their rising self-opinionated voices added to the impression of a honking dispute over territory. Their female partners, coiffured and nail-buffered, made a little less noise in establishing who was who in this perfectly natural of all orders. They selected conversation, rather like items of jewellery, to bedeck the occasion. Caroline, well used to these gatherings at which she chose to remain a cool and sober observer, predicted that by midnight their hair, now anchored by spray and ornaments, would be hanging in strands. Self-restraint would likewise weigh anchor and find itself adrift in a sea of risqué anecdotes and sentimental truths that would slip from slurring tongues.

Already Matilda's nose had turned a little red and waxy. The banquet had taken seven days to plan and prepare during which time she trotted behind Mrs Deeks like an anxious hotelier. That morning she had got out of her bed in what Caroline called one of her nail-biting moods. By six-thirty that evening, long before the guests began to arrive, she took to nibbling the canapes. By seven she had downed a number of gins then squeezed herself into a costume designed for a mannequin. Her efforts only succeeded in concentrating a relatively equable distribution of body fat into a pear shape cruelly emphasised by a tight-fitting bolero-style jacket.

'What do you think, darling?' she twirled drunkenly for Nye's approval.

It was a mistake. Ebury Hall was Nye's stage and he trod its boards like an acclaimed Thespian. He would enter conversation grandly as if sweeping in from the wings. Guests would applaud the performance finding it more prudent to snicker with him rather than banter against him.

'Darling,' he replied, 'I've simply run out of superlatives!' It had been clear that he intended playing the wit with a smirk on his face for the rest of the evening. He started early by honing the edge of his acid humour on his wife's uncertainties.

Deeks, Caroline thought, looked as if he'd been scrubbed all over and stuffed unwillingly into a suit. She imagined his personal odour of tobacco and wood smoke trying to rise above the smell of toilet soap. Mrs Deeks, on the other hand, looked particularly stylish and at ease in a black skirt and white silk blouse. She conducted the traffic between kitchen and drawing room with the air of a Gallic restaurateur, clicking her fingers and signalling orders to the three women she had hired to assist her. She had assigned Deeks the task of servicing the County's aperitif need whilst she marched smartly between the assembled groups introducing guests to canapes with a flourish. She was in her element on these occasions.

Caroline remained in a dark recess next to the chimney breast and spied on the gathering from the comfort of a dumpy armchair. She had never enjoyed the Ebury Meet dinner and had dealt with its irritations by drifting away in her mind in pretty much the same way she had drifted away from Ebury Hall and its culture. It had been a gradual process which she likened to casting off from the bank of a river and letting the current take over. This year, however, the event was beginning to fascinate her. Three gin and tonics had gone down palatably. Usually alcohol mellows perception, at least in the initial stages of drunkenness. Not so on this occasion. Figures and personalities, far from being perceived as if moving and talking behind a membranous screen, came sharply into focus. It was as if the revelation of her father's clandestine partnership with Robert Freer and his cronies had ripped away the fragile tissue between truth and her own self-protecting indifference.

She found herself looking at each guest in turn, focussing intently on Mrs Freer, a well-made sensuous woman. She had a square face which she constantly revealed by pushing back a curtain of groomed brown hair and tucking it behind her ear. The way she kept her eyes on Nye, the way she co-ordinated her conversation with his, suggested an affair. No, not suggested, evidenced an affair beyond all reasonable doubt. Robert Freer, innocent of such goings on, looked proud of his wife and laughed at everything she said as, indeed, she did at anything Nye said.

Caroline moved on to the study of Miss Blinney, the

untouchable, the outcast, the socially invisible, except for the purposes of gossip. There was nothing to be revealed about her because the County had already stripped her down to reveal a hanger-on, interested only in Sir George's money. Caroline didn't believe that. She believed that Miss Blinney's biography and interests lay elsewhere, off camera, protected and hidden behind a pair of unrevealing green eyes. Although she'd never spoken much to the woman, she rather admired her. Miss Blinney had a way of moving , as if she had been a dancer or at least a performer of some kind. If she lit a cigarette, selected something tasty from a plate, or sipped a drink it was with complete involvement in the movements of her body. It wasn't as if she performed for an imagined public, quite the opposite, but as if purely for her own pleasure. She made very little reference to anything going on around her, other than Uncle George whose interests she served from a discreet distance, rather like a professional companion. She didn't seem to mind being on her own at all.

Having concluded that Miss Blinney was an altogether intriguing woman, Caroline then moved on to consider the merits and defects of Thornton Holbrooke-Jones. In contrast to Miss Blinney his performances were unashamedly public. If fashion demanded the garb of a toff then Thornton would be tripping around the night spots of London in topper, tails, kid gloves and swinging a cane. As it was, fashion demanded of Thornton labels and a designer air, ultra individualism, two days' worth of stubble and a passing knowledge of world markets. Since he was a self-constructed stereotype Caroline found him easy to deconstruct. It did not take a very close examination to decide he amounted to no more than his component parts—Versace suits, Armani shirts, Gucci shoes and Rolex watches. Unlike Miss Blinney he was unsubtle and lacked intrigue. Caroline, whose observations were growing more imaginative by the minute speculated about Uncle George's reactions should she tell him she had no intention of teaming up with Thornton and would prefer to go to bed with Miss Blinney. It was amazing that he was so bent on her marrying a narcissistic layabout, but since the Wentworths and the Holbrooke-Joneses went back a long way he had arbitrarily decided that once Thornton had learned to sit up straight and invest his father's money wisely, he would qualify as an eligible match for his great niece.

Thornton was at the far side of the drawing room entertaining three young women she recognised as former pony-clubbers, now graduated to Sloane Rangers. She had departed their company at around sixteen years, exchanging four hoofs for the two cycle wheels that reliably transported her to the preferred milieu of 11 Church Grove. The problem with the pony-clubbers had always been their insistence on rejuvenating old memories. Do you remember when…? Well no, she didn't remember when because she hadn't been in that particular location at that particular time—deliberately. Thornton, she decided, was at his objectionable best this evening.

'Oh Porky's is the place to be seen if you want to get anywhere,' rose above the conversation. Stringfellows was the next venue to be drawn from the mixed bag of places to be seen. One of the former pony-clubbers had evidently met with somebody of celebrity status there. 'Oh wow, did you pull?' Caroline lowered a verbal missile launcher, sighted it at Thornton's pre-frontal lobe and spattered his empty, atavistic thoughts all over the drawing-room walls.

Three stray bullets brought down the Sloane rangers. Stringfellows would never be the same again.

'Hi there.' Caroline's dark recess was about to be invaded.

'Hi, Thornton.' She gave the invader a vague wave of her hand without bothering to leave the comfort of her armchair. Fortunately a handbell tinkled, calling fifty guests to the dining room.

The diners arrived at the table to be politely shepherded according to a seating plan. Caroline made her way directly to the empty seat next to Miss Blinney. This minor disruption of the seating arrangements brought a message from Matilda via Mrs Deeks who, in turn, whispered it to Caroline. Caroline, for her part, whispered back that she preferred to remain seated next to Miss Blinney whose company she preferred to Thornton's. She had the distinct impression that Mrs Deeks was rather amused. On receipt of the reply Matilda frowned like Miss Piggy but could do little about it because the champagne had arrived to toast the Ebury Meet and accompany the first course. Corks began to pop and champagne flutes moved from bottle to table as if from a production line. The first course followed shortly after, Caroline's being a vegetarian substitute for salmon mousse. This year it was asparagus mousse with a home-made sesame biscuit. Perhaps it wasn't going to be such a bad evening after all.

'I think congratulations are in order,' said Miss Blinney. It was as if one of the portraits on the wall had spoken, so rare were Miss Blinney's utterances. 'The competition,' she reminded Caroline. 'You had to compose something, didn't you?'

Caroline replied that she'd composed a sonata and each of the movements represented 'Sounds of the House'.

Miss Blinney didn't ask her to elaborate since she seemed to have an intuitive grasp of which house was being referred to. Suddenly two hugely beautiful green eyes were turned on Caroline, flecks of amusement dancing in them. Her cupid lips extended briefly in a friendly smile. 'Very interesting,' she said. 'Perhaps we'll hear it played at the Royal Albert Hall one of these days.'

It always fell to Uncle George, as Master of the Amwell Hounds, to propose the toast. He rose, picked up his glass and, with the look of a proud bugler about to sound Last Post, addressed the guests. 'Ladies and gentlemen. It has been a critical year for the countryside. Our farmers have suffered huge losses as a result of foot and mouth, similarly our tourist industry has taken a severe blow as a result and, what is of significance to us all gathered around the table this evening, the ancient right to pursue the sport of foxhunting has been seriously challenged. It is with particular sincerity this year that I would ask you to raise your glasses to both the Ebury Meet and the preservation of rural life. Please be upstanding. Ladies and gentlemen, I give you the Ebury Meet and the future of rural England.'

It is always difficult for a non-believer finding themselves in somebody else's church. Amens get muttered, hymns hummed and one kneels, not in prayer but private reflection. Caroline got to her feet with the other guests and stood twisting the stem of her glass between finger and thumb, since she was damned if she was going to toast the Ebury Meet. Usually the half-hearted gesture went unnoticed; this year her ploy failed.

'Not raising your glass, Caroline?' came Nye's incisive tone from the far end of the table.

'Evidently not, Father.' She tried to make a joke of it.

Uncle George coughed gruffly, or was it a suppressed growl? The transgression might have been shrugged off by the guests, now more interested in their food, had Nye not homed in again. 'Perhaps you'd like to propose an alternative toast.'

'The fox,' proposed Miss Blinney promptly. Since a Miss Blinney proposal had never been heard in public before everybody turned their faces in her direction. 'If fox hunting's a sport,' she advised Caroline, 'then you're free to put your money on the fox, if you choose.' So saying she audaciously raised her glass and chinked it with Caroline's. 'Ten to one on the first fox set up,' she toasted. The guests were seated once again and her timely diplomacy should have brought the matter to a close.

'Since we're taking bets,' said Nye, 'I'll have fifty to one on three to the hunt and nil to the saboteurs. What about you, Caroline? Fifty to one on your friends?'

'God,' Thornton sneered, 'you don't support those crusties do you?'

'What do you mean by crusties?' Caroline asked curtly.

'Slobs that don't bother to wash and live off the state.'

'Since we're into stereotypes, Thornton, the Amwell Hunt Saboteurs include a lecturer in animal behaviour, two PhD students, an engineer, an accountant, a farm labourer and a bus driver—people who'd rather go to work than swan around London touting for charlie.'

The street-wise slang was not lost on the guests. The County spine stiffened and Miss Blinney coughed politely. Sandra Freer put her chin in her hands and regarded Caroline as if fascinated by this previously unseen side of her character.

'Do you actually intend sabotaging the hunt tomorrow?'
She licked her lips. There was something about the woman
that reminded Caroline of a lioness draped over a chaise
longue.

'No. I'm not a member of the Hunt Saboteurs, I just know
people who are.'

'Obviously you agree with them.'

'Yes,' said Caroline unreservedly.

'How can you justify sabotaging somebody's enjoyment
of sport?'

'Because it's cruel.'

'Try telling that to poultry farmers round here,' suggested
Robert Freer. She found such empathy with the poultry
farmer a bit rich coming from a man whose only interest
in his patch of the countryside was to develop it.

'Most chickens,' Caroline pointed out in no uncertain
terms, 'are kept behind bars in concrete factories.'

'Rubbish! I can name at least half a dozen farms round
Amwell alone that have gone free range,' said Robert
Freer.

'Okay then how many free range chicken do they lose
to foxes?' Caroline demanded. He didn't have an answer so
Nye involved Deeks in the argument.

'They're not exactly loved by gamekeepers either, are
they, Deeks?'

'They can be a problem, if they're not checked,' agreed
Deeks.

'So how do you deal with them?' Sandra Freer wanted
to know.

'I trap them humanely and shoot them.'

Thornton, now recovered from the blow to his ego came
back in the ring with hunting as a more humane form of

culling. As far as Caroline could remember the last time Thornton sat on a horse he fell off it and never got back on again and certainly didn't ride to the hounds. It was most likely too that his only sight of a fox was an urban one raiding a litter bin around the area of Chelsea Harbour.

'We're talking about hunting for sport, deliberately hounding an animal to its death,' she snapped causing him to raise his eyebrows as if she seemed to possess only half his brain cells.

'So you think trapping an animal and shooting it is better?'

'I didn't say that. I was talking about deliberately hounding an animal to its death.'

'So you're talking about intention not the degree of suffering?' Sandra Freer re-re-entered the conversation. 'On that basis you'd disagree with hunting and agree with trapping.'

'No, I don't agree with trapping either.'

'Is there anything you do agree with?'

'I think we should allow nature to balance things out.'

'My god, there wouldn't be many pheasants left here if you had your way,' said Robert Freer whose plans for a golf course would entirely decimate the stock. Caroline resisted pointing this out to him and offered research findings instead.

'The number of pheasants lost to foxes, without culling, is far less than gamekeepers estimate.'

'According to the experts,' Nye addressed Sandra Freer loudly.

'Oh we all need one of those, don't we?' agreed the lioness who had probably draped herself over his body at some time or other.

'The ancient right to hunt.' Sir George sounded his sonorous authority on the subject. 'You can't just jettison people's rights.'

'There was an ancient right to bait badgers, bulls and bears and watch cocks scratch each other's eyes out but they've all been banned.'

'You can't compare badger baiting to fox hunting,' scoffed Thornton.

'No,' agreed Caroline. 'Baiting and cock fighting were typically pursued by the working classes and foxhunting is supported by wealth and power.'

Thornton was about to point out that, like most saboteurs, she talked like a left-wing bigot when Sir George decided to put a final seal on the argument.

'The ancient right to hunt foxes by people from all walks of life, unobstructed by riff-raff is what I'll be defending at the meet tomorrow and if any of them turn up with the idea of sabotaging a sport we all enjoy I can assure you they'll be given short shrift.' His palm slapped the table and that seemed to be as good as the Speaker's final word in parliament.

'Hear, hear,' chorused the County and Caroline decided it would be better to leave things there. Nye, however, decided otherwise.

'I'm afraid my daughter doesn't appreciate that in banning hunting, shooting and fishing that she would be responsible for putting people out of work which doesn't sound like much of a pro-working-class agenda to me.' There is a point at which temper wells and must spill over. It had been reached.

'That's good coming from you!' Caroline exploded. 'If you had your way Ebury Hall would be turned into a golf club, sod whether it affects anybody's employment.' She should not have opened her mouth, but four gin and tonics don't interact well with champagne and out hopped the truth. Mrs Deeks whirled round from a task occupying her by the sideboard, eyes wide and glaring. Deeks stopped pouring wine and Miss Blinney's elegant little shoe tapped sharply at Caroline's shin. The silence that followed was awesome and threatened to endure for ever. Sandra and Robert Freer sat side by side like a pair of gob-smacked twins.

'Well,' said Nye, 'since Ebury Hall will eventually be yours, Caroline, *virgo intacta* so to speak, I can assure you that neither your mother nor myself would change anything here without your full consent. So, whether you wished it to be a golf club or a sanctuary for lame vulpines would be entirely in your hands. You're in a very privileged position. Isn't that so, Mrs Deeks?'

*Virgo intacta* had been deliberately selected to suggest nunnish moralising and privilege to portray a spoilt little rich girl, a Patricia Hurst fighting the class war. Caroline understood only too well how her father had succeeded in industry. He had spent years rebutting boardroom critics, compared to which his own daughter was a mere novice. She had not eaten enough to mop up the excess alcohol and felt drunk. Observations which had originally struck her as sharp and colourful had dissolved into opaque vagueness. Nevertheless she did notice Thornton leave the table for a moment or two and return with a slight smudge of white powder at the end of his nose. His cheeks were red, his speech accelerating, increasing in pitch and volume. Had common sense not laid a firm hand on her shoulder she would have pointed to him and told Uncle George that this was the way the eligible suitor spent his father's money. The former pony clubbers were decorating his jokes with excessive giggling which rose as if in startled flight above the general drone of conversation.

Boom, titter went the collective voice of the County, clatter went the knives and forks on the plates. Boom, titter, clatter, all of it playing a preposterous pizzicato on her nerve strings. The dinner proceeded, course upon course, until it reached Mrs Deeks's highest culinary achievement, a stuffed boar's head. An idiosyncratic Ebury Hall ritual was to beat in the main course which involved banging knife handles loudly on the table whilst singing 'A hunting we will go'. Thornton seemed to have ditched all inhibitions and sang in a screeching falsetto accompanied by his chorus of Sloane Rangers. Caroline looked from face to face, from the carnivorous Mrs Freer to the charlie-touting Thornton and declared that it would all make bloody good television, if it wasn't so close to home. Thornton and the pony clubbers had hunched their shoulders as if riding horses, banging their knife handles in unison. They gave the impression that they were riding in her direction.

'Oh a hunting we will go, a hunting we will go. We'll catch a sab and put him in the bag and never let him go.' The last thing Caroline remembered before staggering drunkenly to her feet and holding on to the table for support was the way the boar stared back at them through eyes made of figs.

'Come along, Caroline, beat in the boar, beat in the boar.'

Caroline glared, 'Why don't you just grow up, Thornton? Just fucking well grow up.' Having got it off her chest Caroline now had to confront the problem of leaving the dining room without throwing up. Having tracked the early symptoms of total inebriation the competent Mrs Deeks rushed the length of the table, grabbed her arm and steered her into the hall where she produced a projectile of vomit.

In the bedroom where Caroline lay, still stupefied by alcohol, heavy velvet drapes muffled sounds of the meet gathered on the drive below. Close to her window the branch of a naked winter oak configured itself into a shifting lacy pattern of twigs against a dark grey sky. Although a squally south-westerly set them rattling against the glass, the silence within the room seemed to deny the tumultuous weather outside, so too a watercolour in which three nudes basked by an arabesque pool in a quieter and more distant clime.

Before tilting into oblivion the previous night Caroline vaguely remembered Miss Blinney assisting her up the stairs and into bed. Was it imagination or had she said, as she tucked her in, 'I'm afraid foxes aren't the only thing they hunt round here, dear'? A sharper memory returned bringing acute embarrassment. Caroline had told her what a wonderful person she was and worth twice the county women. She couldn't recall Miss Blinney's reply but was left with the impression that she had slipped quietly away without comment.

Caroline woke to take a red-eyed look at the consequences of her behaviour which would have to be redressed. Once the household were off and on the trail of the fox she would slip quietly back to Bristol. If she stayed it would be to face a barrage of Matilda's hand-wringing reproaches, Nye's acidic remarks and Sir George's strictures on common decency.

When a thumping head sent her to the window for fresh air she found herself looking down on the assembled hunting party in the drive below. Observed from this elevated position they appeared to be players who had changed into their costumes ready for the next act. Mrs Deeks, whose role hadn't changed from the night before, was still in her black skirt and white silk blouse as she served glasses of pale gold sherry from a silver tray. As was customary the Master of the Hounds took his last. Astride an enormous dappled hunter, he stooped, taking the stem of the glass between his index finger and thumb, a dapper gesture for such a bullish man. He raised it to his lips and toasted the Ebury Meet.

'To the Ebury Meet,' responded the rest of the field liturgically. Dotted along the driveway, mere extras on the stage, were members of the public in twos and threes and family groups. Caroline caught sight of Spikey moving amongst them with a sheaf of leaflets accompanied by an older couple. At first she had felt isolated from the proceedings, as if immersed in a diving bell, until the sight of Spikey punctured her feeling of disassociation. Since the last thing she wanted was to be hailed as one of his diehard supporters she moved back from the window a little to avoid being spotted. The company below, however, were all aware of her presence and studiously avoided looking up. There was a bad atmosphere, largely generated by Sir George's pent-up fury which superficial good manners prevented him from venting in public. It would be better if Spikey and his fellow believers furled up their opinions and took their leaflets elsewhere.

Uncle George's ill-temper, caused by her behaviour at the dinner, was further inflamed by the sight of the saboteurs. He was edgy, tight-jawed, even his horse rippled and fidgeted as if it had a burr under its saddle. Nye, she thought, looked veritably triumphant. But Nye was not the sort of person to limit his sport to one success, such as the public disgrace of his daughter—there was going to be trouble. Matilda handsomely presented in her riding habit and stoutly in control of her mount was not, however, in command of her anxiety. She bit her lip and looked nervously at her uncle.

Caroline felt inclined to retreat quietly with her regrets. She should not have given way and gone to the dinner in the first place, let alone get plastered to take on the County in such an uneven verbal contest. But the shadowy, patient young woman, who'd spent years avoiding trouble, was now a fiction, a flimsy film of cells nurturing a festering impatience.

The buffoonery between Spikey and his cousin, PC Longfellow, was missed by all but Caroline who enjoyed the spectacle from her window as if from a box at the theatre. Spikey peered through his glasses with ostentatious myopia as the officer explained that the Master of the Hounds had lodged a complaint.

'Lodged a complaint, officer?'

'Trespassing.'

'Trespassing!' The saboteur scratched his head like an ignorant yokel. How could he be trespassing at a public event? He couldn't quite follow the gentleman's logic. Spikey and his cousin's comedy routine, was considerably enhanced by the difference in their respective heights. PC Longfellow being taller and broader than the alleged offender, appeared to loom over him whilst the diminutive saboteur seemed to be looking up his nose.

'Not taking the piss, are we, sir?' Spikey shook his head just a little too earnestly. Walking at an unhurried pace the officer rejoined Sir George to whom he conveyed the idea that, in the absence of any affray, damage to property or threat to persons, the police had no cause to eject anybody from an event to which the public had been freely invited. Meanwhile Spikey and his helpers continued to distribute leaflets.

Sir George's seething was loud enough to turn heads and set horses prancing. 'The public are here on sufferance.'

The press photographer, who had been concentrating on an insipid portrait of a three-year-old with her arms around the neck of a foxhound, missed with his lens that which Caroline could plainly see from her window—the ugly side of human nature. The assault on Spikey was so swift and well co-ordinated that nobody on the ground could have perceived it as such.

As soon as the young police officer turned his back and returned to the car, Nye and Sir George went into conference. They came to an agreement, then parted; Sir George, leaving at a brisk trot, was preparing for the off. Halting his horse between Spikey and the onlookers whom he had been leafleting he then requested all members of the public to stand back whilst the hounds were brought under control. Finding himself stranded between the hounds and Sir George's horse, Spikey moved toward its head only to find himself being barged sideways as the dapple grey was urged into a flanking movement. He walked forward once again, the horse followed. At the same time Nye approached and halted his own mount level with Sir George's leaving Spikey sandwiched between them. To all intents and purposes two riders had drawn level with each other in order to say something. As soon as Nye had halted, Sir George nudged his grey into another flanking movement at which the creature began to prance. As the two horses, or so it seemed, were beginning to fidget, Sir George naturally had every reason to use his riding crop on his grey's flanks—except that the blow, designed to discipline the animal, landed with brutal accuracy on Spikey's temples. The job done quickly, the conspirators parted like pickpockets in a market, leaving the victim with his head in his hands and blood trickling between his fingers.

Nobody could hear Spikey cry for help above the sound of the hunting horn and the clatter of hooves. It was only when the bobbing flotilla of pink and black riding jackets retreated from the drive that his cries were heard. A fellow saboteur rushed towards him aghast, her hands thrust forward as if she expected him to faint. She cupped his elbows in her hands and looked into his face as if trying to persuade him to uncover it. All Caroline could register was his sobbing effort to raise his head, his knees buckling under him as if all he wanted to do was to reach the ground and rest. The woman who had charge of him appeared to know what she was doing: she shouted brusquely at her partner who came forward instantly and together they managed to get him into a car that left the scene slowly. Spikey was borne to hospital with his glasses frame protruding gruesomely from his eye socket. Shortly after the wind caught a sheaf of bloodstained leaflets and sent them helter-skeltering across the drive like russet leaves.

Caroline sat on the floor with her hands over her ears as if the familiar sounds of the house might come and reclaim her. The senses are weak and so willing to be cosseted by creature comforts such as the warmth of a bed. She was not going to go back to bed and sleep it all off. She remained on the floor, devoutly resisting temptation, as if imposing on her buttocks the same discipline that was being suffered by her conscience. She had seen what she had seen—her uncle raise a riding crop and bring it down on Spikey's temple, three ugly blows that he would certainly have spared the flanks of his horse.

Uncle George had always been a peppery old bachelor, intolerant of change, yes, but the man who had struck those blows was not recognisable as the same man. All those years somebody quite different had been hiding behind the persona of Uncle George. Provoked by Spikey's leaflets, out he'd leapt in the form of demonic temper. Uncle George had presided over her childhood, a grandfather figure, a little stern perhaps, respected for his authority rather than loved, but always dependable.

Caroline put her head in her hands and sobbed. This wasn't the first time a dependable male had let her down. One June morning another trusted man had been revealed as naive illusion. Daddy had been charming and good looking, a daddy to be shown off to giggling teenage girlfriends until she'd seen a woman's thighs wrapped around his waist and heard his bestial groans in the wood. That morning dependable Uncle George had become a red-faced brute whipping a man with his riding crop in a regular, orgasmic release of fury.

As the shock and sobs began to subside Caroline confronted the fact that a crime had been committed by her uncle, her father had connived in it, she had witnessed it. Human decency demanded that she go to the police and tell them what she had seen. Peace, comfort and self-interest pointed out that, since she could not both blow the whistle and continue to accept the support of her family she should say nothing. Truth-telling is all very well in theory but it takes courage to stand up in court and denounce those on whom one depends. On the other hand nor could she continue to live silently with the truth. What was seen, said, done could not then be reversed.

Caroline dwelt for a long time on what struck her as an ethical horror story—for the honest human being truth is unalterable. However well one swaddles recollections in comfortable excuses, the facts of the matter will come worming through. If she had anything more to do with Ebury Hall she knew the truth would eat into her conscience with the recollection of Spikey sobbing, conquered by pain, and his cause living on in the way bloodstained leaflets blew in the wind.

Caroline packed a suitcase with a few treasured knick-knacks and some clothes which she hadn't taken to Bristol. She left Ebury Hall for good without leaving a note. One only left notes and explanations for loved ones. Wrapped in their respective embrace of ambition and infatuation she doubted whether Nye and Matilda would even notice she'd gone.

She walked along the drive to the lane, the memory of the Ebury meet receding in flashes of hunting pink and the bobbing black of her uncle's riding hat in arrogant retreat from a crime he thought he had the right to commit. Where the drive met the lane and a trail of horse dung turned right, she turned left. Once her feet were on the public highway, she became a public person, a member of the community with a will of her own. One step led simply to another, her progress daunted only by the thought that she might turn coward and relent. The solitude of the lane and the robust punches of the west wind, entirely compatible with the idea of loosening the moorings and setting sail, urged her forward. Quite what shore she might land upon she had no idea, she only knew that whatever course was set it would lead ultimately to independence from Ebury Hall. She felt a little raw, exposed, but at least she had some money and a room. In six months she would have taken her finals. In the meantime she would return any money belonging to Nye and Matilda and apply for a bank loan to see her through, which is what most students had to do.

She did not take a last look at Ebury Hall but simply turned a bend in the lane and the past went out of mind.

Caroline thought she had been alone in the lane enjoying the first euphoric wave of freedom until round the next bend came a bundle of quarrelsome rags. She had never seen such a scruffy woman before. She moved forward with an air of muttering, dishevelled annoyance, a rag doll that had lost its temper and burst its seams. As the woman drew level with her, she stopped, hunched her shoulders, and screwed her fist as if about to give the young woman a good talking to. Accosted so oddly, Caroline put down her suitcase and waited, since there was something about the behaviour that pinned her to the spot. The strange woman was clearly suffering from an intense internal debate, one that had lasted for so many years it had etched itself into deep furrows across her brow. Although she appeared to be entirely in the grip of a dreadful apprehension, as soon as she began to focus on the young passer-by, her expression changed to one of mild appraisal which Caroline took to be a kind of greeting. Anxiety drained from her face and in its place came curiosity as she studied the long brown freshly-washed hair; with her head tilted like a little bird on a perch, she puzzled over the way it fell over the younger woman's shoulder into the shape of a treble clef.

'Hi.' Caroline smiled politely. The little woman did not smile in return. Instead her arm shot out pointing stiffly in the direction she was travelling.

'Today they'm killing foxes,' she announced and passed rapidly on her way. 'Cunt...cunt...cunt.' The sound of her cursing voice retreated. Caroline picked up her suitcase and continued in her own direction. After a few steps she felt drawn to turn around and study the spot where the ragged woman had disappeared. The encounter was yet one more bizarre image gummed onto the tumultuous collage of the morning.

It was five in the morning before Terence managed to pamper his aching limbs in a hot bath then lay them to rest under warm blankets. He was a very physical man who enjoyed his sleep in the way he enjoyed food, drink, sex, sunshine and belly laughter. He did not, therefore, take kindly to being levered out of his dreams by bad news. Babs's voice, strained and terse from an effort to keep it under control, came through the receiver. 'Terry, I'm phoning from Amwell General. I'm afraid there's been a serious assault on Spikey. He was leafleting at the meet and they trapped him between two horses and beat him over the head with a riding crop. His glasses frame punctured his eyeball.'

153

'Christ!' Terence sat up in bed as if prodded into wakefulness by a cattle probe.

'He's in a bad way, Terry. Alan and I brought him into the A and E. They've told his parents that the retina's badly damaged, the prognosis isn't good. They'll be operating at lunch time but they don't think there's much chance of saving the sight in his left eye. His hearing's been damaged as well.'

'Who the bloody hell did that to him?'

'The Master of the Hounds and the owner of the Hall. Spikey told the A and E that his daughter witnessed the attack. He saw her looking out of a bedroom window.'

'A hostile witness,' observed Terence.

'I don't suppose she'll willingly testify against her relatives,' agreed Babs.

'How's Spikey taking it?'

'He was in a lot of pain when we brought him in so they gave him a sedative. We won't know much more until after he comes round from the operation.'

'I think we should call off the campaign.'

'No way. If you'd seen the mess they made of his face you wouldn't even think of it. During ten years with St John's Ambulance I don't think I've ever seen such a bad injury.'

'That's one good reason for calling it off.'

'Spikey would never forgive us!'

'What do the others think?'

'Alan's for going ahead and so are Ned and Denis. Dave's going to try and bunk off work and join us later.'

It was going to be a bad day, Terence knew it. Nevertheless he laced up boots still clogged with mud and snatched stiff damp clothes from a radiator. He left the house with news of the assault still yapping at his heels as if to drive him back into the fray. Even the scudding clouds appeared portentous. Warm wet westerlies buffeted people, stirred up feelings—it was not a morning for rational reflection, the restless wind wouldn't permit it. What he felt in his rumbling guts was the knowledge that one violent incident invariably led to others. An attack on one saboteur strengthened the resolve of the others, that resolve transmitted itself to the huntsmen who responded with even greater ruthlessness. Each clash engendered its own history until the central issue, blood sports, sank under the strata of legal action. Nationally it was rare for a week to pass during the fox hunting season without somebody taking a blow, taking the wrath of the hunters like punch-bags. It was a wrath that had been increasing proportionately with the success of sabotaging and the turning tide of public opinion. Hunt supporters responded with cunning and violence, laundering their bad behaviour through persuasive barristers and mealy-mouthed magistrates.

The acute injustice of poor Spikey being wheeled anaesthetised into the operating theatre with what remained of his sight and hearing had smudged out the achievements of the night's study. His meticulous field notes, his photographs and recordings of vulpine communication appeared trivial by comparison.

As he walked up Long Coombe toward Pikes Wood Terence became conscious of his stomping boots and expanding indignation. He halted, breathed deeply to regain control of himself and addressed the Master of the Hounds out loud, as if justice was more achievable if enunciated in an imagined courtroom.

'Tell me, Sir George, how it is that a grown man,

chairman of a major electronics company, a leading light in the Conservative Party who has existed on this earth for seventy-odd years could vent his wrath on such a mild bunch of people as the Amwell saboteurs? They're a hotchpotch of animal lovers, conservationists and cautious middle-class liberals for Christ's sake, there's not a single anarchist, or extremist amongst them—nobody there, Sir George to topple you from privilege, yet here you are beating the shit out of one of them like a thug. Some youth with too much booze in him smashes a street light, ah, that would be different, that bit of vandalism would be worth at least thirty hours' community service. You, on the other hand, guilty of GBH, are going to leave the court with a smirk on your chops.'

Nipped by anxiety, Terence headed toward Pikes Wood again until halted by the sight of Ned approaching the same spot from a different direction. He raised his hand in greeting, then pointed back down the Coombe to indicate that he would keep surveillance in the green lane.

Stationed in the green lane Terence unpacked his equipment and fussed over finding a level spot for his camp stool. He took time over the tasks in the same way nervous airline passengers pay close attention to unwrapping the boiled sweet and unfolding the newspaper before take-off. The ritual complete he focussed his field glasses on Ned stationed at the edge of Pikes Wood. There was as much contrast in appearance between him and the hunting party as there was in their respective values. On the one side there was a party of smartly attired riders astride handsome, glossy-flanked thoroughbreds, and on the other a threadbare postgraduate clad in a fading parka astride a lofty bag of bones of indeterminate breed.

Ned was holding a mobile phone and a radio receiver—modern communication juxtaposed with an ancient mode of transportation, if indeed his cantankerous horse could be described as such. When 'Partner' was urged to proceed, he stood where he was, stiff and obstinate. When reined back, the animal would move perversely forward. Thus conveyed, the rider's thin and elongated features would appear over the top of a hedge like an exclamation mark, saying 'whoah' to proceed and 'ged hup there' in order to stop. Having rescued the creature from the veterinary's needle he called it Partner and accommodated entirely to its way of going about things. Partner, having trained his rider, now looked forward to a life of ease.

Terence took another look at Ned and his mount, noting a certain correspondence between the long, gloomy nose of the horse and the gaunt, angular face of its rider. There was something about Ned that reminded him of the proverbial third son of the fairy tale, the ne'er-do-well who was discharged from his father's house to seek his fortune, armed not with brand new sword and shiny shield, but with stick and tree bark.

Ned and Partner provided only a momentary distraction before he returned to his stool thinking about Spikey's operation and what the rest of the day would bring. He closed his eyes to quell his unease and imagined that when he breathed out he expelled his anxiety and when he breathed in he inhaled tranquillity. He paid attention to the mellow song of a blackbird and the way its tune changed to one of alarm when a hedge sparrow broke from cover. Shortly after, a robin ticked its own assertive alert as if to abolish the danger from its territory purely by sound. Birdsong told its own stories.

Perhaps one day he too would tell a story, a simple story for children about a beautiful vixen with a face like a heart. He would call her Pansy. She would have a personality in place of bleeps through a receiver. Her movements across her territory would become adventures not mere co-ordinates on a map. It would be a childishly optimistic tale where wrongs were always righted and nature triumphed. Before he wrote his story he would have to turn off the science in him. Science was all about sharpened pencils and objectivity whereas art was about crayons and subjectivity. Art was a liberal parent permitting irrational sentiment and he was a very sentimental man. Yet...he had laid out dead foxes on laboratory slabs, dissected them, examined their teeth, their entrails and, as sturdily as any forensic expert, had inspected the remains of those subjects that had been poisoned or snared. He had photographed the victims of cruelty, one with a crossbow bolt in its chest that had been left painfully wedged in a garden fence to starve, another that had been shot through the eye with an airgun pellet. Reality could always be relied upon to nudge aside the sentimental man like a bully in a crowd, crop-haired, storm-trooping, brutish.

The hospital corridor was another kind of public highway, visitors coming and going along its length, patients crossing at junctions on trolleys or in wheelchairs. It had been the sense of a public eye on a public highway which had diverted Caroline from taking a bus back to Bristol. Instead she took a taxi to Amwell General. Alter ego, the public eye in one's conscience as she trundled her suitcase into the bus terminus, asked, what would people think of you if you just skedaddled back to Bristol without going to see Spikey and offering yourself as a witness to the assault.

A nurse on duty in A and E guardedly told her that Phillip was comfortable, asleep and his parents were with him—no more than two visitors around the bed please. The drawn curtains around Spikey's bed seemed to signal the seriousness of his condition, further emphasized by PC Longfellow, now off duty, sitting close by with a grave expression.

'I'm Caroline Nye, I live at Ebury Hall, Sandpits. I witnessed the assault on Phillip Longfellow and I'm prepared to make a statement.' The offer sounded unnecessarily formal and seemed to amuse Bouncer.

'I'm pleased to hear it but since I'm off duty you'll have to say it all over again to the duty officer. How would you like your statement presented, hand-written or typed? We like to give our customers choices, see.' The humour brought a wan smile from Caroline.

'How is he?' Bouncer put his finger to his lips to indicate they could be overheard and whispered that the outlook wasn't good. There had been further haemorrhaging in the last hour and the doctor had ordered an MR scan before proceeding with the operation. Spikey would almost certainly lose sight and hearing on his left side. Bouncer watched her face drain of colour and wondered whether he should prop her up on the chair since she looked at risk of fainting. At that moment two nurses arrived to wheel Spikey's bed from behind the curtain. Caroline saw only a head swaddled in bandages with a cheek exposed, livid from the bruising it had taken. A drip followed behind him and behind that, came his parents, shocked and depressed like mourners at a funeral. Caroline burst into tears, shaking and sobbing and repeating, 'I could have stopped them, I could have stopped them.'

'So could I,' said Bouncer. 'I could see your uncle working himself up when he was told there was nothing the police could do. He took it that the law was on the side of the sabs and he didn't like it very much. I think he'd decided then that he'd have a go at Spikey. I keep wondering whether we should have stayed a bit longer to keep an eye on things. Where are you going?' he broke off to indicate the suitcase.

'Back to Bristol—for good. I'm not going back to the Hall, ever.'

'It would be very difficult for you, I mean if you're going to act as a witness against your father and uncle. I shouldn't say this as a policeman but are you sure you want to go ahead with the statement?'

'Absolutely, I've made up my mind.'

'In that case I'll give you a lift to the station. You'll feel a bit better once it's on paper. After that I'll give you a lift back to Bristol.' When Caroline protested that she would go back by bus Bouncer insisted that Denis wouldn't forgive him if he allowed her to go back alone.

'Where is he?' she asked.

'Out sabbing, the mad bugger. Spikey said he wanted the campaign to go ahead, that was just before they put a needle in his arm to shut him up.'

'Where?'

'Where what?'

'Where are they sabbing?'

'If I knew that I wouldn't tell you. The best thing you

can do for Spikey is go back to Bristol and keep your head down. We don't want you undermining the case for the prosecution by being seen with the saboteurs—the defence would claim your evidence was unreliable.'

'I don't see why.'

'That's because you don't think like a barrister. At the moment you're the only witness to what happened. Our star turn, so we'll want you in court looking like a member of the public without any axes to grind.'

'You should have been a lawyer.'

'Did I ever tell you how I came to be in the force? It was like this. I was at Borstal at the time, completing me further education so to speak, when Mr Jackson, that was our careers teacher, called me into his office like and says, "Now then, Bouncer, me son I want you to give some thought to your future. Apart from safe cracking and a few mugging vacancies we don't have a lot on the list, apart from two opportunities, one for a police officer and t'other for a ballet dancer..." '

A nurse passed them in the corridor and, well used to PC Longfellow and his colloquial tales in A and E, grinned. 'Don't believe a word he says,' she advised Caroline. As they reached his car, however, the amiable policeman was replaced by the grave relative of a victim.

'I know Spikey can mouth off a bit when he gets a bee in his bonnet but he didn't deserve this. Thanks for offering to make a statement.'

'I couldn't just turn my back and walk away.'

'A lot of people do.' They left Amwell General and rejoined the public highway, each mile under the wheels putting distance between herself and the influence of Ebury Hall. Deeks's advice was the only memory of the place that she wanted to travel with her. Just get on and live your life the way you want it. Don't let them organise it for you.

What better way to avoid the tiger's eye than to burrow under his den! Old Rogue had been lying curled asleep beneath the gamekeeper's garden shed at Ebury Hall, not a stone's throw from where Sir George's pink coats sipped their sherry. He didn't so much as raise a sleepy eyebrow when a hunting horn sounded the off. Nor did he stir during the first hour of the meet whilst the pack snuffled around, the novice hounds yelping excitedly over every beguiling scent. It was as if the old fox knew that their efforts would not consolidate until the more experienced dogs began to concentrate on a specific trail. As soon as a hunting horn sounded from the north-east, however, Terence picked up a change in Old Rogue's signal indicating that he was on the move. Quite often, at this stage of a hunt, foxes within the vicinity would begin to shift restlessly around their territories, some fleeing their home ranges for good as if the persecution of their species caused a vulpine diaspora.

Tucked behind a hedge, unable to see what was going on, Terence felt as isolated as a blind man in a busy street, his antenna substituting for a white stick that probed experimentally for sonic feedback. He held it up and moved it over the airwaves, tuning it to news of the war. At the bottom of the valley, as the stationary observer, he could only sit tight and wait for Ned to give him the correct bearings for each of the tagged subjects. The mobile phone rang shrilly bringing a sharp rebuke from a robin perched on a nearby tree stump. It was Ned reporting that he had picked up Old Rogue in his field glasses, trotting at a confident pace in the direction of Pikes Wood. It was instinctive for a fox to seek dense cover. In the wood he could pass incognito over criss-crossing trails of animal scent as confusing to a hound's nose as a cluttered map to the human eye. The animal's steady pace indicated that he wasn't under pressure and could afford to conserve his energy.

Terence focussed his field glasses on Ned on his shambling mount, his long arms dealing slowly and methodically with mobile phone, radio tracker, map and field glasses with the air of a lugubrious octopus. Ned's style was mirrored by the horse whose long thin legs tentatively explored the ground under its hooves. This morning Partner was not in a co-operative mood; he had halted and got his head down to chomp swaths into the bright green pasture that rolled down Long Coombe. 'Whoa!' The perverse order rang out across the valley to no avail. How could it be that somebody as laid-back as Ned had chosen such a cantankerous companion?

Ned raised his glasses suddenly and focussed them on a patch of stinging nettles at the wood's edge. Shortly after, he reported that Old Rogue, having milled around in the wood for a while, had just left heading briskly north-east. The animal's chosen course was puzzling since it appeared to put him at risk. The hounds were now approaching steadily from the east. Although they seemed engrossed in random olfactory investigations, if they continued their course it would intersect with Old Rogue's retreat where they would pick up his scent. On the surface it appeared that the animal was throwing himself into the enemy's path, but since another fox had moved off in the same direction an hour previously, Old Rogue was evidently utilising the same scent trail. Terence had often witnessed the phenomenon of a fox using another's trail then looping off a number of times before departing in a totally different direction. It confirmed yet again the cunning devices at a fox's disposal to confuse the nose of its ancient enemy.

Of the project's four tagged subjects one had moved rapidly out of radio contact and out of harm's way. Old Rogue was now retreating briskly northward. Cocky young Paintbrush gave a debonair wave of his white-tipped brush then bolted early in the proceedings toward the Chepton Veins, an uncharted network of underground fissures and streams favoured by cavers. Once a fox went to ground there it would never be caught. A slender vulpine body could squeeze itself through a crack in the ground then follow ancient subterranean highways to appear miles away, often where water spouted from between riven limestone lips, tumbling miraculously into the world as if discharged with the broken waters of a rocky womb.

Pansy was the only subject who had not moved. She still slept at ease under a rusty trailer behind the abandoned tenancy of Harmers Farm; it was about time she too was off. The yelp of a hound caused Ned to swing round in the saddle with the field-glasses to his eyes whilst Terence fidgeted over the thought of Pansy asleep so close to the advancing pack. He hated this stage of the hunt, it was the phoney war that preceded the setting up of the first fox, the stage where every shout and blast on the horn sent everybody into a frenzy, although there was no action to be taken until a fox had been moved. At that point the saboteurs would become a well co-ordinated platoon, observing and communicating with the active unit whose task was to play the tricks and divert the pack from their quarry. To his relief, the hounds short-circuited the path taken by Pansy earlier that morning and continued instead along the route taken initially by Old Rogue.

The hounds came into view, their efforts now more concerted, giving them the appearance of a single body at work. Once the lead hound began to bay it would be with the authority of a baton-tapping conductor. Then the canine choir would sing with one voice and woe betide the fox.

Terence stiffened as they advanced rapidly across Long Coombe toward Pikes Wood, passing less than a hundred metres from Ned and Partner. He could not hear any human voices nor the hunting horn, which gave him the feeling that the dogs were out of range of command. He saw Ned shift uneasily in his saddle, an unease which recommended itself to his own morbid imagination. He seemed so isolated, so vulnerable up there on the hillside. Although he had never heard of foxhounds turning on a man, catastrophes happened, there was always a first time. Try as he might, he could not suppress the scenario in which Sir George's hounds played tug of war with Ned's thighbone.

With a more lofty view of affairs at the top of Long Coombe, Ned reported that an untagged subject, or stranger, had broken from Pikes Wood, with the pack on his scent. He broke off again to contact the active unit who proved to be perfectly positioned. From about a kilometre away in the opposite direction from the flight path of the retreating fox Terence heard the highly amplified recording of a pack of hounds in full cry being trumpeted out from discarded disco equipment. The effect was instantaneous and delightful to watch since it brought complete disarray to the pack, some of which insisted on continuing in one direction whilst the majority followed the call of the fictitious pack in the other. They received a sharp rebuke from Sir George's horn which was immediately countermanded by a hearty blow from the saboteurs' own heavily amplified instrument. The ghostly pack continued to yelp and bay, an utter cacophony but to Terence's ears the sweetest music. He looked through his field glasses at Ned, who saluted the success with both thumbs in the air. The hounds were still galloping down Long Coombe toward Ebury Hall, the decoy sound beckoning like siren song. Soon they would arrive at the end of the run to find nothing more than a mud-splattered vehicle innocently chugging away.

'Is 'er runnin'?' Terence smelt Louise even before he saw her. She stood in the middle of the green lane in a stooped beckoning posture giving her an ancient and wizened appearance that impressed on him the timeless tragedy of her condition.

'Not at the moment,' he explained, 'that noise is made by the saboteurs. It's only a recording played over a loud speaker—it's done to distract the hounds and give the fox a chance to get away.' Louise nodded gravely, satisfied with the explanation. She relaxed then moulded herself into a wheedling shape.

'Chocolate,' she reminded him slyly. The gesture irritated him; nevertheless he took a bar from his jacket pocket and handed it to her. She snatched the offering without thanking him and scurried off to eat it like a cur with a bone. Satisfied, she sat herself down in the wet grass with her arms around her bony knees to observe the Fox Man at work. The way she sat in attendance reminded him of an old collie dog he used to own. Bruce would lie for hours, chin flat to the ground, his eyes miraculously rotating without so much as a quiver of his hair, yet, if his master made a move to leave the room, Bruce would be at the door ahead of him as swift as his own shadow. Sometimes that shadow would appear by a cupboard, the one where biscuits were kept. He had always felt an obligation to reward those long hours of patient watchfulness by explaining out loud what he was doing. Now he felt equally obliged to think out loud for the benefit of Louise regardless of whether her poor diseased mind could assimilate the information. United by their concern for Pansy, Robin Red Breast and the Fox Man sat either side of the green lane. They seemed unlikely comrades, she with her haunches in the mud, he perched on his dry campstool like a local chieftain tuning in to the whereabouts of his subjects.

Having fled into the Veins, Paintbrush was now out of tracking range. Old Rogue's signal was also very weak, his rapid retreat had put him well out of danger for the time being. Only Pansy's signal continued to pulse consistently from the yard of Harmers Farm. Had Terence been able to see her curled nose to tail in a cosy ring he would have had even more cause to worry. Pansy had shrugged off concern for her own safety with a lazy yawn. From time to time the baying of a hound and the hunting horn was registered with a slight tweak of an ear, then consigned to the stream of sensory information that flowed past her sleeping perception. Even the more purposeful baying of the lead hound with its nose on the scent of the stranger did not bother her unduly. Rising from her bed as if woken by no more than a cock crow, she elongated herself in a luxurious stretch, took a sniff at the air like a connoisseur of fine wine, then mooched around her sleeping site as she usually did on rising. Her morning's sleep having been interrupted, she automatically undertook the routines that would precede a night's hunting. She left the site and followed the hedgerow along the lane, her easy-going pace in amiable accord with her surroundings. Within a few paces she halted and sat staring into the hedge as if musing. She seemed to have decided that the furore of sound caused by the hunting party and the volley fired in return from the saboteurs' amplifier came from a distant war that had nothing to do with her.

About a kilometre to the north of where Pansy had taken her morning stroll, another stranger entered the under-growth around the perimeter of Pikes Wood. The benefits of its strategy, however, were short-lived since, within moments, it burst from cover on the other side. The reason soon became apparent. When the pack had shot off to follow the cry of the fictitious hounds, Sir George's furious commands had succeeded in isolating a small number of dogs who thought it prudent to obey. These were now busily investigating scents at the edge of the wood. It was a relief to Terence to see a flash of handsome red disappear in the direction of the Chepton Veins. 'Stranger gone away,' he reported to Ned then followed through his glasses the route taken by the retreating fox. He watched it divert from a westerly course in order to follow a bridleway—muddied, impressed by human feet, dogs' paws, tractor tyres and horse hooves—it was as good as a public door mat over which a fox could pass with impunity. Having astutely taken advantage of the ruined scent map, the stranger then departed from it at a tangent, set a course for a position south of the Veins then disappeared from view.

The hounds ran westward hell-bent on the stranger's trail. They were followed by Sir George who was in turn pursued by Matilda sweating as profusely as her mount. The tantalising lure of fox scent disappeared suddenly through a grinning aperture. The bolt-hole, little more than a fissure in the limestone, provided enough space for a fox to squeeze through but no hound could possibly follow. The abrupt cessation of the chase caused a collision of colours as the black, tan and cream of the dogs merged in a tumbling effort to get at the quarry but their guttural protests and whining were lost in the cavernous spaces of Chepton Veins.

Sir George commanded the rabble to re-group. The defeated pack began to fan out, each hound investigating its own hunch. From a distance they looked much like a group of willing amateur helpers sweeping the area for a supposed corpse. One or two of the novices gave voice without any effect on the older, more seasoned dogs who ignored their tallyhoing. It was the first hunt of the season and relatively early in the day. Once a few more foxes had been moved, the pack would learn to act in concert. With a booming proclamation of its intent, an older hound, which had been concentrating on an area by a drystone wall, set off southeast. Its voice had the instant effect of a commanding officer. The scattered battalion listened alert and tense.

As the stranger bolted into the Veins, Pansy had been

wandering over her home range in a leisurely fashion until she crossed his scent trail. Having picked up the sweating fear left behind in the anxious impress of an almond-shaped paw in mud, she began to trot briskly in the direction of Harmers Pond. She lapped at the muddied water, circled the pond's perimeter once then set her own course in the direction of the Veins. Having agreed her bearings, Ned and Terence were able to pick her out through their field glasses. They watched her progress up Long Coombe; she halted halfway up, then hopped suddenly onto the top of a drystone wall. She trotted along it for some thirty metres before dropping out of sight on the other side.

Her behaviour left Terence to recall how scent trails formed a constantly shifting pattern of highways and byways that crossed fox territory. Certain olfactory signals acted like signposts, urging caution and pointing out necessary diversions from chosen routes. A fox-pad on a muddy track that reeked of fear, the perfume released from broken grass where man or beast had trodden, these were the legends on a fox's map.

'She's coming back!' Ned, having just observed Pansy's apparent flight to safety, now reported her return. 'She's on top of the wall again and heading for Pikes Wood…She's left the wall…still proceeding, same direction. No…no…she's changed her mind. She's just turned around, now following the wall in your direction. Can you see her?' His falsetto commentary hit Terence's receiver at full volume. 'She's going back…what the bloody hell does she think she's doing?' He was beginning to sound like a sports pundit.

The screeched commentary reached Louise's ears too and brought her to her feet, shaking her fist as if to upbraid a bad decision on the part of a referee.

"Tis they diggers,' she said. 'They bin out this mornin'
blockin' up earths. Foxes often go down the Veins, see,
under thik rock up be Pikes Wood. I know, I seen 'em do it
often enough.'

'You saw the diggers this morning?'

'Oh arr.'

Terence had to agree that the blocking of Pikes Spout
would be one of the more obvious reasons for Pansy's
return, although it didn't answer the question as to why she
hadn't simply continued her course due west along the
stranger's trail.

'Because she's frightened, that's why.' Louise regarded
him as if he had been a man who always let the obvious
pass him by. 'They panic, see, when they'm frightened.' She
continued to lecture with her hands on her hips.

He had to agree she was probably right about Pansy's
anxious comings and goings. Very likely they had observed
the partial execution of a strategy confused by panic at having found her exit blocked. Ned replaced his phone in order
to report the blocked earth to the active unit who would then
do their best to remove the obstruction. No sooner had he
done so he was back on the phone again reporting to
Terence that the large group of hounds that had been diverted by the saboteurs were now returning up Long Coombe.
It was likely they would wait by Pikes Wood to muster with
the rest of the pack returning from Chepton Veins. Before they
reached the wood they picked up another scent and began to
head off eagerly westward. This unexpected diversion left
Pansy at the centre of a pincer with only a narrow open
end through which she could bolt to the south.

'I don't think she's going to make it,' came Ned's gloomy
prognosis.

Terence did not pray; he closed his eyes instead since he did not hold with all this praying business. He didn't have a god to pray to, he just had a passionate commitment to life, that force evident in the secret life of the smallest beetle and in the mystery of a swallow asleep on the wing. Eyes closed, fists clenched he hoped, as if hope alone would cast the dice in Pansy's favour.

'She'll be all right.' Louise had been watching him keenly. 'She's carryin' young uns.'

'How do you know, I mean how do you know she's carrying?'

'I bin watching, same as you.'

'Is that why you left her the bread and milk?'

'Helps to build up the strength, see.'

Terence was touched by the sentiment. 'I'm sure you did the right thing.'

'I know I did the right thing,' she said proudly.

'You think she'll get away, then?'

'A pregnant vixen don't leave no scent.'

'So they say.'

''Tis true.' He would like to have believed in the rustic wisdom, although he doubted its truth.

'I hope you're right, I really do.'

Terence could not see, nor did he wish to see, the vixen's ignominious flight, he just hoped her end when it came would be quick. There was nothing they could do since the active unit had been diverted to unblock the bolt-holes. By the time they had trekked back across the fields to their vehicle and their equipment Pansy would be a goner.

Still stationed at the top of Long Coombe, Ned was able to pick her out galloping downhill towards Harmers Pond with the pack now in full cry, closing fast. The lead hound, a large muscular dog, was streets ahead of the rest. Its strength and vitality sent it careering down the valley and Pansy was no serious match for it. Her slender body was stretched to its maximum speed, shifting so fast her little paws barely touched the earth; she was a mere streak of red hovering over the pasture. Ned watched through the glasses, compulsively drawn to follow the horror story to its conclusion. In the green lane behind the shelter of the hedge Terence listened to his report, teeth gritted.

Thirty metres, twenty, fifteen, the gap that separated the hound and the little red vixen was narrowing. She was now level with the marshy fringes of Harmers Pond; her end was only seconds away. At ten metres, she literally flung herself into a violent swerve and the heavy hound behind, lacking her agility, was carried straight forward by the momentum of its own weight. Recognising that it had lost its quarry it eventually halted and took up a quizzical inspection of the marshy terrain under its paws.

Undetected, Pansy neatly wove her slender red body between the pale blonde reeds with the speed and skill of a Flemish weaver. She continued the pattern of movement around the edge of the water, putting distance between herself and the point at which she had entered the reeds. She was astute enough not to bolt, but slipped under a tussock of sedge where she remained perfectly still and hidden by its dense cover.

What was not apparent to Ned's sweeping binoculars and overlooked even by Terence's wildest hopes, was that whilst Pansy lay curled under her thick matting, the foolish hound actually stepped over her! She had not only hidden herself, but had successfully obscured her own scent trail by using the sodden mud at the pond's edge. The rest of the pack arrived in twos and threes, the discipline that had been exerted by the lead hound now broken. They fanned out, a number of them entering the marsh whilst the rest concentrated on trails at the dry side of the reed bed, their noses missing completely what Ned picked up through his field glasses—Pansy breaking cover at the opposite side of the pond and streaking south-east towards safety.

It was just as the vixen had succeeded in putting a hundred metres between herself and the hounds when Nye's hunting pink came over the brow of the hill. He had been keeping an eye on Ned for the last thirty minutes ever since the active unit had succeeded in diverting the hounds away from the stranger. He was amused by the lanky do-gooder astride a nag that should have gone for dog food years ago. A mobile phone velcroed to his parka, a radio receiver and field glasses, did this wet liberal buffoon really believe all that paraphernalia was going to bring his foxes special dispensation? On the contrary, Nye would not consider it a good day in the field unless he took the brush from a radio-tagged fox. Those radio antennae and field glasses were every bit as reliable as a pointing finger. Strange how good old George got so hot under the collar over his ancient and immutable right to hunt. A saboteur in the field had the efficacy of chilli up a mastiff's bum. As for himself he relished the idea of pitting his wits against them, they added to the day's sport as much as the fox.

He hailed the Master of the Hounds and pointed in the same direction that Ned focussed his field glasses on a sprinting vixen. 'Tally ho,' he roared and left Sir George's flank laughing, urging his chestnut into a full gallop down the length of Long Coombe. No other man was going to deny him what he coveted, be it power, property, a woman or a fox's brush.

Under the command of the horn, the hounds began to muster again at the edge of Harmers Pond from where they set off hot on Pansy's trail. Now out of sight of their field glasses, Ned and Terence began to track her progress electronically. At first she appeared to maintain a course that would ultimately bring her into Sandpits village, which formed part of her home range and provided plenty of cover, not least the gardens at the back of six Edwardian terraced cottages. The hounds could mill around there as much as they pleased, but it was to be doubted that any of the residents would open up their neat gardens to a pack of foxhounds. 'Home and dry,' Ned summed up optimistically.

Neither he nor Terence could fathom what it was that caused Pansy to change her mind at the last moment. Presumably in response to a threat that her protectors could not perceive, she headed back in a north-westerly direction towards the shelter of Pikes Wood. Not long after changing course she came into view, clearly under considerable pressure. Once again she took Long Coombe at a gallop, but this time uphill thus tapping a vital reserve of energy. Instantly Ned broke off from his report in order to alert the active unit, leaving Terence incommunicado behind a hedge, seeing nothing, but reading everything in the approaching sound of hounds and horn. He remained hunched and listening with his arms folded jerking involuntarily when the phone rang.

Ned reported grimly and rapidly that the active unit had gone to unblock Pikes Spout to find a group of terrier men guarding it. There had been a confrontation leading to an injury, they thought Alan might have a broken rib as a result. By the time he had recovered sufficiently to be helped back to the van, they found their vehicle had been broken into and the equipment smashed to bits leaving them entirely disabled.

'Bastards!' It was a globule of a curse that Terence spat into the mouthpiece causing Ned to start at the other end. Partner, mildly surprised, raised his head from a bit of amiable grazing and took a few lumbering steps forward. Normally the beast's contrary behaviour would have brought some light relief, but under the circumstances it underlined how ill-equipped they were for this sort of campaign—Ned on a horse rescued from a knacker's yard possessing a brain that had been wired back to front, a handful of saboteurs, two of whom had been injured. 'Those bastards get as much pleasure from a fight with a saboteur as they do watching a fox torn to bits,' he concluded.

These people, and Peter Deeks agreed with him, were not the old-style terrier men and diggers of popular perception whose livelihoods were threatened by a ban on hunting; these were thugs who would rather wager on dog fights than do a day's work. Terence wondered whether Sir George was aware of this nasty little fifth column, but turned a blind eye since they saved him from having to dirty his own hands. Following the assault on Spikey he was beginning to feel the Master of the Hounds shared a cosy symbiotic relationship with them across the distance of social class.

Louise had been standing on the opposite side of the green lane, her fists screwed in apprehension, her body contorted by the intensity with which she listened to what was going on around her. Strangely, her grey eyes remained expressionless. Terence watched her and suddenly felt terribly tired. The lack of a good night's sleep and a decent breakfast had caught up with him causing him to feel detached from the reality of the situation. It struck him that they were actors in a black comedy. Her intense posture had been well rehearsed, she had slipped it on like a costume before setting foot on the boards. The way in which the hedge bulged in and out either side of the lane, the subdued browns of winter reminded him of dark velvet theatre curtains—on stage was the Fox Man and the Mad Woman, enter the Huntsman cued by a horn. What the bloody hell do I think I'm doing here? Terence asked himself. I'm not a campaigner, I'm a scientist. The facts are that far more foxes die painfully by the bullet, poison, trapping and traffic; foxhounds are the least threat to the fox population.

He watched Ned on the hill, the way the wind tousled his hair made him look younger than he was, bringing out a paternal concern for his safety.

At the top of Long Coombe, out in the open and carrying all that equipment, he was as good as an archery target. It would be nothing for Sir George's terrier men to have him off his horse, on the ground and putting the boot in, after which they would make off with equipment borrowed from the fox project. The best course would be for Ned to pack up and join with what was left of the active unit.

As if his own anxiety had rippled through the air, Ned phoned to confirm, in a tone that suggested he was swallowing on his nerves, that Pansy was still in Pikes Wood and shifting around quite a bit. Terence suggested he kept the equipment out of sight, a waving antenna would give away Pansy's whereabouts. He did not add that it would also make Ned a target; to do so would only provoke stubborn resistance from this young Don Quixote on the hill. He asked tactfully whether Ned could be of any help to the unit. 'There's not a lot we can do without the amplifier, I might as well stay here and blow a horn.'

Pansy's erratic signal suggested she was constantly changing direction. Louise listened to the bleeps, her hand over her mouth, looking somewhat like a maiden aunt in receipt of a shock. The shifting restlessness of a frightened animal and the tension expressed in the body of this strange little woman combined to charge the atmosphere with an unnatural energy.

'Pansy's still in Pikes Wood,' Terence told her factually, as much to calm himself as to keep her informed.

'She'd be better off in they reeds by Harmers Pond.'

'The hounds might fall for it a second time, but I don't think the huntsmen will! She'd stand a better chance if she bolted along Old Rogue's trail.'

'He fathered 'er young uns, didn't 'er.' Louise's quaint observation withered the science in him.

'Yes,' he agreed, 'he fathered her cubs.' Back came the sentimental man, the man who said that cruelty in any form is abhorrent. Then he found himself saying crossly, 'We should have cancelled the campaign this morning. We've got one of our group in hospital, likely to lose part of his sight and hearing and now somebody else with a broken rib.'

Spikey undergoing surgery, Alan in A and E, grown men and women yowling for an animal's blood. Is this what people chose to call civilisation? If it was, then the evolutionary route that began at the origin of the universe and trekked across the aeons must have taken a wrong turning. Did those early hominids, now at rest in their fossil graves, show any inclination to dress up in funny clothes in order to impose suffering on each other and the beasts around them? Not that Terence idealised man in his so-called natural state. Nature was a system, mechanistic. Cruel on account of indifference it might be, but at least it was predictable. Birds, beasts, trees and plants all bowed to the rule of physical law. Mankind was the chaotic element. Mankind the unpredictable, the disastrous, the inexplicable.

Through his field glasses Terence caught sight of the hounds streaking up Long Coombe with a scattered party of riders following behind. When the dogs entered the wood and the riders encircled it he switched off the radio receiver. Pansy's audible, zigzagging panic had pommelled Louise into catatonic immobility. She had taken on the appearance of a lifeless puppet that might jerk into movement at the pull of a string. Her grey eyes were glass orbs set in a crudely chiselled face of wood. She was pitifully thin, little more than an animated skeleton covered by hide. The malady that was eating her brain was also a leech that had sucked her body dry leaving behind a hyperactive nervous system. It would take only the sound of the hunting horn or a baying hound to flip the switch. How odd it all was, he and this poor psychotic woman, both of them wedded to the chaotic day by their love of the fox.

It was Louise's sighing that drew Terence out of his reverie, it came from her in little melodic wheezes that grew into choking pants as if from a woman in labour. She crossed over to his side of the lane and looked up into his face with such earnest anxiety it was as if she were about to despatch him to do something heroic.

'They wankers have bin an' made 'er bolt,' she spat out. Spittle caught his chin unpleasantly and he wiped it away with the back of his hand. As there was nothing else he could do other than track the vixen's rough direction, he switched on the radio receiver only to find it promptly switched off again by the perfunctory intervention of Louise's index finger.

'Listen,' she ordered in such a sharp, school-marmish way that he found himself doing as he was told. After a few minutes of concentration on the direction and tone of the hounds he was able to pick up their individual tongues, some holding more vocal authority than others.

'Over 'ere!'

'No, over 'ere.'

'Forget it, dick head, it's 'ere.' They were a crude canine platoon in disarray, gradually learning the battle cry. He didn't really need to listen to the hounds to know the progress of the hunt because it was written on Louise's face. She was now hunched with a fist held against her teeth; even more distressing was the way her whole body jerked spasmodically in response to the bays and yelps. She took the whole business as if it were an excruciating pain. He wished he had something to say to her that would take the sting out of it all.

'She's runnin' for thik pond.' Her eyes lit up with hope and her enthusiasm exploded with such a childish faith in the vixen's survival that he simply didn't have the heart to prepare her for Pansy's inevitable end.

'Yes,' he agreed gravely, 'I would expect her to do that.' After some minutes of watching Louise take the sounds around them like body blows, it came as a relief when she stood stock still in the middle of the lane, raised her arm and pointed like a prophet of doom.

Fox corpses were nothing new to Terence, there were one hundred and one ways for a fox to die and he had seen most of them, but a corpse in a laboratory is factual, and death no more than an objective statement. What he had never seen before was a creature dead on its feet. He had always thought the phrase fanciful since something could not be both dead and on its feet. When Pansy came into view in the green lane she was dead on her feet.

He and Louise had been standing shoulder to shoulder like children listening in the dark, they parted reverently in order to allow a little red shadow to pass between them. Pansy was not alive, it was her body that was being driven by its autonomic nervous system. He had heard of such things before, how a dog with its head severed still wagged its tail. Her eyes had rolled upward, he supposed from a fit; the staring vacancy left by the departed life reminded him of roller blinds being suddenly released and something taking flight through an open window.

It was a sad and quirky notion that haunted him for months to come that Pansy's final hope had been to reach her hawthorn lair, the site she had prepared for her cubs. It was as if the intention had gone on ahead of her dying body which, without volition of its own, had simply trailed after it. He did not propose watching her final submission, as far as he was concerned the ripping to bits of her body by hounds was a mere formality. She was dead.

The hounds were now at the top of the lane, a broad-shouldered, mud-spattered brigade announcing their arrival with cacophonous triumph. The effect on Louise was that of contact with a high voltage cable. She leapt, electrocuted, then set off in the opposite direction with her unique stiff-legged way of walking yet managed to produce the speed of a run. Within feet of Pansy's corpse she turned around promptly as if she had determined to confront the oncoming hounds, threw herself at the hedge then took to snatching at it, indifferent to the dagger-sharp bramble and hawthorn. Within seconds her hands were slashed and bloody.

Terence stared aghast, unable to deal with such an insane outburst which seemed to be driven by fear and fury, their contradictory demands being resolved through self-mutilation. His own instinct urged him to get out of the way of the pack, but if they ran away with Louise in such a high state of agitation, her hands pouring with blood then the pack, stirred and ready for a kill, might pursue them. Similarly if he allowed her to remain there, shaking her bloody fists at the dogs then she, not Pansy, would become their quarry. To do anything other than remain as still as a rock and look confident placed them both in jeopardy.

'Keep still, you stupid bitch,' he bawled ineffectually at the solid wall of hysteria that placed her beyond the reach of common sense. He might just as well have hurled a stone at a hurricane. Turning on his heels, he headed toward the oncoming pack, driven less by courage than by the gruesome prospect of a fellow human being torn limb from limb by a pack of dogs. Before the hounds levelled with him he stood stolidly in the middle of the lane.

Time changes as a crisis approaches, stretching itself, extending enough to allow the brain to take on board quite irrelevant information. Terence became acutely aware of a tri-coloured stream of fang, fur and lolling tongue. He could feel damp, inquisitive noses investigate his hands like gentle kisses, the condensation of their sweating breath, the mild whipping of their tails against his thighs. He breathed deeply to calm himself whilst they passed him by, parting either side of him as if he had been no more than a boulder in their path.

Next came a man on a glossy chestnut hunter. Terence was aware of an extraordinary handsomeness, a cool, photogenic male beauty entering the scene as if presenting himself to a camera. Terence grabbed the reins and shouted, 'Call them off, there's a woman down there, she's had a seizure.'

Nye looked down from arrogant horseback height upon the shouting man, noting the radio receiver and mobile phone. Did this man seriously think that a fiction about some woman in a fit, clearly a ploy, could possibly sabotage his day in the field?

'The fox's brush,' he replied, 'I want and the fox's brush I will have and if it pleases me to cut it off and paint my face with blood to celebrate the kill, I will.' Nye spurred his horse forward in the wake of the hounds, laughing.

Terence stood glaring and cursing at his departing back, so square and so neat in its tailored jacket. Choked by an incapacitating fury, he bawled at him loud enough to fill the valley.

'Don't you care, don't you fucking care?' His curses and his pleas for Louise's safety had no greater impact than that of a man shaking a flower at a dictator. The huntsman's wicked laughter was the distillation of everything cruel.

Mankind's indifference to his own species as well as the planet and the life it sustained had donned a black riding habit and taken on the persona of this despicable man.

'Cunt...cunt...cunt...' Louise's terrified shrieking rose above the yelping of the hounds, ascending to an inhuman pitch. If only it were the cuck, cuck, cuck of Pansy turning in gekkering defence of her life, at least her end would be swift. Horrified Terence flung himself at the next horse, grabbing its reins. Sir George stooped over the shoulder of his grey mare scowling to listen to the distraught stranger. As if taking a reluctant precaution he sounded the horn and urged the mare forward, Terence following behind.

At the end of the run the pack had become one indistinguishable body of seething fur intent upon eating whatever struggled for life beneath its suffocating mass—Louise. He thought of the poor vagrant woman who'd hurt nobody, struggling to get to her feet and suffering the excruciating agony of being eaten alive. He began retching and sobbing as, through his tears, he watched Nye dismount and wade with astonishing confidence into the middle of the pack, barging aside the dogs as if he had been first amongst them. He stooped, growled a command and when he turned again he held aloft his bloody trophy. It was not Louise's severed head topped incongruously with its dimpled brown beret, it was simply Pansy's brush. Like the show-man he was Nye raised it to his forehead and blessed himself with her blood.

'Oh well done, Dickie, well done, sir.' Sir George never

stinted his praise in the field. He sounded the horn to rally the hounds and returned the way they had come, passing Terence, isolated and distressed by the trauma, as if he'd been invisible. Nye, on the other hand, tilted his hat in mock courtesy.

'Amwell Hounds one, Amwell Saboteurs nil,' he said.

The wind dropped taking the temperature down with it. The dark came suddenly at four, escorted by a calm winter solace, a most suitable afternoon for a funeral. Had anybody been there to carry a tiny box of bones to its final resting place they might have said in memoriam: 'Oh well, Pansy survived her brief season and nature will not take much account of her departure, after all it's only the passing of one event, as is birth the introduction of another.' One event has no meaning amongst the trillions generated in the infinity of time and space, no meaning at all beyond that assigned to it by the human onlooker. Dressed in the protective clothing of a philosophical attitude, Terence had taken himself home to sleep off the unpleasantness of it all.

He slept surprisingly well without dreams and it was quite dark when he returned to re-claim Pansy's radio collar which still transmitted a token heartbeat. At least that's what he told himself he had gone to do, but really he had returned to give his vulpine friend a decent burial by shovelling her remains under the protective roots of her hawthorn lair. He assumed that he would have to search amongst scattered bones for the transmitter and had not expected to find the site of her slaughter cleaned and tidied, nor a tomb of neatly interlocking twigs over her lair.

The work was astonishingly meticulous, giving the impression of a large upturned bird's nest. On the surface of it six small corn dollies had been placed, each skilfully woven into a traditional pattern. One, larger than the rest, he assumed commemorated Pansy, the five smaller ones the embryonic life that Louise had been anticipating.

It was beyond words. Here was this unkempt, filthy, diseased woman who owned nothing but the rags on her back yet, with bare hands, that must have busied themselves all day long, she had woven this superb monument. It was the purest act of devotion. It had not been left there to look pretty, it was too profound a statement for that. The sad day came bubbling up accompanied by big loud sobs echoing in the dark lane. Conscious of the noise he must be making, he blew his nose manfully, discharging sentiment through his nostrils.

It would have been desecration to have disturbed her work of art in order to retrieve the transmitter so he walked away. After a few paces he turned around to shine his torch for a last look. In the splash of artificial light the tomb showed as a simple and natural piece of architecture, an outgrowth of the hedge. Given a few months it would decay and return to the earth, rightly so since it is from that single atomic fact that everything comes and eventually returns, the earth. She knew that and had woven her ancient knowledge into the immutable statement. 'Listen.' Louise's finger had switched off the radio receiver during the hunt and went to her lips to shush away everything he knew, or thought he knew.

Was she really mad, or just passionately different? Terence emerged out of the green lane, a huntsman's cruel smirk endorsing the horrible possibility of those hounds tearing Louise to pieces. Would anybody have troubled to weave a monument for her? The night closed behind him like heavy black drapes. From the direction of Pikes Wood came the wow...wow...wow of Old Rogue's contact call, a call that would never be answered.

Caroline's letter to Matilda was starkly to the point and judicial in tone. The indictment against Nye and Uncle George was presented from the witness box of her bedroom window. She had to admit, as she wrote, to a feeling of jubilation in visualising the hunting party, alarm on their faces as they listened to her evidence in court. Since she had not just decided to leave home but had vowed never to go back again, the profound distinction called for a time to be added to the date of the letter. It was the time precisely when she had learned from Bouncer that the operation on Spikey had been unsuccessful, leaving him blind and deaf on his left side. The only good news was that the haemorrhaging had been staunched and he had not suffered the brain damage the doctor had first suspected. Not a detail of his injuries was omitted from the letter which concluded that the attack had been so vile and brutal she had voluntarily given a statement to the police.

Under the circumstances there was no possibility of her ever returning to live under the same roof as her father; through his complicity with Uncle George he was equally guilty, and when charges were brought she would be prepared to testify against them both in court. The final paragraph bluntly rejected any further support from her parents. She would complete her course aided by a bank loan. If Matilda wished to see her it would have to be at the student house in Bristol which she was planning to share with Denis Tunstall.

Mrs Deeks watched her employer's face flush brightly then drain of all colour.

'Is there anything I can do, Mrs Nye?'

Matilda stared at her blankly as if the question were incomprehensible.

'Mrs Nye, are you all right?' she prompted.

Matilda handed her the letter in silence. Now it was Mrs Deeks's turn to flush scarlet. 'Oh my God,' she put her hand over her mouth.

'You were there,' said Matilda, 'you saw what happened. It was an accident. We didn't even know anything about it until after the meet when Deeks told us.' Matilda snatched the letter back and jabbed at it with her forefinger. 'Is this the way she thanks us for all we've done for her? She's had the very best of everything. We've given her a wonderful start in life, and now she's throwing it back in our faces. Why, what have we done? Do you believe any of this nonsense?' She shook the letter as if to upbraid Mrs Deeks in advance for any disagreement.

Mrs Deeks fished deep down into her conscience where her suspicions writhed like a nest of vipers and said, 'Well, Sir George was beginning to lose his temper...'

'What are you saying, that my uncle and my husband were responsible for assaulting this Phillip Longfellow?'

'Of course not!'

'It was an accident.'

'Of course it was,' came Mrs Deeks's prudent agreement.

'You and Deeks saw what happened and I hope you'll both testify in court.'

'Is there anything I can get for you?' Perhaps Mrs Nye

could be appeased with a large slice of gateau At least all the time she was eating she wouldn't be insisting on any commitments.

'No, there isn't,' Matilda snapped at her. 'I want to be left to speak to my husband in private, if you don't mind.'

Mrs Deeks returned to the kitchen only to be ordered back to the drawing room by the insistent tinkling of a silver bell, undermining any hope that the morning was going to be hers in which to discuss with Deeks the implications of Caroline's letter. Although both had their suspicions, neither of them had seen the incident, only the aftermath and Mrs Nye's demand that they should testify otherwise was thoroughly unreasonable. She found her employer in a state of fluttering ferment, fingers, surprisingly delicate for such a well-built woman, dancing as if over a stringed instrument.

'What the bloody hell am I going to tell him?' Mistakenly believing that her opinion was being sought, Mrs Deeks gave it.

'Well, if I was in your shoes, Mrs Nye...'

'Well, you're not, are you?'

'Will that be all, Mrs Nye?'

'No it will not be all, Mrs Deeks.'

'You rang the bell, Mrs Nye so I assumed you wanted something.'

'I rang the bell,' Matilda explained as if her housekeeper had been too dense to comprehend it, 'because I needed to express my feelings about my daughter's letter.' The letter was snatched up again and seemed about to be used in place of a paper tissue. Mrs Deeks regarded her employer's sniffing efforts to control her tears, recalling a ten-year-old Matilda Wentworth stomping around the village demanding her own way because she came from the Hall. When she didn't get it she would burst into tears declaring nobody liked her because she came from the Hall. Mrs Nye's tears engendered a range of emotions ranging across humour, anger and pity. Even all these years later she found herself still trying to balance the emotional equation. 'Well?' demanded her employer.

'Well what?' asked Mrs Deeks.

'What do you think?'

'Well, I'm not sure I should be giving an opinion.'

'Well, I'm asking for one.'

'In that case don't tell Mr Nye anything. Wait and see if the police press any charges. If the police don't press charges then Caroline can't testify can she?' She watched Mrs Nye's expression change from apprehension to puzzlement then finally relax into contemplation of the advice. 'Can I bring you some gateau, it's a new recipe?'

Sir George's bad behaviour didn't slip by unchallenged. Within a few days of the Ebury meet he found himself and Richard Nye being closely questioned by the Amwell police. Since the culprits had already agreed upon what had happened, as opposed to what had actually happened, the police got seamless and consistent statements from both of them. The horses had become fidgety because of the number of people milling about. For public safety supporters were asked to stand back whilst the hounds were brought under control ready for the off. Sir George's horse began prancing, they often do at this stage of the meet, which is why members of the public are asked to stand clear. It was necessary to discipline the animal to avoid an accident. Sir George was not aware in doing so that he had inadvertently caught his riding crop on a bystander's head, in fact he hadn't even been aware of the accident until the gamekeeper at Ebury Hall told him some hours later. As Master of the Hounds he naturally took responsibility for anything that happened during a meet. The Ebury meet was fully insured and Sir George would be writing to Mr Longfellow and his family expressing his sympathy and pointing out that they were entitled to make a claim under the terms of the insurance policy.

'Bollocks!' was Caroline's unadorned response to Uncle George's statement. He was a leading light on the show jumping circuit and his command of dressage was equally applauded. What Caroline saw from her window was precisely that—dressage. There hadn't been one moment when the grey mare was out of control. Surely the Amwell police weren't going to swallow that one whole! Bouncer assured her that there wasn't a single officer at the station who believed the story either. He had no direct dealings with the incident himself because the victim was a relative; nonetheless he passed on whatever information he could to Caroline, off the cuff and strictly in confidence otherwise he would be hauled over the coals for unprofessional behaviour.

Caroline further learned that one obstruction to pressing charges would be that there was only one witness so far. Although she had seen the incident, she had been thirty metres away and had not been privy to any conversation that had passed between Nye and Sir George on the ground. For this reason, to make any charge stick, they would have to interview others present, including hunt supporters, bystanders and saboteurs. The police had warned Spikey's family that existing evidence would look flimsy in court and their immediate response was that they would pursue a private prosecution if necessary.

Nye's discovery of Caroline's letter was followed by a week of hissing recriminations. Matilda should not have tried to hide it from him, particularly now the incident was in the hands of a solicitor. 'It doesn't make any difference, you're still culpable,' Matilda pointed out.

'Culpable, culpable!' Nye parroted back at her. He'd never heard such a long and intelligent word pass her lips before. Uncle George, presiding over the argument with a more lofty scrutiny, blamed them both—they should have monitored Caroline's friends. By consorting with saboteurs she had effectively given them carte blanche to barge in and sabotage the meet. No two ways about it, they had an undue influence over her, that much was evident on the night of the dinner; she had set out to denigrate everything that the alliance of rural interests stood for.

'I don't need to point out,' he continued his summing up, 'she attacked the very things that have seen her through her school and university years.' Nye desisted from reminding him that it had been his own urban salary that had seen his daughter through her school and university years, not any wealth generated by Ebury Hall. 'As for living with that lout, Tunstall,' continued Uncle George's unremitting tirade, 'his agenda's bloody obvious—shacking up with a girl who's heir to a fortune, Dickie, that's where our Mr Tunstall's coming from.'

Nye looked up from his lunch with nothing but admiration for his wife's uncle. Sir George had distorted reality with such authority nobody dared contradict him. Having skilfully deflected any suspicion Matilda might have about the accident, he then placed the blame for the whole incident squarely on Caroline's shoulders. Did he really believe that Tunstall was after the family fortune? What fortune? There was only debt attaching to the Hall. As for any trust he set up, it would pass initially to Matilda to manage, thence to Caroline on her mother's death and so on, down through the years, passing from generation to generation until the capital sum had been whittled away to nothing. If Tunstall hoped to marry into a fortune, it was a forlorn hope. He watched Sir George chomp heavily on his food, his brain no doubt fully occupied by keeping Ebury Hall in perpetuity by marrying his great niece into a wealthy family.

'Duped, that's all I can say and frankly, if she was my daughter I'd get her away from that lout and back here to confront her responsibilities.' Uncle George wiped his greasy lips on a napkin and threw it down on his plate truculently.

It was now time for Nye to underline the fact that Caroline wasn't coming back to the Hall in the foreseeable future. It was time to talk about a different future, one in which Sir George would have to re-think the inheritance and how best to place it in order to secure the best outcome for Ebury Hall.

'If Caroline was duped, George, she was a very willing dupe.'

'That may well be the case, but it's still your responsibility as parents to see she does the decent thing.' Even amongst the antiquated customs of Ebury Hall doing the decent thing sounded archaic.

'Caroline's very much her own woman, I'm afraid. Since

she's over twenty-one and about to graduate I don't have any more levers to pull.'

'You're being remarkably phlegmatic about it, Dickie, that's all I can say.'

'Realistic.'

'Uncle's right, Richard, you're being very complacent.' Complacent! Nye sat bolt upright as if having taken a shot in his chest. Who was this new woman contradicting him, she who had always clung limpet-like to his every opinion? Sir George placed his palms firmly on the table, the thump they made having the authority of a judge's gavel.

'I'm sorry, Dickie, but I'm going to have to re-think the terms of my will. As you're both aware I had always hoped that Caroline would marry somebody with the means to support the Hall after we've all passed on. The income from the estate isn't ever going to be sufficient to keep it going and I had hoped to make my own contribution through a trust. It would have been my brother's dearest wish, clearly this isn't going to be fulfilled. Caroline has made her own intentions clear, she doesn't intend to return here having decided to testify against her own family in court.'

'You must do as you see fit, George, naturally,' Nye answered from behind a screen of neutrality that hid the busy calculation of self-interest.

'Unless Caroline drops these silly allegations and decides to come home, minus that lout Tunstall, then I'm afraid the future of the Hall is in jeopardy since there certainly won't be my legacy to support it.'

Blackmail, bully and blame, the three devilish prongs of Sir George's managerial fork had always pitched Wentworth Electronics forward and there was no reason to suppose that he was going to employ softer techniques to get his own way in his private life. Ensure that Caroline drops her allegations and comes home or say ta ta to five million quid to secure the future of the Hall.

Matilda excused herself and popped out to preside over the preparation of the dessert leaving an opportunity for Nye to square up to the facts of the matter. Two could play the blackmail game.

'George,' Nye introduced the subject without any subtlety, 'Caroline has a mind of her own. She saw what she saw and if I cajole her into saying otherwise she'll simply dig her heels in. We both know what she saw. If her evidence is supported by other witnesses I'm afraid you're in the shit.'

'I rather think we'd both be in the shit, Dickie. Let's hope it doesn't come to that. What Caroline saw was an accident, as we've both agreed. Coming back to the question of my will any endowment is conditional.'

'Then you leave us no choice but to sell Ebury Hall.'

'So be it, if that's what Matilda decides to do, there are other projects to be endowed I'm sure.' Sir George rose. 'Say goodbye to Matilda for me. I must go, I've got an appointment with my solicitor.'

'I hope he advises you to do the decent thing, George.'

'I doubt he'll advise me to endow a golf club,' came Sir George's parting shot.

During the days following the Ebury Meet Terence saw nothing of the vagrant woman. Before the hunt she had dogged his heels, her constant presence mildly irritating, her bad breath and acrid body odour unwelcome until he grew used to her presence, tolerating her in the way one might an old flea-bitten dog that seeks neither attention nor any reward other than human companionship. He had devised manageable tasks for her to keep her occupied whilst he worked. After a while his tolerance had grown to respect.

From time to time he glimpsed a personality that must have been there before the onset of the disorder that had fragmented it. She possessed an astonishing ability to store information. He only had to point a finger at a wild plant for her to promptly supply its botanical name, its preferred habitat, its medicinal and culinary uses and its mythology. She embraced life with the passion of a Jain so that he had to mind his biological 'p's and 'q's whenever she was around, mindful of where he trod.

'Weeds ain't just weeds—' she'd look up into his face earnestly, '—they'm life patterns.' If one of his clumsy boots happened to tread on one of her more favoured life patterns her tutting and clucking would pursue him. She became woven into those cold nights, appearing as if summoned from the dusky fields by his presence.

When she arrived he would get out his map and ask, 'And where did we leave Old Rogue last night?'

'Yer.' Her dirty finger would stab accurately at the exact co-ordinate on his OS map.

'Oh well done!' He never forgot to praise her, his praises causing her shoulders to hunch like a child about to giggle with pleasure.

After Pansy's death she simply withdrew from human contact, and the events of that grisly morning when a little red vixen came back to her lair to die. Louise's explosive distress haunted him all through the raw wet January days, so too Old Rogue's contact call piercing the silent aftermath of the hunt. For seven days his sharp, tri-syllabic phrases echoed across Long Coombe as the dog fox returned to the green lane where he had courted his vixen. Within yards of Pansy's remains he would undertake a tentative and anxious pawing at the ground, tail lashing from side to side uncertainly. Terence avoided the anthropomorphic conclusion that Old Rogue was bereaved, but he was nonetheless convinced that what the dog fox did express was puzzlement and uncertainty. When the contact calls went unanswered, Old Rogue submitted to whatever animal understanding he had of the situation and returned to eke out his living at Ebury Hall.

# The Season

# of the Hedge Gypsy

It was a grey, boring afternoon in March and Nye's irritability was provoked further by the cold easterly insinuating its way into the drawing room. He had watched Matilda bob plumply up and down along the drive on the back of a new dappled grey mare they couldn't afford and seethed. When he broached the subject of selling the Hall she had flatly refused. Sir George would only subsidise its future conditionally and, as for investing in its development as a golf course-cum-leisure centre, forget it.

Nye mooched around, prodded further into antipathy towards his wife and her uncle by the deteriorating fabric of the building around him and the debts bequeathed by winter storms. This second-rate place in the country had fastened onto his income like a leech and caused burgeoning regrets—for this he had thrown himself away on a woman who looked like a fattened bullock! His cruel imagination draped a lacy bridal veil over sprouting horns and a thick woolly brow then, to compound his spite, pinned a rosette to it—it was the highest accolade Matilda Wentworth would ever win out of him. He should not have placed that gold ring on her finger, but stuck it through her nose. What had his marriage brought him? A house that threatened to fall apart in the wind and leaked in the rain. Croquet on a summer lawn, himself numbered amongst the dinner-jacketed county elite. He had grown tired with the very idea of it. It was a role he'd played for far too long in a play that ran interminably.

There was little point revisiting old illusions, they were as dried up as a pressed flower in an old maid's prayer book. Life at the Hall was beginning to take on that one-dimensional quality of a film set, behind its facade was the mundane, the daily ordinariness and the indescribable malaise of having to wait between social events in which he took the leading role. Life at the Hall was just another way of growing old.

Having created an unworthy effigy of his wife he felt justified in wearing the uniform of a disenchanted husband. Donning his wax jacket and slinging a gun over his shoulder, he went in search of sex. 'I'm going shooting,' he told Mrs Deeks.

Suzanne had not troubled to scrape the chicken bone from a plate left on the coffee table. A decorative display of feathers had tumbled against it in the draught from the open door adding to the impression of a carcass picked clean. Meagre light filtered through narrow leaded light windows creating dark nooks and crannies in the cool stone interior of the cottage. The place was a den, something had taken refuge there in the gloom.

Nye stood in the doorway ready to flush it out with his shotgun whilst savouring the bestial ambience of it all. The smell of cooked meat and butter hung over the room, a heavy gas tinged with something sharper—the wild garlic, perhaps, that grew in abundance by the front door, or more likely the cannabis that she smoked from time to time. He dilated his nostrils and took in the smells from the room pretentiously, amusing himself with the evocation of a fox gone to ground and a hound tasting the air. A silk basque, deep red in colour, lounged over the arm of a chair like a shed skin. Rather oddly, the room did not contain much of a personal nature, no ornament nor artefact, nothing that would expose the personality of its occupant. There was no reading material either; did she read? It all had an air of transience, of somebody merely passing through, leaving behind them intimate yet anonymous signs like spore on a track, the impress of a pad in the mud, tell-tale hair scraped from a pelt by barbed wire. He entered, picked up the basque and buried his nose in it.

Suzanne lit a cigarette in a dark corner of the room. 'Help yourself.' Smoke left the corner of her mouth in surly wisps. He did not remove the undergarment startled and red-faced because his was an unashamed enjoyment of her odour. He was an egocentric man and egocentric men are not overly sensitive about others' opinions of them, even about their most intimate habits. Whores have revealed to them every twist and turn of male sexuality, and Nye was more than happy to show off his. This was what he had come loping across the fields to do—express himself. Dressed in a red, but not flamboyant, robe to match her basque, Suzanne stood with one hand on her hip, smoking as if she had all the time in the world. But, Nye noticed, there was an open suitcase on the settee and the indolent pose belied the fact that she wanted to transact the business quickly and be off.

They were not lovers and most unlikely ever to be friends, which left only cash on delivery for sex. He meant nothing to her and as for her meaning, well... women in general were either decorative or predatory. The decorative/submissive type, like fast food, were there for his instant gratification, any emotional leftovers being quickly discarded. The predatory type were there purely for sport. This one did not fit easily into either category, there was something about her that caused his throat to constrict. Those green slanting eyes, sometimes flecked with yellow in certain lights, the broadly furrowed brow, the way the face narrowed to a small chin caused him to believe that something vulpine was regarding him whilst remaining hidden itself.

He examined the red basque, her flesh by proxy, and pinched it sadistically before allowing it to drop onto the settee. The gesture was meant to say your ability to satisfy my needs is not worth the mention—Suzanne had got the better of him. He sat, seemingly at ease, in an armchair, his knees parted either side of the shotgun, his chin rested on the butt. It was a self-conscious, interrogative pose. Having always looked at himself as if through a camera lens he knew staring to be an indispensable tool in the interactive game. Moreover years of self-study had also taught him how to bully space with his physical presence.

He watched her leg swinging over the arm of her chair; an inner thigh showed like a white surgical scar where her red gown parted. There was, he noticed, a long blue vein; she was no chicken, forty at least. Suzanne took a prolonged look at her watch indicating that he was wasting her time. The gesture caused him a gloomy anxiety over his future, time calibrated by visits to a whore. Of late he began to acknowledge his dependency, as an addict would his drug, with a kind of excited revulsion. Nevertheless he ameliorated his resentment toward the cost of addiction by taking his time over its satisfaction. He wanted no more from this tart than any other woman—sport.

Most women, in his experience, played the game of hide and chase according to his rules. Suzanne didn't even enter the game in the first place, tolerating him with a shoulder-shrugging indifference. What she thought, felt, perceived, was stacked neatly behind their transactions as if they had been goods reserved for another more favoured customer. Yes he resented it, at the same time found it baffling and enthralling. Back and forth he had trotted between her cottage and Ebury Hall for twelve months to the syncopated rhythms of desire and frustration. He wasn't a man in love by any means; he was a man enjoying its physical sensations without the burdensome nonsense of having to give anything up for it—other than money. As for Suzanne, if she wanted his money then she must be prepared to give him a good run for it. He reached for the silk basque again getting body odour and stale perfume: incense that sanctified cold passion and lurid fantasies.

'Well?' she asked impatiently. He did not answer but continued to regard her whilst stroking the smooth metal surface of the gun barrel. His needs were as exposed as those of a patient in a VD clinic.

'Next please,' he said.

The bathroom door had been left open on purpose to reveal Suzanne astride a bidet. Nye could watch or avert his eyes for all she cared as long as he got the message that it was most inconvenient when he didn't use a condom.

'Clippety clop, clippety clop,' he accompanied her intimate ablutions. She stooped to dry herself, then threw the towel in an untidy heap with other dirty washing. 'You cut a fine figure astride a bidet.'

'You should use a condom and spare yourself the sight.'

'Not at the price you charge.'

The post-coital exchanges often took this particular tone, distancing them both from the sex act so that their intimacies appeared no more than something displayed on a market stall. The wood burner in the sitting room below had gone out causing Nye's fingers to become tinged with blue. He goose-stepped them across the coverlet toward his wallet lying on the pillow where Suzanne's head should rightly be. Nye had not come just for sex, he had also come to wheedle the truth out of Suzanne about Sir George's intentions regarding his will—given the cantankerous old bugger bared his soul whilst under the intimate cover of Miss Blinney's blankets. If he wasn't going to endow the Hall and wasn't going to invest in its future as a thriving business then what the hell was he going to do with his money? Would he leave it solely to Matilda unfettered? Somehow he doubted it. The trouble was Miss Blinney had a keen sense of which side her bread was buttered and could be as unforthcoming as a closed clam when she chose. She watched his marching fingers halt at the wallet and salute the bank notes displayed to beckon her interest, but when she moved to take what was owed her, they magically disappeared.

'Your little conjuring trick, is it, dear?'

'Client, him want chat-chat.'

'Just pay up and piss off.'

'Not until we've talked.'

'We haven't got anything to talk about.'

'Oh, haven't we?' Words for Nye were as clumps of grass and tree stumps for a cat, they obscured his pussy-footing around the subject, namely Sir George's will. 'Poor old

Uncle has taken his great niece's defection from the Hall very personally, hasn't he?'

'Has he? I wouldn't know.'

'The old boy's got too much faith in the future of the Hall. Like all true believers I'm afraid he doesn't understand why others don't worship the same god. Such faith can turn the head of even the most astute businessman.'

There was not so much as a flicker of interest in Suzanne Blinney's eyes. 'I haven't got all day.' It was hardly an encouragement to continue the conversation.

'Do you know, Foxy, I've always wondered what you spend mine and Sir George's money on.'

'I've got commitments as a matter of fact.'

'Commitments, and what commitments might they be?' Nye imitated her Lyons Corner House way of talking.

'I've got three boys to bring up.'

'In the care of the local authority, are they?' asked Nye spitefully. Suzanne turned her back on him and remained staring out of her bedroom window. The door to Sir George's intentions had been firmly closed in his face. The man for whom others' feelings were chaff in the wind was about to learn a salutary lesson. He could not see the expression in her eyes; usually they were given to floating up and away like green bubbles giving the false impression of detachment from whatever was going on around her. Had she faced him he would have caught, full blast, the look of utter distaste and contempt. As it was the stiff backbone was message enough. Silent seconds ticked by and he regretted his stupidity, thinking it prudent to get dressed and leave.

He was taken completely by surprise when she announced, 'They're all in public school, a very good public school as a matter of fact.' She turned, deftly snatched the bank notes owed to her, then returned to the window, her back to him.

He couldn't leave now, not after that sort of revelation. He lay stunned by the possibility of Sir George's progeny, like Banquo's issue, stretching into the future. They waved their spectral fingers over his last will and testament. Could it conceivably be...? He glared at the turned back and was just about to demand the truth when she appeared to be taking an interest in something below the bedroom window.

When she turned she seemed not to have taken umbrage over his remark. With her arms folded under her bosom she smiled with unexpected grace. 'Before we have our little tête-à-tête, why don't you pop downstairs and get me my ciggies? I left them on the coffee table.'

If ever she found the door to the cottage unlatched Louise would enter and forage, swooping beady-eyed on any cigarettes, fruit or biscuits that happened to be lying around. She would fill her pockets efficiently and be off without so much as a shudder of conscience. Suzanne's cottage had become just another collecting point on a circuit of resources. Like Pansy she too had a home range, hers taking in the kitchen at The Plume of Feathers, the milk float, the post office to which somebody sent a beneficent gift of a cheque exchangeable for cash, and a convent where silent and mystical women dispensed hot soup, bread and blankets without seeming to expect anything in return. Louise visited these sites with a clockwork regularity that lent structure and purpose to her daily life. Hers was a scavenging, foraging lifestyle. If unlocked doors opened onto resources then it was no crime to pass through them and help oneself. Occasionally she caught sight of a slim, dark-haired woman who paid her no more attention than she did the independent tabby cat for which she scraped leftovers into a tin bowl.

On this dull afternoon in March Louise slipped through the cottage door and began to cast about Suzanne's sitting room. She noted the half-packed suitcase, which contained nothing of interest to her, the picked-over chicken carcass on the coffee table and the full packet of cigarettes, a gun barrel that gleamed coldly under a red silk basque on the settee. She was not aware of the man who lay in a bed in a room above her head. She examined the gun with guilty curiosity knowing, as a child knows, that the possession of such a thing is both wrong and dangerous.

When she heard her benefactress mumble an instruction upstairs she started back into the shadows taking it with her. The bed squeaked in protest as somebody left it. Heavy footsteps on the stair came shortly after. She would have fled had the stairs not been close to the door. Instead she watched the naked man descend confidently, his bollocks swinging from side to side like those of a prize bull at a show. As he reached the bottom step his hand was already extended towards the cigarettes on the coffee table. They would have disappeared into Louise's pocket had she not loitered to inspect the shotgun.

Fate is a house of cards waiting for a puff of wind to bring it down. The puff of wind that sealed Nye's fate was a beam of sunlight breaking through the grey afternoon and catching him full in the face. For Louise his features, so brightly illuminated they appeared to be detached from his body, were apocalyptic. What she saw in the burnishing

208

light of revelation was the face of the heartless huntsman who had slaughtered her vixen. She jerked involuntarily and up came the gun level with his chest.

He swung round, shielding his eyes against the sun to find the shabby vagrant hunched over his shotgun like a seasoned combatant at the end of a sten-gun.

If ever a man had cause to say if only, Nye was to have such cause. Alarm pulsed along his nerves sending his palms upward in surrender. The instinctive signal was ineffectual against the memories that deluged Louise's senses—snarling white fangs, a glinting knife severing a vixen's brush, vermilion blood on a huntsman's hands, raw, ugly, constricting terror sitting on her heart like a demon. She jerked the gun barrel upward into Nye's ribs causing his gawping jaw to snap shut on his tongue.

'Foxy!' he bawled up the stairs, spitting blood.

Sir George's whore had already descended and stood smirking triumphantly.

'Now get out of that,' she assigned a title to the bizarre tableau in her sitting room. Another autonomic jerk of Louise's arms brought the gun metal under Nye's rib-cage again. Wincing and cursing, he screwed up his fists ready to strike out at the withered woman. Had she not clung to his shotgun so ruthlessly he would have kicked her to the floor to avenge the stinging pain and indignity of being cornered without his clothes on. He glared savagely at a face that was pinched and pensive and as yellow as candle grease, the only colour in it was where the thin skin, stretched tautly over cheek bones, had been pumiced by weather into a superficial glow of ruddy health. In spite of this the face was disconcertingly ageless. An even more disturbing feature was the expression of its eyes—cool, grey

209

and absent of any concern for the here and now. He was convinced their owner saw, heard and attended only to the commands of an alternative authority, one he was not prepared to challenge or test in spite of her diminutive form.

Nye took a step backward with one hand fending off another blow whilst the other trawled the settee for his clothes. Since her posture suggested the coiled, poisonous readiness found in snakes and scorpions he kept a wary eye on her. There was a risk that any sudden move might cause a reflexive response from the finger that rested lightly on the trigger. His random sweep of the clothing brought him what he assumed to be his boxer shorts. Hopping nervously from foot to foot he attempted to stuff his feet into Suzanne's silk basque.

A shriek of laughter came from the stairs. 'Aw my gawd, I've never seen anything so hilarious!' Suzanne collapsed into an hysterical heap.

Louise looked quizzically at the laughing woman seeing in place of humour the red sheen of her dressing gown, white fluffy carpet slippers peeping from beneath it and the manner in which the woman's head was thrown back in a snarl to reveal sharp white canines. It was Pansy resurrected in her russet coat, flashing the white tip of her brush, not laughing but gekkering.

'Fuck off, Nye, and don't come back here again,' Suzanne managed to blurt out.

To Louise it was as good as an edict from the god of life patterns. She levelled the shotgun at Nye, her right hand leaving it to snatch the ammunition belt and hang it around her neck. She dropped Suzanne's cigarettes into her copious pocket then sidled crab-wise along the dining table requisitioning whatever took her fancy—an orange, an apple, a banana and a bunch of grapes. Pigeon-beak fingers pecked amongst discarded toffee wrappers in a bowl, confectionery entered the same marsupial space as the other goods.

Eyes fixed on the gun barrel pointing at his chest, Nye despatched his own hand again to collect whatever he could of his clothes. He bundled them together and stood shivering. It was too much for Suzanne who fled back upstairs to the bathroom to avoid wetting herself. Louise's foraging was beginning to take on the ominous preparation for a long hunting trip. A torrent of filth soon followed his indignation and found its way up the stairs to the lavatory. 'Ha...ha...ha,' he heard Suzanne above the flushing of the cistern.

'Run!' Louise ordered Nye curtly. He just had time to stuff his right foot into his left wellington boot before she prodded him into the cold spring afternoon as if he'd been a big pink pig at a market. Suzanne, who wouldn't have missed Nye's comeuppance for the world, flew instantly to the bedroom window and flung it open in order to savour every delicious moment of his hobbling retreat, white buttocks looking terribly vulnerable.

'Give him a run for his money, Loopy Lou,' she called raucously. Her crude cawing summoned the retired school-teacher from next door. He emerged from the back of his house with the expression of one hailed inconveniently by bad behaviour. He mounted his caravan step which was kept close to the fence for the purpose of delivering com-plaints. When he looked up he found his dubious neighbour leaning from an upstairs window and pointing down the gar-den, housecoat drunkenly awry, a naked breast swinging generously over the sill. It was anarchy, bedlam and certainly not what he had retired to Sandpits for.

'Do you mind!' he thundered from the top of his step which only provided him with an additional nine inches of authority.

'Hah, hah, hah...' was all that Suzanne managed by way of explanation. He could not see what she could see—Nye, stark naked with the exception of one wellington boot on the wrong foot crashing through a garden gate into an orchard beyond. He stumbled towards the setting sun which presented itself as a streak of dying red light amongst the gathering clouds. 'Mind your nuts on those nettles, ha...ha...' accompanied his undignified flight.

Two hours after Nye had been flushed out of her cottage and set to run, 'Foxy' painted on her urban mask and headed for London in the wake of Sir George. Her high heels clicked smartly along the flagstone pathway behind a taxi driver who carried two leather suitcases. Shortly after, Miss Blinney departed Sandpits in a haze of diesel fumes. The cottage she left behind, briefly illuminated by car headlights, was as neat and as silent as the day she had entered it; apart from two feathers and a dried flower on the carpet nobody would have known she had been there at all.

To the north of where she had wintered over, like crumbling vertebrae in an ageing spine, a drystone wall runs the length of Long Coombe from Pikes Wood, forming a tousled head at the top of the valley, to the wispy tail of water at the bottom known as Harmers Pond. Had twilight not cast a discreet veil over the scene a watcher there would have seen a naked man clad only in a single wellington boot stumbling and cursing alternately along its length, his white flesh contrasting starkly with the greensward. They would also have seen him halt by a bush to take in desperate lungfuls of air. A small brown-coated woman toting a shotgun advances upon him with rapid clockwork steps, urging him to continue the ascent with a loping, painful gait. Anybody witnessing this impossible scene would have been forgiven for imagining they had seen a legendary white ape being driven uphill, and seeing that he had his arms around a bundle of some kind, thinking that such a creature had stolen something from the woman who both chased and chastised him at the same time.

After the first kilometre of his flight Nye bawled breathlessly over his shoulder, 'You and that fucking trollop...you hatched it up between you...' His words barely peppered the damp evening atmosphere of the Coombe let alone penetrated Louise's iron intention to keep him on the run. As soon as he stopped to draw breath for another curse then she would advance with the gun to prod him violently forward with the barrel. It was in this stop-go fashion that he eventually entered the shelter of Pikes Wood, bursting out of the twilight into the dark woodland having first run the gauntlet of waist-high nettles that daubed his unclad thighs with spiteful venom.

In a wood there should be a thousand places to hide, stretching by a fallen trunk, merging with the shadows, curling beneath the bracken, yet all Nye could do was stand and seethe with his arms about his bundle of clothes. At the bottom of the valley the dark haven of the wood looked as if it could swallow him up; now he had arrived he didn't know how to take advantage of its cover. A hominid ancestor would have extended a long hairy arm and looped it over a branch in order to effect a treetop escape. A hairless white ape he might appear without his clothes but a man trained to the peak of performance on a squash court is not necessarily adapted for life in the canopy of a mixed woodland: his prehensile skills having disappeared into prehistory.

Commonsense might urge that he drop his bundle and flee unencumbered into the dark. The trouble was he found himself in the grip of a dilemma, facing the choice of naked retreat through brambles that claimed their deposits of flesh, or putting on his clothes in order to keep warm. He did neither, instead he dealt with the astonishingly hot pain of nettle stings.

Moments later Louise burst through the same patch of nettles, brushing aside their astringent attack as if they were no more than sticky cobwebs. She sat promptly on a log and remained there stiffly upright with his gun resting on her knees and his belt of ammunition around her waist, looking like the subject of a sepia-tinted photograph of a scruffy pan-handler. Surely this was a role, Nye reasoned. Foxy had hired the services of this apology for womanhood in order to...but Suzanne's in-order-to motives eluded him.

A sensible man would have postponed the natural desire to demand explanations and put on his clothes whilst he had the opportunity. Not so Nye, who flung his on the ground in anger, placing his foot on them as if they were likely to scuttle away. He stood with one hand on his hip; the other he used to remonstrate by poking at the atmosphere with its extended forefinger.

'Don't think you and that fucking tart are going to get away with this...' He broke off, his thoughts snatched by the memory of Sir George's whore pissing herself with laughter. 'She might find it all very amusing, but I can assure you that a court of law won't...I'm taking the pair of you for every last penny you've got. Do you understand, do you?'

The penniless schizophrenic remained silent. Do you...do you...do you...hung in the air; it could have been the territorial proclamation of a large woodland bird and was indeed answered immediately by the alarm trill of a blackbird. Nye remained fixed in his pose for quite some time and Louise paid no more attention to him than had he been a marble muse in a stately garden. Perhaps it was the classical evocation of his naked posture that caused her to extract a bunch of grapes from her pocket and begin to pick fixedly at the small purple fruit. She nibbled away, scoffing the lot whilst he waited for an explanation until finally distracted by his big toe that had been pushed sockless into the wrong wellington boot and had rubbed up a nasty blister.

The silence of the wood was an ominous precursor to night and the injured toe throbbed like a native drum. He looked around for somewhere to sit; spotting a severed limb of hornbeam, he spread his wax jacket over it and lowered his arse cautiously. With teeth gritted against expected pain he began to lever off the boot. The blister, having burst, presented itself as a suppurating, dirty wound that would turn septic if left untreated.

He took a tally of the clothes he had succeeded in grabbing from Suzanne's settee. It was a poor catch, netting two wellington boots, a wax jacket, a pair of trousers of some lightweight poly-cotton mixture and a small top belonging to Suzanne that he had mistaken for his own T-shirt. Since it was far too small he threw it away in disgust; the branch of a holly bush caught it by the neck and it hung, a small white corpse swinging from a prickly gibbet. Neither the wax jacket nor the trousers brought much protection from the cold. He eased his cut and blistered feet into the wellington boots, deciding that he was just going to have to grin and bear the discomfort of it all until he got home.

Half an hour had passed since entering the wood and still Louise had not moved. She was so still that a pheasant had wandered into the clearing to peck confidently around her feet. She was as much a part of the woodland scene as the lolling tongues of bracket fungi growing from the rotten log upon which she sat. He studied her blank profile for signs of awareness, finding nothing there but a monumental emptiness as if she were a crudely chiselled wood-carving. Nevertheless a cautious instinct warned him against placing any faith in that staring vacancy. Her thoughts might well appear to be absent, if one judged by her expression, but he sensed that her attention loitered at the periphery of her awareness waiting to focus should anything untoward alert it. Any sudden move would be a mistake.

He looked toward the gap in the trees that could provide a gateway to freedom; nettles shivered there in the breeze. Their shadows were no longer sharp, but fattened, merging together in the light of the dying day. Soon the security lights would switch on automatically over the stable doors at Ebury Hall. The parish clock chimed; he rose and strolled to the edge of the wood as if offered an exit from his dilemma by its reassuringly domestic sound. Propping himself against the trunk of a silver birch, he folded his arms like a man enjoying the evening air at his own front door whilst, under cover of his seeming calm, he looked eastward toward the Hall. Who, he wondered, would be the first to raise the alarm? The thought of alarm bells, however, did not bring him any feelings of security: on the contrary the word alarm transposed itself into a prickly sensation of unease. How was he going to explain being flushed out of Suzanne's cottage without a stitch on him? There was no story, however devious, that could bypass even Matilda's flabby naïveté.

Anger welled and focussed itself on Sir George's whore. Suzanne Blinney's motives for instigating this dangerous prank were purely psychological. Foxy's meanings, opinions, personal history lay hidden behind elegant clothes and a mask of makeup. What elegance and cigarette smoke obscured was a distorted lesbian view of men. It was often the way with women of her ilk, their prostitution was a way of getting back at the sex they despised, a way of sneering behind their hands. It stood to reason that she had got hold of this half-witted woman, promised her money, sexual favours even…he paused to consider the disgusting possibility…then wound her up tight as a coiled spring before placing a gun in her hands and despatching her with the order to give him a run for his money. Mind your nuts on those nettles that dirty tart had bawled cheaply from the bedroom window. Very well, she had set him up to satisfy some lesbian whim, forcing him to play her reckless game, and play it he would have to, if he wanted to get home in one piece, but not by her rules. Having decided to create a few of his own he quite welcomed the challenge.

He looked down the valley toward the houses on the outskirts of Sandpits, visualising himself as a kingly playing piece in some topographical board game. A throw of the dice might have determined his present position in Pikes Wood, but it would be his superior wit and skill that would ensure his safe arrival at the finish. He investigated the scenery in terms of the cover that it might provide for a man fleeing before a gun. The trouble was the map that he held in his head was not the same as that on the ground. His mental map was smaller with more features to shelter him. In reality he would have to run full pelt over pastureland with only the drystone wall for cover. The physical obstructions to his escape sent him retreating into thoughts of a successful public indictment of Miss Blinney and her demented crony until he recognised that any legal action would resonate domestically as well as publicly. The best course was to effect an immediate escape and return unobtrusively, minus his gun, to Ebury Hall as if nothing had happened.

He began to edge experimentally from where he had propped himself and since it did not bring any response from his abductor he edged a little further, telling himself that at least he had started the game with a double six— his greater intelligence and strength pitted against an undernourished half-brain. He further cradled his bruised ego by entertaining a gratifying impression of himself sprinting, zigzagging to avoid gunshot and throwing himself into muddy hollows like an SAS officer. He took a deep breath and tensed in preparation for a flying start.

He had not covered a metre before his boot hooked under a tree root and he fell flat on his face. A startled pheasant broke from cover. Louise, as if violently aroused from torpor leapt to her feet, jerked the gun upward in an involuntary gesture and let go a resounding shot.

'Don't shoot, for Christ's sake, please don't shoot me,' whimpered Lieutenant Nye of the SAS with his nose pressed to the wood's mossy floor.

'Run!' It was not his own volition that raised him to his feet and launched him into flight, but the vicious thrust of gun metal in the small of his back. His first reaction was one of disbelief as at the thunderous crack of a car accident, this is not happening to me. The first wave of understanding came with pain, and pain means more to one who has always cosseted his body with good food and holidays in the sun.

He staggered to his feet cursing and curled his fists, only to encounter a second blow under his ribs delivered with a reflexive jerking of his abductor's forearms. He had never experienced a pain quite like it, this pain was acute and breathtaking, this kind of pain was omnipotent and most people will do anything to avoid it. She told him to run so he obeyed, throwing himself into the night ahead. Using the drystone wall as a guide he staggered down Long Coombe dragging behind him, as if shackled to his ankle by a chain, the swish of his pursuer's boots through the wet grass.

Darkness settled and the nocturnal life of Ebury Hall Park came on duty like a small industrious shift of night-workers. Beneath the brightly lit drawing-room window a hedgehog went about its business with snuffles and grunts. Above its head Matilda, wearing a bright orange housecoat, paced animatedly back and forth. Viewed from the outside her fretting demand to know what had happened to Nye appeared to be the silent mouthing of a plump goldfish. 'And now this, now this!' she told Mrs Deeks apropos of Nye's unaccountable absence. Her hands spiralled toward the ceiling to take in Caroline's vacated bedroom as well as an estimate for roof repairs received that morning. Winter had not been kind to the old brick mansion. The levering of gale-force winds had lifted the eaves and shaken off tiles. Running repairs had revealed woodworm in the rafters and three still days of frost had highlighted plumbing defects. 'It's just expense after expense. I might just as well have a bonfire made of banknotes.' She concluded the tirade by returning abruptly to the question of Nye's whereabouts. 'And where's my husband, do you suppose?'

'I've no idea, Mrs Nye.' Mrs Deeks stared out of the window, thus avoiding eye contact with her employer. 'Shall I draw the curtains?'

'No,' Matilda snapped rudely.

Mrs Deeks straightened her white cuffs and returned to silent vigil. Mrs Nye was being determinedly truculent.

'Perhaps Mr Nye had an appointment and forgot to tell you.'

Matilda, in a dismissive and arrogant frame of mind, waved aside the idea.

'He's a very organised man, you know he is.'

What Mrs Deeks also knew was that Nye had probably gone where he always went whenever he donned a wax jacket and slung a gun over his shoulder.

'He writes everything down in his diary, you know he does,' Matilda appended, then slipped into a pool of silence, leaving Mrs Deeks to wonder when she would have the grace to re-surface and dismiss her so she could take the pressure off her aching feet. Perhaps now was not the best time to resurrect the issue of court shoes versus flat ones. 'It's ten o'clock!' Matilda announced.

Mrs Deeks, having last eaten at lunch time, was well aware of it. 'Will that be all?' Tiredness and irritation was beginning to bubble up, threatening to boil over. Mrs Nye's behaviour had become intolerable following Caroline's letter. More of this selfishness and she would hand in her notice, tied cottage or no tied cottage.

'Oh, yes, yes, I suppose so,' came her employer's ungracious reply.

It was midnight, an open fire in the drawing room maintained a lively dance not quite in step with Matilda's husky sighing. The lace cuff of her night-gown, held to her forehead, gave the impression of a tear-stained handkerchief, its fringe of cotton knots substituting for worry beads. Sir George drank whisky in regular draughts and speculated.

It was one in the morning when Matilda snatched the phone and against his advice telephoned the county police of whom she demanded a senior officer. What she got was the duty officer from Amwell who offered the consolation of his personal experience—many men disappear overnight and reappear the next morning, most of them with hangovers.

'Is he a drinker?'

'Certainly not!'

'Depressed, worried about things?'

'Not at all.'

'Ill in any way?'

'He had a shotgun with him for God's sake!'

'Is it licensed?'

'Of course it's licensed.' The squeal of frustration brought Sir George to his feet. He took the phone to relieve his niece of the burden and began to explain, in a codified fashion, that Nye was most unlikely to take his own life.

'Then it doesn't sound as if you've got very much to worry about.'

Having accepted the advice that they should leave things until the morning he returned to his whisky and the point where speculation had left him before his niece's telephone call. Nye was not a drinker and on the rare occasions when he did go over the top he always came home sober. There had been affairs but always well-managed and short-lived. He might well resent the confines of marriage, but Nye knew which side his bread was buttered and accordingly kept these extra-marital activities within the bounds of discretion. He was more likely to leave behind indignation than pregnancies and broken hearts.

It was not a woman who kept him out so late. Fraud? The possibility had nagged him ever since Matilda had summoned him from London. More than any other board member Nye would have both opportunity and motivation. The upkeep of the Hall and its lifestyle ate into his income. Returns from rents had been falling steadily for a decade as tenant farmers were driven off the land by economics. Shooting and fishing barely compensated for losses. Nye had the main responsibility for a multi-million pound government contract...the temptation was there. Whisky heated and expanded the suspicion until it became conviction. He watched his niece pacing up and down the room with a heavy equestrian regularity. Whenever she reached the night-black window she would balk, seemingly at her own image reflected there, then retreat from it.

'I know,' she announced inspired. 'I'll look through his organiser.'

'If you think it will tell you anything,' he yawned. If Nye was guilty of corruption he was most unlikely to reveal it in his personal organiser. He would rather have returned to London and a reasonable night's sleep than witness her fruitless search; tomorrow there would be the prospect of an internal audit.

The black leather-bound book on the study desk was much like its owner—handsome, square-edged. It lay there deputising for Nye in his absence and had about it a forbidding aura that said, touch me, if you dare. He was a fussy man when it came to personal space and kept certain aspects of his life safely compartmentalised. Business matters were associated in Matilda's mind with Sir George and the head office staff, Nye's clothes and their care with Mrs Deeks.

It was with a slightly disconcerting thrill, therefore, that she opened up the organiser. Had the book not been left face down, causing her to flip open the back cover, she would never have found 'Foxy' faintly scrawled there in pencil, in a style uncharacteristic of Nye's normally neat hand. The pale letters implied a temporary note like a name on a betting slip. A tip for a winner perhaps? Clearly he had put money on a horse and didn't want her to find out at a time when the Hall and its repairs had prior claim on their income. That was it, Foxy was a horse and the London number belonged to a bookie.

Having been prodded round five complete circuits of Pikes Wood the quarry was pursued down the length of Long

Coombe to be about-turned and driven all the way up again. Nye found that the only way he could avoid the sharp rebuke of the gun barrel jabbing his spine was by keeping up a steady, albeit stumbling, pace without stopping to argue. It was impossible anyway to parley with her insane determination to keep him moving. Although his captor did stop to draw breath from time to time it was with a sudden cessation of movement as if she were driven by a mechanical power source. Whenever the rapid swish-swish of her boots ceased he too halted to draw in lungfuls of air and hug his ribs to relieve the acute attacks of stitch. When it seemed they were about to embark on the sixth circuit of Pikes Wood she halted again and he supported himself against a tree trunk.

This crazy woman might have a gun and a maniacal energy but he was by far the healthier and stronger. It was a matter, therefore, of running the course until she dropped from exhaustion. Taking a tally of his aches and pains he concluded any damage was minor compared to ten hot and swollen toes which had suffered the constant pressure of rubber boots on bare flesh. If anything gave way it would be his feet, only a bowl of cool water would alleviate their burning discomfort. It was pitch black; the last time he managed to see his watch it had been six o'clock, after that he had lost touch with time, guessing that he could have been walking in this stop-go fashion for some six hours. No doubt Matilda would be in a flat spin over his absence.

'My family,' he said, 'they'll call the police. There'll be trouble, they'll put you away...they won't let you out again, not after this... . If they had any sense they'd keep you in a padded cell for the rest of your life.'

His threat did not bring Louise hand-wringing to her knees. On the contrary a spontaneous eruption of fury followed, the physical and emotional upheaval causing her to leap in the air like a jack-in-the-box. She came rushing at him shaking his gun so violently that he prudently put the tree between himself and her oncoming fury. Quite inexplicably she rushed straight past him exuding a foul gust of body odour to halt some six feet away where she stood shouting and bawling in an alien tongue. Clearly her hallucinations were as real to her as his own current predicament was to him and he reasoned that it would be to his advantage to promote and manipulate them.

'That's right, you tell him,' he encouraged aiming to deflect her fury from himself. 'They'll arrest you, they'll put you in a padded cell, they'll lock you up and throw away the key.' The spontaneous explosion of activity was wonderful to behold. His taunting had the efficacy of a bag of sugar thrown on a fire. Watching the leaping sparks of paranoia he began to edge further into the shelter of Pikes Wood. This time he was not going to be stupid enough to make a dash for it down the Coombe and risk drawing her fire. Instead he would lie doggo in the bracken until she tired of searching for him. She seemed to be winding down, it was time to stoke the paranoia again.

'Who's there, Loopy Lou, Old Nick is it...? That's right, give him what for.' He began edging away, a few paces at a time... Nye of the SAS, officer in charge of escape, was confidently reinstated with an increased faith in his tactics. When he recognised his captor's passion had burned itself out as spontaneously as it had ignited Lieutenant Nye's escape plan was aborted. She marched toward him then stationed herself by a birch tree. Stiff-backed and holding his gun like a sentry she stared, her cold grey-eyed surveillance fixed firmly on his intentions.

When Matilda left the drawing room Sir George had been regarding the exit of a forty-three-year-old who had spent most of her adult life chasing fatuous notions of love like somebody ineffectively trying to net butterflies. The forty-three-year-old who re-entered the room, however, had undergone an alarming metamorphosis. She held Nye's black leather organiser aloft like a bible in the hands of a fire-and-brimstone preacher as if expecting him to pledge undying support for the truth contained therein.

'It's a woman,' she blurted out in her fury, 'a bloody woman! Did you know about this?'

'It doesn't surprise me.' Alcohol and sheer relief had induced an incautious candour. He thanked God it wasn't fraud that had leapt from that little black book of revelations.

'Does he love her, do you suppose?' she demanded.

'I doubt it, Dickie doesn't love anybody but himself.'

'What a shame,' said Matilda with equal candour, 'you didn't tell me that before you arranged my marriage to him.'

It was two in the morning when Matilda's bitter observation sent Sir George climbing the stairs to bed, dragging Nye's infidelity behind him. Not being au fait with Suzanne Blinney's nickname, he had no idea who Foxy might be. Another passing fancy, no doubt; certainly it would not be anybody of any significance to Nye, but what would Matilda do now? Nye was her *raison d'être*, the pivot around which her world revolved. It wasn't just Nye's stupid indiscretion that climbed into bed with him and insisted on sprawling heavily across his tired mind, it was a feeling that something had gone kaput at Ebury Hall. The regular and reliable order of the place was disintegrating, he could even see it at a physical level in the decaying fabric of the building. There was ivy on the walls with lateral arms as thick and fibrous as the muscles on a navvy. There was worm in the loft, dry rot in the cellar...and there was Caroline's defection. He knew, even though he could not bring himself to admit it, that Denis Tunstall was not really after his great niece's fortune. There was no fortune, only debt and worry would come with Ebury Hall. Caroline had turned her back on it anyway, effectively disinheriting herself.

Too much whisky sent him to sleep but did not dispel that subversive notion of a hidden hand sabotaging his efforts to maintain the Hall and its traditions. Kee vit...kee vit...came the contact call of a tawny owl perched on a branch outside his window. Such a song from a guardian of the night should have been as reassuring as the cry of a lamplighter, but kee vit...kee vit only succeeded in pecking his eardrums and stirring his doubts.

The same call that pierced Sir George's dreams was promptly answered by another delivered from a branch above Nye's head where he sat in Pikes Wood with his arms hugging his knees and cursing under his breath. 'They should burn you at the stake, you old lesbian hag.' His mumbled insult, produced for the sake of pride rather than effect, was little more than the defiant yap of a defeated cur. Whatever detonator he had pressed to cause a volcanic eruption of her psychosis, it was not going to work a second time without danger to himself. He closed his eyes as if to shut out the abhorrent presence of his abductor. She remained so still and silent she could have been carved out of limestone, yet there was ferocity in her pose. As with a scorpion, who could say what would cause her to come at him all sting and venom? His only hope of getting away unscathed would lie in thinking of her as an animal, by getting to know her behaviour and finding the predictable in it. He peered through the glutinous dark of the wood, searching the space she occupied mere feet away but his senses reported only an intolerable waiting stillness resonant with malice.

After a while his concentration waned and his brow dropped wearily onto his knees again. He dozed intermittently, drifting into mere seconds of sleep before being alerted by cold, hunger and a sense of the danger he was in. If, he speculated morbidly, a shotgun went off in Pikes Wood, down in the village it would just be taken for somebody out shooting rabbits or a car backfiring.

Moments later Nye's brief doze was interrupted by an investigative nudging of the gun barrel as if it had been summoned by his guttural snores.

'Run,' his abductor ordered sharply.

He got slowly to his feet with a great deal of grunting and groaning in order to exaggerate his injuries and borrow a little extra time. He massaged his calves, loosened his knee joints with a wincing expression then tried his weight on the swollen foot. It was a performance rivalled only by the limping, fluttering display of a ground-nesting bird distracting a predator's attention away from its nest. His abductor was not overly impressed and regarded the antics with a school-marmish patience.

'Run,' she ordered again.

'Where? Don't you think we—' he selected the inclusive term deliberately, '—ought to find somewhere to doss down for the night? In fact I know a cottage, the owner's away, there's plenty of grub there—plenty of chocolates, cigarettes.' He recalled her addiction to both.

With his hands in his pockets he set off, seemingly nonchalant, in the direction of Ebury Hall. The cottage he had in mind belonged to Deeks and was situated on the edge of the estate in a small copse bounded by a high stock fence. Two big black Labrador bitches slept in the kitchen and as soon as anybody came anywhere near the place they would raise the roof. It was quite simple really, so simple he cursed himself for not thinking of it sooner. Loopy Lou would be caught with his gun, his predicament would be self-evident and that would be the end of the matter. A smirk of victory began to crease the corner of his mouth. He even began to feel a little excited, like a small boy whose trickery is kept afloat by a giggling buoyancy. He formed a picture of Deeks's dogs unleashed, all fur and fang, security lights flooding the area and the gamekeeper emerging with his own gun. Not long now and he would be home and dry, curled up with a malt whisky, giving a heroic account of his adventures, which would studiously exclude Suzanne's cottage.

As soon as he reached the stock fence, reality presented him with a quite different scenario. As predicted, Deeks's dogs set up a shindig. They were not in the kitchen as usual but had been let out to roam freely. On hearing his approach, they hurled themselves at the stock fence which bulged under their combined weight. Deeks must have been expecting trouble with poachers because moments later a light came on in an upstairs window. It was the familiar sight of the gamekeeper's face peering out that caused Nye to lose control. 'Deeks, Peter Deeks,' he managed to bawl before the gun barrel struck his ribs in the most vicious blow he had received so far. The sound of his anguish and attempts to draw breath were smothered by the sound of the barking dogs.

'Run, run, run, run,' came Louise's staccato order.

Nye pulled himself to his feet, his fingers clinging to the stock fence. Briefly he saw Stella and Babs, normally benign and friendly animals, gun dogs he knew well and had taken out shooting, bare their teeth and growl at him. 'Stella, Babs,' he appealed through the wire, to be answered by hot and rancid breath as if the dogs had just fed on raw meat. As he peered into their yellow eyes an aberrant thought struck him that the dogs were no longer animals but people, combatants blacked up for night combat. A dagger-like canine caught his finger and he withdrew his hand as if from a shock. He turned and stumbled away in the direction determined by his captor. Accompanied by the sound of snarling dogs, he found himself driven southward into an unknown night. Forced to turn his back on Ebury Hall, he looked over his shoulder, seeing briefly the light coming from Deeks's cottage before it bobbed away like the lights on a distant ship.

Now he was all at sea, flailing and floundering, his efforts enervated by anger and indignation. Fear had been there right from the very first encounter with the insane administration of pain, its thin wedge prising him from his hope of an early escape, but as soon as he acknowledged that fear it was rivalled by an indignant and furious determination to survive the ordeal. A man who'd always been successful in the life game, he told himself, does not allow himself to drift on a current determined by somebody else.

Nye was despatched down Long Coombe with the gun barrel prodding at his buttocks, his abductor showing as much respect for his dignity as an auctioneer at a cattle market. She moved closer to him now, the inexorable swish, swish of her boots sounding more rapid, and resonant in the cold dark night. It was clear that she wanted to get somewhere in a hurry. He had no idea of his destination and what would be expected of him when they arrived, nor whether he would be permitted a drink. Thirst had been stealing up on Nye all night, now the increased pace caused it to become a desperate need. It was not the kind of thirst that could be slaked by a pint of beer at the squash club, but the kind that turned the saliva to glue and constricted the windpipe. His uncertainty translated into panic at the prospect of not being able to find water. The need began to rage hotly, insistent, demanding immediate satisfaction to the extent that even his escape became secondary.

If Nye had never known failure in his life neither had he encountered such a primitive drive as thirst and the panic it could generate. He began to swallow convulsively as he stumbled gasping through the night, the taste of moisture in the air teasing and provoking his need. 'I need water,' he cried out but the swish, swishing of his abductor's clockwork steps did not halt. 'I need to drink, for Christ's sake,' he shouted with tears in his eyes, but was answered with a nudge in the small of his back. He reeled, bawling,

'A man can go without food, but he can't go without water.' Nye bellowed with such sincerity he sounded as if he'd been the first to discover a universal truth that no other had grasped before.

Another nudge caused him to shut his mouth and proceed down Long Coombe. His knowledge of the area told him that he was being driven towards Harmers Farm. There would be no water there, the tenancy had been abandoned over thirty years ago and any mains water would have been disconnected. His only hope was that they would pass close enough to Harmers Pond for him to drink. It was little more than a dew pond that would swell and shrink throughout the seasons. Although he had a rough idea of its location it would be difficult to spot in the dark. There was a slight paling of the sky provided by a few streetlights in Sandpits. Against it, dimly smudged, he saw a group of alders that he knew grew by the water's edge; he ran towards them, crashing through some reeds, his boots releasing the smell of marsh gas. Nye waded towards the middle of the pond where he assumed the water to be cleaner and before his abductor had the opportunity to prevent the satisfaction of this most basic need he stooped, cupped his hands and drank greedily expecting any moment to feel the gun in his back. He drank noisily in huge swigs and when he had finished stood with his ear cocked, anticipating his abductor's approach but heard nothing, not even the sucking of mud at her wellington boots.

It was too much to hope that the mad woman had abandoned the chase and gone home, wherever that might be. She lurked waiting for him, perhaps only feet away, camouflaged by the thick black night, as indeed he was.

Darkness rendered them equals. If he made a dash for

it, by the time she had located him from sound alone, raised the gun, aimed and fired the remaining cartridge in the assumed direction of his retreat he would at least have gained a head start. He rehearsed his escape, sprinting away, lead shot zinging...common sense pulled him back, cautioning him that they were not equals; she was unfathomable, beyond reason and he had no better chance of predicting her next move than guessing when a coiled snake would strike. It would make more sense to move only when he heard her move, thus using the sound she made to scramble his own. Assuming he could reach the other side of the pond without drawing fire, he would not risk catching a lead pellet by bolting immediately; instead he would snake his way around the perimeter of the pond, then lie flat in the mud, obscured amongst the sedge and reeds until she abandoned the chase.

Having told himself that he had not come thus far in life to be outwitted by a woman with only half a brain, he stood feet apart, hands on hips like a local colossus bestriding his waterlogged empire, listening whilst sinking slowly into the silt. Minutes passed and no human sound came to him from the pond's marshy bank. Close by there was something that sounded peculiarly like a duck grumbling, the dripping of condensation from the alders and the regular pop, pop of marsh gas. She was out there too, poised, listening, and the thought of it brought an eerie sense of connection with her. The night was a substance to which they both clung, a black gel that quivered whenever either of them moved. A male frog croaked its spring courtship invitation, the sudden outburst, a seeming pronouncement on Nye's dilemma, caused him to startle and totter forward. Anchored as he was by his wellington boots in the mud his body's momentum carried him forward, fingers splayed. His noisy descent into the water was as good as shouting, yoo hoo, here I am, over here! By the time he righted himself his boots were full and his trousers soaked to the crutch.

Kee vit...kee vit came the territorial proclamation of the very same tawny owl that had sung outside Sir George's bedroom window. Convinced that nature itself connived at his downfall, Nye pulled his wellington boots out of the mud—yet another noise to loud-hail his whereabouts. He waded towards dry land lifting his feet against the contrary sucking of mud. He might just as well have tried to walk on two sink plungers. The elegant tactic of snaking his way through the reeds and lying low until the danger had passed now aborted, the most he could hope for was that he would be allowed to bale out his wellingtons before being nudged into the chase once more.

What he had not expected to find floating on the water just ahead of him was a neat circle of yellow light as if somebody had taken the moon and set it adrift on the black oily surface of the pond. An electric torch was the last thing he would have expected this vagrant half-wit to possess. The beam of light, however, was not focussed on himself and his predicament but settled instead on a ripple by the reed bed. Revealed as if by a spotlight upon its watery stage, a male frog mounted its partner and clung to her in a hug of procreative triumph.

''Tis the time of the year,' announced his abductor.

Nye regarded the amphibious pornography and experienced a rush of indignant disbelief. 'What's this supposed to be, a fucking nature walk?' he yelled at the ambiguous shadow behind the torchlight. 'Absurd, absurd,' he mumbled to himself unable to dispel the impression of his abductor as a prim infant teacher labelling the sex act somewhere in the corner of the stick insects' glass tank. 'Absurd,' he repeated as if to convince himself.

The torchlight skimmed across the pond and settled on his face. Kee vit...kee vit, the tawny owl launched itself from a branch of alder which hung over the water like a diving board and drifted off into the black sea of night; it passed his cheeks like a small silent spirit, causing a mild flutter of air. Shortly after something died with a squeal of angry protest.

'Run.'

Amongst rusting agricultural equipment at Harmers Farm, bramble and barbed wire rose entwined in a coiling contest. A crop of luxuriantly green nettles had conquered the heights of an old dung-heap. Ivy, having deprived itself of space on the exterior walls of the crumbling smallholding, now probed inside through windows that had shed their glass years ago. Here nature was in the ascendancy and the evidence of human agriculture lay strewn around like the relics of an ancient magic that had lost its potency against the forces of sun, wind and rain. Into this scene of abandonment and failure, well after midnight, Louise prodded her quarry.

Too exhausted to remain on his feet Nye sank to the ground like a sagging bag of grain. Multiple discomforts stabbed his body, but he had neither will nor energy to deal with them. He couldn't even be bothered to bale out his boots. Under drooping eyelids, he made out a bobbing torch. An animal-like scuffling came to his ears as his abductor foraged close by. He did not ask what it was she was looking for in the dark. She was mad, her malady placed her beyond the interrogation of reason. She didn't even possess a language to reason with—run seemed the only discernible word she ever spoke, the rest being a tirade of incoherent cursing spat out in globules.

When the torch clicked off and the scuffling ceased, Nye tensed anticipating the gun barrel in his guts, but all he could see was a candle flame of embryonic fire that came from a neat pile of kindling. The flame grew and so too his hopes for a little physical comfort. Louise had propped three stout logs together wigwam-style over the flame. Steam began to rise into the night carrying a pleasant fungal smell just before the wood caught fire. He began to edge toward the warmth cautiously, inches at a time least even this small comfort might be withdrawn.

Louise ignored him, her attention being attracted by one of the numerous trinkets clinging to her coat. It swung on a loose thread, a child's plastic bead bracelet, the sort of thing found in a cracker and discarded. Worthless as it was, it sent her into purse-lipped tutting as she searched her pockets, patting away at them like a smoker feeling for a box of matches. Eventually she found some sewing cotton and a needle which she threaded by the light of the fire.

Bizarre as it was, Nye felt drawn to watch her fastidious attention to such a trivial task. There she sat amidst all the dereliction, dirt and poverty, bending over her work like an old biddy attending to her crochet. The sight of her stretched his credulity. 'Why?' he asked, his tone more mystified than indignant. 'There I was, minding my own business, then suddenly I find myself at the end of my own shotgun, forced to run without any clothes on, prodded and poked all the way up Long Coombe, five times round Pikes Wood, out to Chepton Veins and back again. What fucking game do you think you're playing? There's no sense in any of it.' He shook his head wearily. 'What have I done to you? You don't even know me.' He broke off, almost intrigued by her motives, then pounced, inspired, on an idea 'I know...I know...I think I've got it—I remind you of somebody, somebody who upset you and you're getting your own back.'

The repair job done, Louise bit through the cotton neatly and restored the needle to its packet. Her silence dismayed him; it was an extension of her self-sufficiency. This woman carried her world around with her in her pockets—torch, matches, chocolates, cigarettes and now she had purloined his gun. 'I'm hungry,' he grumbled, only to be ignored again. Very well, he would approach the subject from a more cunning angle. Allowing a few minutes to pass he said slyly, 'If I'm starved I won't be able to run for you. I can't run without food inside me.'

Far from prompting any concern for Nye's welfare the word food sent her hand delving into her pocket to bring forth a chocolate bar; she peeled off the wrapper like a banana skin and ate with the concentrated energy of a shrew. Such flagrant dismissal of his hunger whilst satisfying her own left him facing an horrendous possibility. He was going to be held hostage until he starved to death. His lip curled. Had he been able to sprout two long white canines he would have willingly sunk them into his abductor's throat.

'You can't do this to me,' he snarled, his chin thrust out like a bristling yard-dog whilst his mouth dribbled rabidly from hunger. He was answered only by the sound of a

237

mousy nibbling that placed her beyond the niceties of human manners and himself beyond human law. Nye swore to himself that if no other means of escape presented itself this woman would die at his hands. 'If I had my way,' he told her with such malice that it seemed to burn his eye sockets, 'I would nail you to a stake, roast you on a spit and feed you, bit by bit, to Deeks's dogs.'

Through narrowed eyes, he watched her confidently light a cigarette and smoke it in the same intense fashion she ate. Puffs of smoke hit the night air as if released from the funnel of a miniature steam train. Her eyes, he noticed, darted constantly to the shotgun that rested on her knees.

Diminished by such grim circumstances, his bitter threat sounded no more potent than the whining protest of a chained dog. Louise continued to puff imperviously. His fury now exhausted, he capitulated to fatigue. Threats were just a waste of energy, so he propped himself against a rusty trailer and hugged his wet knees. The mad woman possessed all the resources; he had nothing, no food, no fresh water and no means of self-defence, leaving him entirely at her mercy with nothing but his native wit.

Feverish, Nye put his hot brow on his knees and belched loudly; the release of air from his guts bringing back the slimy flavour of pond-water. A pain stabbed through his bowels causing him to flush in panic. 'I need a crap,' he groaned. 'I suppose I'm allowed to have a crap in peace, am I?'

'I int stoppin' 'e.' Nye crawled away on hands and knees, anus tightened, accompanied by his abductor's observation. ''Tis thik water from Harmers Pond what's upset 'e— contaminated, see.'

Nye managed to find some privacy amongst the vegetation on the dung-heap and gave way to the indignity of diarrhoea. He cleaned himself as best he could with dock leaves which he found after a painful search amongst the nettles. He shuffled miserably back to the trailer and wriggled under. Here at least he would be safe from the malicious prodding of a shotgun barrel. A little warmth came to him from his abductor's fire, the only comfort he could find in this bankrupt environment. Although his bowels had succeeded in dispelling whatever microbe he had ingested with the water from Harmers Pond, the fever still lingered to sabotage his concentration. The ideas he had tried to assemble into a plan of escape had scattered, perversely refusing to be rounded up; petulant sheep they seemed, moving further afield with each attempt to pen them in.

Mesmerised by the fire's juggling sparks, he gave up the effort of thinking and began to drift into the alternative dimensions of sleep. He found himself clad in evening dress dancing in a clearing in Pikes Wood with Suzanne who was naked. She drank champagne from a cut-glass flute with a faraway look in her eyes. Her presence in his dreaming dance had no substance. She was as wispy as morning mist and would be abolished by the rising sun. Although he could not see them, others laughed and clinked glasses somewhere amongst the trees. From time to time the shadows of phantasmagoric dancing partners fell sharply across the clearing. He and Suzanne drifted back and forth in a foxtrot accompanied by the genteel rhythms of a Palm Court sextet—until Matilda burst upon the scene astride a handsome grey, dressed and numbered for a show-jumping event. Her fury on finding the pair together filled the wood with the legendary sound of a giant's footfall. She sidled her bristling mount toward the dancing couple, growing bigger with each advancing step until it became impossible to see her as a whole.

Suzanne and the dancers had evaporated leaving Nye to watch his wife expand until the palm of her hand alone filled the clearing. With no room in which to escape Nye fell into one of the numerous salty pools of sweat that dotted its surface. He slithered about in an effort to stand upright only to find himself elevated horribly before she threw him away in disgust. He fell spinning and sickly, waking up in the harsh reality of a night spent in the open.

The fire had gone out and the weather had turned bitter, gusting sleet as hard as gravel. His abductor had built herself a crude shelter and withdrawn inside. Whether she slept or remained on guard it was impossible to say. The shelter looked ominously like a crude sentry box. Dare he take the risk of wriggling past it along his only escape route? He lay shivering, still wet from his immersion in the pond and peered into the dark with all its uncertainties. Did people with such gross abnormalities actually go to sleep or did their nervous systems suddenly go on red alert at the merest stimulus as hers seemed to?

He listened miserably to the repetitious beat of sleet on his metal roof and longed for the dawn with its chorus of birdsong, tuning up like an orchestra before the curtain rises on a well-lit production. A childish aberration had always presented the night to Nye as something to be held at bay by street lamps. If not halted it would encroach, filling the air with an inky substance. It had always struck him that at night nature took on singular and bestial purposes that distilled to a single personality. Out there, in the black substance, a mad woman sat as still as a bat in repose. A bat; he shuddered instinctively, horrified by the thought of that membranous skin stretched between skeletal fingers—now there was a creature that exemplified the dark. Half a mouse transported by wings that folded like black umbrellas, possessing feet where hands should rightly be, enjoying its rest upside down, flying blind yet with expert seeing.

The grey dawn came stealing over the derelict farm-yard, the damp air bringing with it a faint whiff of fox urine; perhaps one had glided past him in the night. The lightening sky was cheerless and sinister, there to prologue the story of how the farm's previous occupant had been found hanging from a beam in an outhouse. Nye found his eyes wandering irresistibly around the yard to seek the place where the deed had been done. He could see the stark outline of a dutch barn, a holly tree growing in the entrance to the old milking parlour, an ivy-clad granary, dagger-backed bramble tumbling over the side of the former silage pit. A shed door hung loosely on a single hinge, seeming to tremble a little. Perhaps it was there they had found him.

The whole place spoke of defeat and surrender, of a man's flight from failure. A battle had been fought and lost here and the detritus that lay around was the armoury and ammunition abandoned in retreat. Who had been the enemy? Fungi, it was said, had got the barley, foot and mouth had taken the cattle and despair the man. Nye told himself that he would never have let things get the better of him like that. He wouldn't have kowtowed to nature and the vagaries of the market. Telling himself that he could never share such plodding and blinkered attachment to the land, he scraped a shallow depression in it in order to rest his head. Exhausted, freezing cold, aching from head to foot, he closed his eyes, and tried to will away the grisly notion of a desperate man dancing at the end of a rope.

At breakfast time Matilda presented herself in the hall, red-eyed, yet wearing Nye's betrayal with the dignified air of the bereaved. She found Sir George trying short-sightedly to poke a small gold key into the locked drawer of an antique writing table assisted by Mrs Deeks.

'Can I help you, Uncle?' she asked curtly.

He mumbled something about looking for papers that might indicate Dickie's whereabouts.

'We know where he is, we don't need any papers to tell us. He's with that woman.'

Sir George looked as if he were about to dismiss Mrs Deeks out of earshot.

'And would you happen to know anything about Mr Nye's assignations, Mrs Deeks?' The question was grandly amplified by the hall, the acoustics turning Matilda into a prima donna assured of an audience.

'I don't think it's my place to comment, Mrs Nye.'

'Other than behind your hand.'

The locked drawer sprung open in response to Sir George's fumbling, springing Matilda's own indignation at this invasion of personal property.

'Really, Uncle, I don't think you'll find anything more in there than a few old hat pins. Close it, will you, Mrs Deeks.' Sir George was taken aback. He had been used to coming and going in the house at will and could not comprehend such a trivial objection to him opening a drawer.

'This is a family matter, Mrs Deeks, perhaps you'd be good enough to...' He inclined his head in the direction of the kitchen and Mrs Deeks turned on her heel to be instantly pivoted round by Matilda's countermanding order.

'You will wait until I have dismissed you, you are employed by me, not my uncle.'

Sir George's chins wobbled like the loose folds of flesh under a turkey's beak. Mrs Deeks straightened her white cuffs and waited to be formally dismissed to carry on in the kitchen. Mrs Nye, she thought, appeared as if she was ready to sing an aria. Uncle and niece, seemingly in competition for the heights of dignity and self-control, froze into a parody of themselves. They could have been taken for two characters in a West End farce. Sir George fiddled with the little gold key as if compulsively drawn to open the desk drawer.

'You seem to have forgotten, Uncle, that the desk belonged to my grandmother.'

'My mother!' he pointed out.

'You also appear to have forgotten that this was my father's house.'

'My brother's!'

They paused to consider their respective claims to ancestral property.

'And now,' summed Matilda, 'it is my house.'

Sir George's cheeks turned a hypertensive purple. 'Bring my coat, Mrs Deeks, I'm going back to London.' He marched to the front door, chin thrust forward like an old fighting bull released from the stockade, God help anybody who got in his way that morning, they would be gored to the ground.

Hung over after a night on grief, Matilda paid no more attention to her uncle's departure than a thought dismissed from her mind. Nye's infidelity was paramount, there could be nothing to equal the treason committed by one who had been unswervingly believed in.

The little gold key protruded from the lock of the disputed antique writing table, but it was not this key that concerned her, since it unlocked no more than a few Victorian millinery accessories. It was its modern counterpart hidden in her pocket which troubled her. She postponed inserting it into Nye's desk drawer. She knew what it would unlock, her search for further evidence in the early hours had already revealed it. No, she would defer the moment a little longer, there was no point overdosing on misery, she'd had a surfeit of that particular poison the night before.

The wind mixed its own brew of sleet and dry leaves along the drive. It was springtime, renewal time, but the season had only brought invidious messages of decay. It was a wicked whisper that planted surreal notions—a herd of plump white woodworm grazing upon the timbers in the lofts above her head, regiments of dry rot spore in the cellar below her feet. Those solid old timbers upon which the whole structure depended were surrendering to a crumbling disease like the bones of the elderly to osteoporosis. Nothing was sustainable any more, even the house martins that glued their conical nests under the eaves each April were more capable of holding the old Hall together than either she or Sir George.

Ebury Hall and Nye had been linked in a silly, insubstantial dream about marriage to a clever, witty, charming, handsome man. What mean little trick of the psyche had obscured the truth all those years? A name scrawled on the inside cover of an address book, a key to a desk drawer. These things were the advance guard of the gross invasion of reality, a reality that had always been there waiting to storm the bastions of self-deception. Uncle George had been quite right, Nye did not love anybody but himself. She had squandered more than twenty years on a cold, provocative, egocentric. Her marriage, like the old Hall itself, had been eaten from within and what remained was the brittle shell of pretence.

At two o'clock that morning Nye's desk drawer had opened to present the backs of some photographs, faintly inscribed with pencil in the same lazy, sensuous style that had written Foxy. Now, in the silent aftermath of Sir George's angry departure, she recalled photographic portraits of the woman who trailed like a wisp of smoke behind him wherever he went. Whenever Matilda had thought about Suzanne Blinney, which was only fleetingly, it was as one of those decorous females that puffed on cigarette-holders. She was never referred to publicly, but privately understood to be one of the privileges of rank and wealth. Who was Matilda, the niece, to question her uncle's bachelor habits since there seemed to be no particular disgrace in enjoying the companionship of a younger woman?

It was the sound of a diesel engine that woke him. To him its retreating throb was like hearing the mother tongue above the chatter of a hostile and foreign crowd. 'Help! Help!' he bawled after it and, with hope overcoming his aches and pains, he began to wriggle from beneath the trailer only to confront the over-sized wellington boots of his abductor and the barrel of his shotgun. His head retracted instantly in the manner of a startled tortoise. Appeased by this obeisant gesture, she then sat hunkered close by, keeping an eye on him whilst she drank from a carton of milk. Having slaked her thirst, she peeled the foil cap from a fruit yoghurt.

Nye watched her, his mouth salivating. In the time it had taken for the milk truck to reverse in the dead end of Harmers Lane and for his captor, unseen by its driver, to divest it of a pint of milk, he could have escaped. There were no bars around this bizarre world, his ankles were not shackled, his view was not confined to a slit of daylight but he was imprisoned as surely as if an iron door had slammed behind him. With the custodial confidence of a gaoler in charge of the keys she had 'popped out' for a pint of milk. Having been driven hard across the countryside followed by a night of brutal discomfort he now understood that all his actions were determined by her. Together captor and captive had crossed that psychological threshold where the behaviour of one affirms the role of the other. He glared at her from beneath the trailer as she sucked and licked the yoghurt from her fingers. The milk had left a greasy moustache on her upper lip. Whilst she drank her coat had parted revealing two skinny, dirty knees above the level of her wellington boots. How could he have been so stupid as to have lost his freedom to such a poor apology for a human being?

Suzanne Blinney—his brain spat out her name—had dropped him into this pit of shit and she was the only one who could haul him out again. He curled his fist and beat the earth, cursing feebly. There was little point in hiding his distress since her lizard eye, that unblinking, unsleeping, mythological surveillance saw everything, not least what went on in his brain. Fatigue overcame resentment and his head fell back on the earth. In the mean space afforded by the height of the trailer he felt around him to clear away stones and twigs in order to make a crude bed for himself. There was an irritating chunk of rock beneath his knee, which he rocked until it eased away from the soft soil. One end, round and smooth, rested in his palm. The other end had been chipped away, perhaps by a ploughshare, to form a flint cutting edge over which he ran his thumb. It was an edge for whittling wood, butchering a carcass, scraping a hide; he looked malevolently at the brown, weathered skin around his abductor's throat. The gun barrel prodded experimentally under the trailer. He rolled out of reach to find it coming at him from a different angle. Pocketing his flint weapon he wriggled out and remained swaying on all fours giddily regarding his guard's wellington boots. 'Water,' he told her feebly, 'I need fresh water.'

'Best go and find some, hadn't 'e. Run.' She hunched her shoulders around the word and frowned as if sighting her authority along it. 'Run.'

The word flushed him out of Harmers Farm. 'Run' sent him along the lane stumbling and cursing.

It was not the obscene nature of the photographs that first struck Matilda, but the expression of sublime indifference on Suzanne Blinney's face. Her eyes floated above the filthy inquisitiveness of the single glass eye that held her in its gaze. Such detachment gave the zany impression that somebody else's face had been pasted, pastiche style, onto the wrong body. The pictures weren't even sexy; they were just cold, two-dimensional exposures of one man's pornographic choices. Surely Nye could not love this woman whose body he had treated like a pliable doll, bent and twisted into positions that pleased him the most. Matilda blushed, a consuming blush of indignation and shame. How could this woman have allowed herself to be used in such an absurd way?

She sank heavily onto a chair, red and sweating, aware of Nye's smart leather organiser that had initially unlocked the truth. The next blush was not for Suzanne Blinney's sexual compliance with his demands but her own stupidity. She too had contorted her body by stuffing it into haute couture to catch the eye of an indifferent man. Had she not spent the best years of her life pivoting around his every mood and opinion? When that failed to win his affection she had thrown money away at health farms and on faddish eating. When her food-denying strategy failed, then she would try cooking for him. Seeing him pick and peck deliberately at the haute cuisine she had served with a flourish, she would stuff her own face to compensate for feelings of inadequacy. They had been wasted years spent in planetary orbit around a man who didn't even like her, let alone respect her. Was she really any different from Suzanne Blinney?—at least Susanne had detached her soul from Nye's dirty little lens. Matilda returned the photos to the drawer then stood clasping the key. The marriage might be over but she was damned if she was going to shed her tears in public.

'Mrs Deeks, Mrs Deeks!' She flung open the study door and shrieked into the hall. Mrs Deeks arrived like a breathless stretcher-bearer. Her dutiful attention brought a flush of fury to Matilda's cheeks—she had not been summoned by concern, but by the juicy prospect of scandal. She must have known, everybody must have known. 'You will remove Mr Nye's things to the stables, every last sodding thing. I want nothing left in this house to remind me of him.'

Nye had only ever known wants in his life. I want that car, that woman, this level of income, but he had never known need until he caught sight of Harmers Pond knowing he could not drink there, the water was filthy, contaminated and would make him ill again. Fresh water, food, shelter, fundamental necessities were being denied him. He shook his head wearily over the sheer incomprehensibility of it. 'You can't do this. You can't hunt a man down…I must have fresh water, for Christ's sake. Don't you understand that, you cretin!?'

His protest whimpered in the morning air and in response his abductor merely waved an arm indicating the direction she wanted him to travel. It was the gesture of an admonishing infant teacher shepherding in a difficult child from the playground. This pedantic arm-waving sent him back up Long Coombe toward Pikes Wood. Nye stumbled up the rolling pasture driven by the swish, swish of her wellington boots, a sound to which his own movements had become firmly hobbled. Her rapid steps formed an insistent offbeat as she scuttled behind him like a giant rodent with inexhaustible energy. She had lost her human personality and taken on an it-like identity. People had defensive layers that could be peeled away to reveal an essential core. She had no core, only a demonic motor force.

When her footsteps ceased abruptly halfway up the valley, Nye gratefully leaned against the drystone wall and breathed deeply. He fixed his eyes on the grass at his feet to avoid the sight of the sweeping hill ahead, an interminable green distance without rest, food or water. He heard her muttering behind him, but did not turn. From now on everything he did must be aimed at conserving his energy. It was a Latin phrase that made him look up and regard his pursuer with astonishment. He found her stooped over something on the ground, cupping her hands around it all of a pout-mouth and fuss, with his cartridge belt dangling around her skeletal hips.

It was all so unbelievable. Surely he had been watching a second-rate pantomime with her cast as the comic desperado who had leapt off the stage, chased him out of the theatre and all over the countryside, in a joke that had gone too far and a role that had taken over the player. The safety catch on his gun, he noticed, was still released.

'Tut, tut, tut...tut, tut, tut...' she chattered with maternal concern for the primrose his boot had crushed, one of a cluster growing at the base of the wall. Although she cradled his gun with one arm, her face was turned away from him, unguarded. Weakened by his ordeal he might be, but he was still considerably stronger than her, moreover, uphill of her. Six short metres, it was nothing for a former striker, a leading light in his old university team. Her head would be the ball and his escape the goal. He took in a lungful of air and made ready to launch himself; within seconds he would be putting the boot in.

'Primula Vulgaris, Primula Vulgaris.' Louise looked up sharply as if admonishing him for his lack of attention. Nye remained rooted whilst his intentions lunged forward into abject dismay. 'Primula Vulgaris,' she chanted as if by repeating its Latin name she would restore it.

He screwed up his fists in fury and appeared about to beat them on his chest. 'Why?' he raged. 'If you're not doing it for that fucking whore, then why?' A crack of thunder over their heads followed his question bringing Louise instantly to her feet with her bony fists shaking at the clouds. Although she let forth a torrent of mumbo jumbo, Nye sensed that she was not shaking her fist at some devilish hallucination or the storm, but at the question itself. This was not anger; he had seen her anger exposed before, but extreme frustration at having been cornered by a question she hadn't wanted to answer.

'Run,' she instructed brusquely. Nye went shambling off again before she had the opportunity to poke him in the ribs. This time he moved off, taking a glimmer of hope with him. Ever since his brutal abduction, he had not encountered a personality beneath the surface of her insanity, but what his question cracked open and revealed was a kernel of childish truculence—a character.

It was a bitter woman who stood at the drawing-room window watching Nye's possessions migrate from the house to the stables. The Deekses made a number of return journeys conveying items in a bed sheet giving the uncanny impression of Nye himself curled in a hammock. Matilda's first incendiary reaction had been to create a funeral pyre out of everything representing their life together, until the financial and legal implications tolled their sonorous warnings. Besides it was more gratifying to think of his clothes hanging amongst bridles, saddles and bits in the stable. There they would remain, neatly suspended, her husband in absentia; after all if he chose to behave like a stud with a permanent erection, then the best place for him was the stable.

Having evacuated all memories from the house, it was her intention to initiate divorce proceedings immediately, that very morning. Nye certainly wasn't going to be given the benefit of time to create excuses for himself or deny the evidence of her own eyes. She watched Mrs Deeks pass the window, her cheeks flushed, intoxicated by the excitement of it all, savouring the task and hungry for further issues stirred up by the upheaval of her employer's marriage. Even more provocative were her corner-of-the-mouth comments to Deeks.

Yes, it was a very bitter woman who regarded the housekeeper and her gamekeeper husband. Her embittered observation extended to include everybody who surely must have known. How they would all gossip, telling each other how they had always told each other so. They, that indefinite collectivity called The County, had been making insinuations for years and she, like an idiot, had chosen to ignore them. Nye's exposure would provide enough fuel to keep them motoring until the next hunt ball and beyond. There wouldn't be any sympathy for Matilda Nye, that was for sure. Whatever way she accounted for the failure of her marriage, she would continue to be fashioned by the implicit view that it was a woman's responsibility to make a marriage work. It was an expectation evident in every silly, insipid magazine article on how to dress, how to slim, how to eat, how to cook, how to please. She caught sight of Nye's briefcase still in the hall and eyed it with burning resentment. She was going to come out of this marriage cradling her pride, her public persona a rock of resolution.

Having decided as much, she picked up the briefcase and threw it the length of the hall. It skated over the polished wood block floor and landed upright against the front door. The suggestion that it waited there ready for its owner to depart for work infuriated her further. She opened the door and flung it out, bawling at Deeks, 'Take that bloody briefcase away.'

Moments later, the gamekeeper holding a black umbrella against pelting rain and carrying Nye's briefcase, walked towards the stables accompanied by his wife who held a shopping basket full of Nye's toiletries. 'It looks as if he's going to have to spend the night with Mrs Nye's mare,' she mouthed.

'He's spent the night with less reputable females!'

'I shall be in the study,' Matilda informed the couple crisply through the drawing-room window. 'I don't want to be disturbed. I have some very important matters to discuss this morning. I'm at home to nobody. Is that understood?' The window slammed shut.

Nye's eviction from the Hall completed, Mrs Deeks returned to the kitchen wondering whether to prepare dinner for two and if Mr Nye returned that evening whether his should be served in the saddle room. Now was not the time to enquire, perhaps it was best to wait an hour or so and approach the subject obliquely with Mrs Nye.

Matilda returned to Nye's study, locked the door and re-moved his dirty photographs from the desk drawer like a bundle of state secrets. Although the house was silent the atmosphere was tainted, charged with whispering conspiracies. She tried the door handle several times as if Mrs

Deeks's curiosity knew no barriers, then turned over the first. As her initial shock wore off the pictures took on the objective quality of medical illustrations. She imagined the clinical obscenity of Nye dipping the negatives in a tray of developing fluid then pulling them out with a pair of tweezers. But it was not this that disturbed her so much as the titles scrawled on the back of each photograph. If Suzanne Blinney's body had been obscenely posed, then Nye's sexuality had been disgracefully exposed as lewd arrogance with a hint of sadism.

She selected a number of photographs and pushed them into an envelope addressed to the family solicitor, another sample was selected for Uncle George. 'Dear Uncle,' she wrote, then balked at the endearment. If Nye's infidelity had shaken her faith in men, the thought of her uncle sharing the same woman dissolved it entirely. She had always thought of him as a father figure and the relationship with her uncle and guardian had never developed with her age; he had remained in a time capsule, seen through a child's trusting, dependent eyes. She had never considered him having sex with Miss Blinney whom she thought of as a cheap but elegant companion who had draped herself over an old man's bachelor life, serving his ego rather more than his libido. Even his Westminster flat she had visualised as an extension of the exclusively male gentleman's club. Miss Blinney would hang on his arm when he went to the opera, the theatre, the races, but that, Matilda's imagination told her, was where it ended because Miss Blinney always went home alone in a taxi. Now she glided silently along the densely-carpeted corridor that led to her uncle's flat. Next to Sir George's cufflinks deposited tidily in a little leather box on the dressing table were Miss Blinney's earrings. Next came the intimate stages of undressing, then the ugly facts of a liaison in her uncle's double bed.

'Dear Uncle,' she tried again but felt compelled instead to think about Miss Blinney, Suzanne, Foxy, the catalyst who had caused a new alchemy, the mixing of Nye and Uncle George in the same fleshy, libidinous fluid. The uncle whom she had thought of as father and her husband sharing the same woman, the thought of it plumbed psychological depths leaving her shocked and angry and desperate.

Louise sat in stony immobility on the tree trunk in Pikes Wood that she had occupied the day before. Nye sat on another, dwelling on his discomfort. He wanted to rant and rave at the top of his voice, except that such an expenditure of vital energy would be pointless, like hurling ping-pong balls at a fortress. Her insanity was unconquerable, totally beyond the call of either passion or reason. He glared instead at the tongue of bracket fungi sprouting from her tree trunk. It did not help matters since its smooth grey skin implanted the idea that it was a removable appendage of hers. There sat his abductor's extruded tongue deliberately poking out at him in childish triumph.

Perhaps he was going a little mad himself, her insanity being communicable. Was it, like the fungi, a parasitic growth clasping the brain cells with tendrils, drawing out vital nutrients as it crept across the mind? Nye eyed the plant, resenting it for having taken metaphoric root in his own mind, hypnotised by its horrible, tumorous comparison with his abductor's brain. Was there any healthy tissue left in that head of hers, a cluster of brain cells that continued to function normally?

'I need a piss. I suppose I've got to get permission first.'

'I int stoppin' 'e,' she replied reasonably enough.

Nye got to his feet and wandered to the end of the invisible leash which tied him to his gaoler. Pissing did not bring relief, only a hot, stinging pain. In the distance across the valley he saw somebody ploughing on a tractor and cows being herded into a milking parlour, people going about their business unaware of his existence, let alone his predicament.

'They look so far away,' he whispered to himself as it struck him that they belonged to a world to which he might never return.

To counter the morbid thought he calculated his chances of being rescued. He began with the Deekses' discretion over his womanising. No doubt they would be discreet too with the police, he felt sure. The trouble was did they know about his fling with Foxy? Even if they did, the consequent enquiries would only lead the police to an empty cottage on Milestone Terrace. Yesterday there had been an open suitcase on the settee, lid up, an unzipped mouth consuming negligee, flesh-coloured underwear, the tools of Suzanne Blinney's trade. Sir George's autumn and winter needs had been serviced—time for Foxy to enjoy the spring in West London.

She was as much part of the sporting year as were the beaters who thrashed hell out of the heather, the men who catapulted Sir George's clay pigeons for him or the terrier men who pushed their dogs down foxholes. It was springtime, the season of politics, time for Sir George to preside at Tory Party HQ.

He tried to calculate what Matilda's frenetic flapping would reap. Oh do something, do something ... . The ear of the Chief Constable himself would be battered with her squawking insistence on a nation-wide search. The trouble was, however much the local bobbies danced to the tunes of her arrogant panic, they were not going to think of looking for the missing husband at the end of his own gun sitting on a tree trunk in a wood only a mile from his home.

George knew nothing about his visits to 'Foxy' and it wouldn't therefore occur to him to direct the police to her charming little mews flat in Kensington. As for Foxy herself, it would hardly be in her interests to volunteer information. If anything George Wentworth would be looking for him in quite a different direction—via a multi-million pound contract. A businessman to the core he would instantly set an internal audit into motion. Not that it would uncover any major fraud but might well expose a thousand pounds short here, a thousand pounds short there. Nye propped himself weakly against a tree and watched the last of the cows enter the milking parlour at Kemps Farm.

'You're in deep shit, Dickie.'

A motorbike courier left Ebury Hall with a letter addressed 'strictly confidential' to a solicitor in Amwell. The first stages of the divorce proceedings had been despatched, but not so Matilda's anger which remained behind to rattle at the bars of its confinement. It was a padding beast craving the freedom to run and to roar. Since the letter to the solicitor had not provided the cathartic outlet hoped for she tried dispelling her feelings by preparing a speech for the moment Nye had the audacity to put his foot through the door. She paced around the study experiencing alternate highs and lows, holding her stomach as if to contain the emotional upheaval. Finding it all too much, she snatched a silver bell and set off ringing it along the length of the hall.

'Mrs Deeks...Mrs Deeks!' Her voice entered the kitchen where the housekeeper relaxed in her slippers. She pushed her feet back into the black court shoes as if summoned by a peppery drill sergeant. 'If Sir George calls,' Matilda told her, 'he is to be told that I am not at home. He is not to be invited in and you will hand him this letter from me.'

Mrs Deeks' normally tolerant expression changed to the shape of an exclamation mark, its dot formed by the O of her small round mouth.

'Is there something wrong?' demanded her employer.

'To be honest, Mrs Nye, I'd find it a bit...'

'A bit what?'

'I'd feel very awkward with Sir George being your uncle.'

'This,' Matilda's imperious arm-waving took in the mezzanine, grand staircase and portraits on the panelled walls, 'is my home. Perhaps it might come as a surprise to you to learn that my uncle does not have carte blanche to come and go here as he pleases.'

Her sharp eyes queried her expression as if expecting to find contradiction there but saw only astonishment. Mrs Deeks had grown used to a woman who flapped around the place with bossy anxieties. She was inconsistent, lacking in self-esteem, albeit arrogant, fussing and interfering in the kitchen occasionally, but essentially good-hearted as far as that type could be, willing to share a joke even. Mrs Nye had undergone a metamorphosis. Betrayal had unzipped the plump caterpillar and out flew the grand duchess.

Matilda, momentarily recognising that she was being a

little unreasonable in her demands, crumpled into uncertainty. 'This is very stressful for all of us, I know,' she excused herself, then, recognising that the apologetic tone sounded like capitulation, she began to bawl like a fishwife: 'As for my sodding husband, if he shows up take him to the stable, it's where we Wentworths have always kept our prize studs.'

Another silent hour had passed in the wood. The man ploughing the field had left, the last batch of cows were filing from the milking parlour at Kemps Farm yet she remained as still as a cacoon. The chance of being rescued appeared so remote, Nye abandoned the hope altogether. His abductor held two strong cards, her unpredictability and his double-barrelled shotgun. He was not prepared to test the limits of the first, but quite prepared to risk the remaining cartridge in the gun. From the way she handled it he guessed she knew little about shotguns and would not be able to re-load one in a hurry. His escape would be entirely reliant on getting her to fire that last cartridge in the wrong direction. He would wait until nightfall which would give him an advantage.

He studied three scenarios, the first and worst being that in which the strategy failed entirely, and he caught the full blast of the shot, the second where it partly failed and he sustained a minor injury from stray lead shot and the third a successful execution of the strategy. The risks confronted, he concentrated on the objective of reaching Ebury Hall before enquiries sniffed out the fling with Foxy or indicated the need for an internal audit. At best, he risked instant estrangement from Matilda and the Hall, at worst, dismissal from the Board followed by criminal prosecution. He closed his eyes and willed night to fall and kindly assist his escape.

He had only dozed for a few minutes before being alerted by a sharp metallic click. He opened his eyes to see his abductor pushing a cartridge into his gun barrel. Fear, dismay and fury brought him to his feet shrieking. 'What drives you, for fuck-sake? Just tell me what drives you.'

There was no answer, only that cold, hard, grey-eyed stare.

Nye sank onto his tree trunk again, convinced that not only did this woman have absolute power over his body, she had free access to his thoughts as well. She wasn't merely mad, she was insanely intelligent. 'Everybody's driven by something,' he reasoned out loud, more to counsel himself than to communicate with her. 'Money, power. Nobody's driven by motives that don't bring benefits. Money!' he shouted triumphantly. 'This is some cunning fucking plan to wear me down to the point where I'm willing to offer thousands for my own release—that's it, isn't it? Okay, I'll go along with it.'

Feigning confidence, he limped towards her across the clearing. Nye presented himself by the side of Louise's log with one hand on his hip, the other pointing its index finger in order to prod home the common sense of his offer. 'How much?' he pressed on boldly. 'Five hundred, seven hundred?' His voice ascended to financial heights then ceased abruptly. He stooped over her, convinced that her greed, hidden behind stubborn silence, would be coaxed out. 'Come along, come along, woman, name your price.' He folded his arms. 'Very well, a thousand, but that's my final offer I'm afraid. A thousand pounds in cash and I won't say a word to the police.'

Louise stared toward a distant horizon that excluded Nye's offer of money.

'Good God, woman!' he exploded. 'Think what it could buy—chocolates, tobacco. You like chocolate, don't you? You could buy a new coat, some jewellery to sew on it. Perhaps,' he appended his offer with less enthusiasm once he realised it wasn't getting very far, 'perhaps you need time to think it over.'

He returned to the other side of the clearing and balanced himself on the same broken arm of hornbeam that he'd occupied the day before, giving him a gloomy feeling of déja vu. Nevertheless he sat in determined hope, silently willing her to accept the money and give him back his freedom. Minutes passed and life in the ancient wood went about its business but Nye, intent on bringing off the deal, was immune to the chirruping, rustling, and the fluttering courtship display of a wood pigeon.

When his abductor did deign to address him, she turned slowly and told him with a pert, self-important air, 'When they do chop down the very last tree, 'tis then they will learn they can't eat money. That's what they do say, don't um? Can't eat money,' she told the man sitting on his hornbeam executive chair.

'No!' he roared so loudly that it sent the amorous wood pigeon into instant flight. 'But you can buy things with it, you demented old crusty.'

Having been instructed not to admit Sir George should he call, Mrs Deeks called her husband to a conference in the kitchen. There were going to be changes at the Hall that might not be to their advantage. Deeks sat for a while quietly considering which side to support in the divided household, that of the uncle or that of the niece. He watched his wife waving the letter, exclamations sounding off like firecrackers. 'She's being bloody unreasonable. If she wants an argument with the old boy she can slam the door in his face herself if he calls because I'll just pretend I didn't hear the bell.' Deeks watched his wife glance furtively at the kitchen door knowing exactly what she had in mind.

'It's in our interests, Pete,' she said as she brought the kettle to a boil and held the letter intended for Sir George over it. Neither had the least idea of what had caused the rift between Mrs Nye and her uncle; they assumed she blamed him in some way for Nye's womanising. When the naked Miss Blinney fell out of the envelope and landed crutch side up on the kitchen table all became clear. Mrs Deeks slapped her hand to her mouth, suspended between sordid curiosity and sheer astonishment. She silently handed the photographs to Deeks who regarded them with studied dignity then placed them face downward on the table as his wife read the letter to Sir George.

'Listen to this, Pete. "Dear Uncle. Since losing Daddy through that dreadful shooting accident I have always regarded you as my father. I am shocked and appalled to think of you and my husband sharing a bed with this obscene woman. It seems to me that it is not just in the field where you and Richard ride neck and neck."'

Matilda had spent the best part of the day pacing between the extremes of exquisite fury and utter self-worthlessness.

Common sense scuttled behind emotion like a diplomat trying to counsel a moody monarch. Out of her restless journeying rose the stark facts of the matter—if she divorced Nye, then she also divorced the lifestyle that floated on the halcyon flow of his income. No more winter holidays skiing en Les Alps, no more sumptuous dinner parties nor restorative weeks spent at expensive health farms. As for Ebury Hall with its creaking joists and the hardening arteries of its plumbing, it would just have to drag itself out of its geriatric complacency and start earning money. Various options began to present themselves to her—an equestrian centre, a hotel-cum-country club with fishing and shooting. The trouble was the counsel offered by pecuniary interest was offset by that side of her brain which insisted on giving vent to revenge. It was really Nye she wanted to think about. He would be made to pay dearly for having made an idiot out of her. He could either cough up the capital for her projects at the Hall or face a very public and embarrassing disclosure of his disgusting sexual proclivities. She felt sure that Uncle George would be the chief instrument in persuading him to toe the line.

And so Matilda strode over kilometres of carpet clasping a white leather-bound photograph album to her bosom, her agitated thumb tracing Our Wedding embossed on its cover. Soon this too would join all the other mementoes, letters and photographs associated with Nye. She opened it at the first chapter in the narrative told by fixed and grinning images. It began with herself and Sir George who had come to give her away in the absence of her own father. What an apt phrase, to give away. If the giving away was the prologue then the epilogue, narrated under the very same lych-gate, was a portrait of herself and Nye posing arm in arm. She was plump, billowing and lacy in a gown that overstated her size. No longer could she re-live the positive impression of herself as the stunning bride. It was a picture of herself grasping her prize, a man who looked like a film star. Look, look what Uncle George has bought me, she seemed to be saying to the camera.

Nye had never loved her. She had always sensed it but never confronted it, even though the evidence lay beneath life at the Hall like a clandestine message secreted between the leaves of a book. Truth hides in the unstated. Nye's infidelity had been that something unstated in Mrs Deeks' discretion. He's gone shooting, Mrs Nye, always accompanied by a blink. It was readable on her uncle's brow whenever he frowned a warning at Nye's acerbic humour: watch yourself, Dickie, don't overstep the mark.

Matilda looked at herself again in her wedding garb and extrapolated from the photograph an inevitable history of being led into dinner parties, functions, balls accompanied by her husband's barbs, and titters from the county women. She had been paraded like prize stock, and it was a bovine creature indeed that didn't even know it had a ring through its nose. Flushed by the fury that truth can often bring, she sent her wedding album spinning frisbee-style into the hearth to join the other relics of a bygone marriage.

'Mrs Deeks, Mrs Deeks!' Her summons raged along the hall. 'I want you and Deeks in the drawing room, now.'

Miss Blinney, as naked as the day she was born, slipped under the cover of a tabloid together with Sir George's opened letter.

Nye sat on his hornbeam branch, arms folded, as if having

just stormed out of a board meeting. 'So, you can't eat money, eh? We'll see about that when the police catch up with you!' No revolving blue light bobbed its way along the green lane by Harmers Farm. No siren wailed across the valley and through the interminable silence that followed he clung to his conviction that he could still buy his way out of the dilemma but the tactic had failed him: now he was reduced to depending on pure chance. The very thought of another night without food, shelter and fresh water panicked him. Already he was swallowing hard on a sore, dry throat and the thought of water came to haunt him again. He tried to close his eyes and doze but fresh water in all its forms lodged in his brain: fat raindrops falling on the earth, filtering into the Chepton Veins, spouting from Chepton Shoot, then joining the brook beneath to babble cool and clean over a bed of bright, round pebbles. Water, the essence of life, tortured his thoughts until he couldn't bear the craving any longer.

He struggled to his feet and limped off in the direction of Long Coombe. 'I'm going to find water,' he told his abductor, careless of any punishment that might be meted out and began his descent down the valley. If, on passing the cluster of primroses, Nye had been able to elevate himself above the scene, he might have felt that their delicate but tenacious return to the landscape each spring seemed to possess, in its own pale way, a greater legitimacy than his own lumbering presence.

In the drawing room, Mrs Deeks and Deeks stood side by side, heads inclined towards Mrs Nye's proposals, discomforted by the thought that their employer's blue-eyed glares might bore through to the truth about Sir George's letter.

'As you might have guessed I intend divorcing my husband and this will have certain consequences for the Hall. So, we will have to pull in our horns and Ebury Hall will have to start earning us some money. I've been thinking along the lines of an equestrian centre together with a hotel-cum-country club which will support the shooting and fishing.' She broke off and bitterly regarded the photos set aside for burning.

'Shall I light the fire, Mrs Nye?' offered Mrs Deeks.

'And deny me the pleasure?' The photograph of the Nyes, arm in arm under the lych-gate, lay upright on the hearth, untorn. Mrs Deeks, feeling that whatever Nye had done didn't seem to justify this death-by-effigy, picked it up as if to plead for its retention in some way. 'He wouldn't have given me a second look if I hadn't been the chairman's niece.' Mrs Deeks opened her mouth as if to offer something consoling, then closed it again. It was, after all, the truth.

Finding the spectacle of herself and Nye on their wedding day unbearable, Matilda looked away to be confronted by another equally critical reminder—a glass case containing a plump-chested pheasant cornered by an agile red fox, its lip raised to expose brilliant white fangs. 'That was my marriage.' She pointed to the boxed-in tableau; 'I was the pheasant cornered by my husband's sneering.' She rounded on Mrs Deeks who still regarded the photograph uncertainly. 'Tear it up.'

'I'm sorry, Mrs Nye, but I don't think I should.'

'I said tear it up, then get out of here, the pair of you.'

Harmers Pond looked smaller and shallower than Nye had imagined it during the night. He stood amongst the blonde, waist-high reeds only yards from the three crook-fingered alders that had met in stooping witch-like conspiracy against the night sky. His boots sank in the mud, releasing greasy slicks that refracted into purple, green and blue chemical snakes swirling on the water whenever he moved. Oil? The diplomacy of darkness had hidden from his eyes that which he was about to offer to his lips. God knows what toxins had doused his guts, what nasty little virus had colonised his bowels. Although the memory of biliousness and diarrhoea caused him to heave, he still craved water. He wasn't merely thirsty, he was desperate; water was the only thing that could put him out of his misery, yet here he stood with a plentiful supply of it, not daring to drink. What sort of chemicals leached off the land into this pond, what were they putting on the fields these days? He eyed the corner of a bright blue plastic sack that had been dumped amongst the reeds—herbicide, pesticide, fertiliser? Poison could so easily enter the body through water, insidiously doing damage that might not be apparent for years.

Nye waded to the centre of the pond where he assumed the water might be cleaner and stood there, seeking some biological indicator of the health of the pond. At one end there was a small muddy shore, pock-marked by cattle hooves. If cattle drank there, that was a good sign, wasn't it? There was also the quivering gelatinous frogs' spawn trapped amongst the reeds, that too was a good sign. He certainly hadn't seen any bloated fish floating on the surface either. Louise waited at the pond's edge wearing his cartridge belt, bandolier-style, like a prison guard escorting her charge to a filthy water-hole in some dried-up banana republic. Without inhibition she squatted and urinated freely in the water.

During the course of the day, the husband's sin had expanded disproportionately. His mere eviction from the Hall to the stable was not punishment enough; he needed burning at the stake. Matilda built up the fire in the drawing room and then fed the flames, watching memories coil into grey worms of ash. Even greater than the husband's infidelity was the sheer audacity of his continued absence. Having been denied the benefit of a furious row with him she substituted with a number of symbolic acts. The trouble was, the burning of that man Nye had only a limited catharsis.

With no symbols left to smash, tear, reduce to ash, Matilda flew to the other extreme of contemplating self-destruction. Wallowing in the thought of suicide, she created a full-blown theatrical production of the event, giving herself sole directorship. She would take the car, drive it recklessly. They would find her slumped over the steering wheel. Her departing soul would ascend with ethereal triumph over grief. The funeral would be a solemn, dignified occasion, the coffin, smothered in flowers, would emerge from the mist on top of a carriage pulled by her favourite mare. Nye would be beside himself with remorse as her body passed under the very same lych-gate that had featured in her wedding photograph.

So far so good, until the more perceptive lens of common sense focussed upon the expression of relief on Nye's face; when he read her will he would inherit everything, leaving him free to dispose of Ebury Hall and the park as he saw fit. Matilda's departing soul that had been drifting wispily, untethered by worldly considerations, came plummeting back to earth like a burst balloon as soon as she considered the possibility of Nye benefiting from her death. She would disinherit him, now, this very day. Finding pecuniary revenge far more satisfying than self-destruction, she made plans for the future which began with a list of business objectives for the Hall including the appointment of a properly qualified manager and sound financial advice.

Nye turned his back on the unbearable sight of his abductor urinating by the edge of the pond as if to deliberately foul his drinking water, only to find himself confronting the blue plastic sack still winking wickedly at him from the pale reeds. Had it spilled its toxic contents in the water or had it blown there? His environment was being bombarded by risks. He regarded his haggard and dirty face floating on the pond, concluding that if he did not drink he would die, if he did drink, he ran the gauntlet of unknown risks. Thirst overcame him, and he cupped the water in his hands with the feeling that even death was worth risking in return for such sweet relief.

Having satisfied his thirst, he washed his face and hands, prolonging the task in order to delay the moment when he would be set to run again. So far the day hadn't presented a single opportunity for escape. Rescue seemed even more remote since he simply couldn't picture the twist of circumstance that would send a search party in the right direction. As he washed himself, he weighed his chances against his abductor's unnatural energy which fed and grew on his own exhaustion. 'She sleeps and doesn't seem to,' he found himself muttering at his own reflection. 'She keeps watch when she seems to be asleep.'

'Ah,' replied the man from the surface of the pond, 'but the filthy old hag still has to eat, shit and piss the same as anybody else and you're going to wait for one of those off-guard moments to provide your window of escape.' As if for reassurance that such a moment would arise soon, he put his hand in his pocket to feel for the chunk of flint, the ancient tool being his only ally in these hostile circumstances. He hissed at his abductor under his breath as if words could convey poison. 'You see, you flea-bitten freak, I've got a nice little cutting edge and I'm going to bring it down on your skull, again and again, chopping and hacking you to bits.' A powerful memory returned; it was Deeks's spade coming down on an adder's back, chopping away at it until the last venomous quiverings of life had been obliterated.

'Ah,' counselled the man floating on the pond, 'but what about the blood, gristle and bone on your chunk of flint?'

Nye presented the gore to his conscience and concluded, 'Yes, I think I can cope with that, I can despatch Loopy Lou to her maker, no problem.'

'The trouble is,' came back his watery counsel, 'how might a court of law judge reasonable force?'

The agitated sucking of his abductor's boots in the mud brought him swinging round. Perhaps his murderous thought had gone skating across the surface tension of the pond like a water boatman? But she was not looking at him; her attention was fixed on a distant point over his shoulder. He followed her gaze up Long Coombe in time to see a tall and well-made man striding towards Pikes Wood. He was dressed in a black anorak and carried a rucksack to which had been tied what appeared to be a small camping stool. The man halted, consulted a radio receiver then strode on. Nye filled his lungs and bellowed, 'Oi...Oi!'

With his arms outstretched as if to embrace the departing figure he began to wade across the pond, but his abductor, having already anticipated the move, skirted the perimeter and appeared in front of him. She looked up into his face and said with an expression of childish triumph, 'He can't 'ear yer, not with they phones over his ears. 'E do listen to foxes through they, see.'

Nye watched the Fox Man recede with an unreasonable hostility toward his turned back. The dark figure striding away with such earnest devotion to his task seemed to Nye provocative. ''E's following foxes.' His abductor rubbed it in unnecessarily.

'It's a pity he hasn't got something better to do than radio-track fucking vermin.' His condemnation of the creatures and their benign benefactor was a mistake. Louise snapped into action like a triggered mousetrap.

'Run, run, run!' came the staccato order sighted along the barrel of his shotgun. By this means she headed him back to Harmers Farm.

For the second time that day the Deekses were summoned to the drawing room to listen to their employer's proposals for the future of Ebury Hall. Within ten minutes their expressions shifted radically from deference to stony disbelief. Mrs Deeks, having entered the room prepared to review the proposals with a healthy degree of self-interest, now bristled with indignation. Mrs Nye had felt it incumbent upon her to explain the realities of the changed domestic situation. It would be necessary for her to commercialise the Hall and her plans would not include the full time employment of a gamekeeper and a housekeeper. She hoped they would appreciate her position, of course there would be due notice and gratuities to say nothing of excellent references. Sadly, however, Cartwrights Cottage would not be available for them.

Tight-lipped and fuming, the Deekses left the drawing room without waiting to be dismissed, leaving the door wide open for Mrs Nye to close herself. They returned to the kitchen, Deeks to sit in silence assessing their joint chances of finding similar employment elsewhere whilst Mrs Deeks rediscovered her working-class origins.

'They're all the same, Pete,' she burst out, jerking her head towards the drawing-room society above their heads. 'We've done nothing but dance behind their backsides and this is all the thanks we get.'

'Yes,' he agreed but the militant tone of her observation did not succeed in straightening his shoulders. He put his elbows on the table and his head in his hands with a prolonged sigh. All those dwellers in Drawing-room Land had to do was click their fingers, incline their heads, raise their eyebrows, ring their bells to get the service they required. Slow, slow, quick, quick slow. Indeed, Mrs Deeks had danced back and forth over the years between drawing room and kitchen to the stringed accompaniment of Mrs Nye's demands, but not any more.

She leant forward and withdrew the naked portrait of Miss Blinney from its tabloid hiding place, and slipped it back into the large brown envelope intended for Sir George's letter. Shortly after a letter to Mrs Nye joined it.

She sealed it grimly, slipped into her black court shoes as if for the last time and conveyed their terms on a silver tray to the drawing room.

Mrs Deeks found her employer breathing deeply to regain control over her emotions. The sight of the housekeeper, who surely knew about the Foxy affair, did not help to this end. 'What is it?' she snapped.

'A letter for you, Mrs Nye,' she said coolly and stood by to watch her read with a smug sense of having penned a less than subtle form of blackmail. If she read their terms thoroughly it would be clear to Mrs Nye that she and her husband were demanding a year's salary in lieu of notice and suitable gratuities to acknowledge their redundancies without which their discretion, vis-à-vis certain matters, could not be guaranteed. Overtaken by other events, Mrs Deeks was never to find out how closely their employer scrutinised the terms. On seeing the letter she snatched it from the tray and held it in her fist like a crumpled handkerchief.

'Oh Brenda,' she wailed. 'It's all falling to bits, the Hall, the estate, my marriage...the whole sodding shooting match. Oh Brenda what the bloody hell am I going to do?'

'Since I'm not in your employ any more, it's not my job to advise you.'

If the hope of escape through the Fox Man had acted like an analgesic, briefly damping Nye's discomforts, its denial brought them back again: 'Run!'

'I can't, you stupid bitch, I've got a septic toe.' He slowed, to accentuate his limp, and entered Harmers Farm cursing like an old dosser and made straight for the farmhouse, determined not to spend any more time in the open. Standing in the doorless entrance he announced, 'I'm going inside.'

'I int stoppin' 'e.'

'I'm going to make a fire,' he added, hoping that the sight of smoke coming from the abandoned building might attract attention. The word fire set his abductor immediately to the task of collecting kindling. Nye watched her, his thumb massaging the smooth end of his flint, her own fingers pecking at minute strands of combustible material. The kindling grew in her sagging pocket until it resembled a bird's nest in a marsupial pouch. Although she worked with assiduous attention to the task, not once did she let him out of her sight, always working towards him, his gun at the ready.

He despaired at ever escaping from this improbable woman. When she flushed him so violently from Suzanne Blinney's cottage, a door had opened into an alternative reality—hers. 'Why?' The question knotted his guts with anxiety. She didn't want money, asked for nothing and deliberately obscured her motives. She didn't want to kill him, he felt instinctively convinced of that, but she did want his captivity, his suffering.

Unable to tolerate the sight of her dipping and diving to accumulate a mere handful of kindling, he strode toward a pile of rotting logs balanced against a garden shed. Selecting three of the driest he returned to the house impatient to get warm again. In the former sitting room, filthy and bereft of any comfort, he found some yellowed newspaper underneath the cracked linoleum. He rolled a number of sheets into cylinders then wedged them under the tripod of logs in the grate. Hunkered by the hearth, he waited for his abductor to return with the matches. He had not expected her to rush in from the garden, all of a tut and fuss, to knock him off balance with the gun barrel.

'Leave!' she ordered, nudging him into a corner of the room as if chastising a dog.

'All right, all right, pea-brain, I was only trying to help.'

'You'm no good at it. I'll show 'e how 'tis done.' She dropped to her knees by the hearth to demonstrate fire-making bossily. In one pocket she had collected dried grass and straw, in the other twigs. The lesson began with the ostentatious removal of Nye's unworthy efforts, accompanied by a great deal of sighing as she set aside the logs and newspaper. It was the impatient gesture of one having to clear up after a child. This done she carefully created a ball some six inches in diameter from the smallest pieces of kindling. Over this upturned, perfectly neat nest, she began to construct another from twigs, removing them from her pocket one by one. For thirty minutes she squatted on her heels, her mouth working away as if in suppressed commentary.   This seemingly rapt attention to the lowly task was deceptive, her eyes shifted constantly with the gun close to hand. Once the job had been completed she did not set light to the kindling, but remained contemplating it as if mesmerised by her own craft work.

'You're supposed to light it, not look at it,' Nye snapped.

'I made it so I shall light it when I feel like it,' she replied and remained in a pouting squat before the stone cold hearth. The passing of time meant nothing to her personally. After a while she took a chocolate biscuit from her pocket and removed its wrapper in a finicky manner. Nye watched her dirty fingers at work with malignant loathing. They had been extended by long, horny nails reminding him of chickens' claws scratching in the dust. She took a quick bite from the biscuit, then placed it on the floor between them before producing a box of matches. She returned to the business of fire-making, leaving him to eye the chocolate like a dog waiting for food. He licked his lips, seized by a painful desire to eat it. He could smell the confectionery, almost taste it in his mouth; his salivary glands became so active he was forced to swallow repeatedly. Aware of his salivating interest Louise snatched it away. 'You int havin' it.'

'You shit, you utter shit-house!' Nye was reduced to a growling fury over the way food had been snatched from under his nose.

''Tis mine,' she yapped back at him.

'Yours, yours!? You stole it.'

'Then 'tis mine.'

Nye watched the chocolate disappear like a fish down a gannet's gullet. 'If you stole it from the whore, how do you suppose she came by the chocolate in the first place?' With the chocolate safely en route to her stomach Louise didn't give a damn one way or the other. 'I'll tell you, I'll tell you how she came by the chocolate,' he roared having lost all claim to self-control. 'She bought it with the money I gave her in return for sexual services, so the chocolate is mine, not yours.'

'She bought the chocolate so 'twas 'er chocolate.' She regarded the little flame dancing around her pile of kindling and then concluded, 'Once I had it off 'er then 'twas mine.'

'Theft is not legitimate ownership. Don't you understand anything, isn't there just a molecule of healthy grey matter left up here?' Nye pointed strenuously at his temple. 'Or is there just a dried pea rattling round in that skull of yours?

Listen to me, just listen. If possession is nine-tenths of the law that gives me carte blanche to take the next bit of chocolate off you—right?'

Louise licked her fingers complacently. Nye looked with detestation at her brown beret sprouting rats-tails of thin grey hair with the eggs of head lice gummed to them. She broke wind, the revolting intimacy causing his disgust to turn into another wave of murderous resolve. His finger returned to stroking the flinty edge of his stone-age weapon whilst his palm cupped the smooth end. The primitive axe, he avowed, would crack open her skull as easily as a knife decapitating a breakfast egg. She was now busily ripping the newspaper into thin shreds and adding them, a few at a time, to her embryonic fire which radiated a surprising amount of heat. Judging the time to be right, she propped two rotten logs over it. Wood smoke, unable to find its way through the blocked chimney, billowed back into the room distributing a pleasant incense.

Drawn by the heat, Nye edged towards the hearth and propped himself against the wall. Warmth and exhaustion made it impossible to keep his vow to remain awake and alert. His head simply slumped onto his chest, observed slyly by his abductor. From time to time his aching neck woke him and he would find himself looking blearily through the doorway into a kitchen garden now strangled by weeds.

Hints of its former order added dismally to the farm's atmosphere of failure and abandoned projects. A squirrel descended suddenly from a nearby hazel bush to appear in the doorway with a unique agility that seemed to shape its body into frequency curves. It stopped without momentum as if driven by a small electric motor and dived into a cache of acorns hidden under a light cover of soil and leaves. Emboldened by their silence, the creature had come close enough that its little clawed toes were visible clasping the nut. Even so it remained perfectly still, listening. It struck Nye as possessing the perfection of an ornament, its acorn fashioned from buffered wood, its dark and liquid eye from polished onyx. Assured of its safety, its front feet delivered the nut to its sharp teeth which gnawed with ruthless efficiency.

The clean white fur that covered the squirrel's belly gave it an oddly domestic character as if it wore a white cook's apron. There was something reminiscent of Mrs Deeks about the creature which led Nye's thoughts back to the kitchen at Ebury Hall. 'No hope of rescue from that quarter,' he muttered feverishly. The Fox Man came into his thoughts again, a tall dependable figure disappearing into the landscape wearing headphones, oblivious to Nye's plight.

'Where was he going, your Fox Man?' he asked Louise as if continuing a conversation left off only minutes previously. She stared at the fire, her resolute silence deflecting further questioning. 'Those earphones,' he persisted through the fog clouding his concentration, 'what does he wear them for?'

'I told 'e already,' she answered with an emphatic impatience designed to end the conversation.

Nye stared through the doorway to where the squirrel continued its excavations. He watched and marvelled at its self-sufficiency. He had been following a path back to Ebury Hall via the Fox Man, but it was cluttered with ifs and buts and his needs were too immediate to try and clear them away. He needed food for example. Where would he find something to eat in this desert of a place? How simple it was for the squirrel hopping off a branch, locating its larder, then cracking open a nut. The question of how to feed himself directly from nature formed a hazy picture of blackberries and an equally vague notion that the only edible fungus was the field mushroom.

What do I know about self-sufficiency, a mere director of finance he asked himself? I know how to store and retrieve money. I know how sworn enemies can be drawn into the commonality of the market place by self-interest, but I can't, in spite of my superior intelligence, feed myself independently. 'I know about the cash nexus and you know about the cache nexus,' Nye found himself telling the squirrel.

It was not amused by the intrusion which caused a perplexed grimace before it vanished as miraculously as it had appeared. His abductor must have been watching it as well because as soon as it left she got to her feet and went into the garden to stoop by the patch of excavated earth and collect bits of discarded acorn shell, presumably for kindling. When she returned to settle by her fire Nye asked, 'Why does he listen to foxes?'

'He takes his map,' she began as if an explanation of function was equal to an exposition of purpose, 'then he listens through his phones, then...where two lines cross, that's where they be.' Her finger pointed at an imagined co-ordinate as if she held an OS map. ''Tis called trigonometry.' She pounced importantly on the word.

'Oh is it indeed? And where does he go to do his trigonometry, eh?'

'Yer, there, everywhere,' she answered evasively. His abductor might be mad but she was far from stupid. Behind the veneer of her malady, there lay a feral cunning. His hope routed slunk away and he closed his eyes resigned to the prospect of another day of deprivation.

'I wonder if the Fox Man ever visits Ebury Hall,' he asked more by way of comforting himself.

'Old Rogue do live there,' she answered mysteriously.

Although the fire died towards dawn, leaving the derelict farmstead damp and cold, to Nye, in his fever, it felt as steamy as a sauna. He belched gas from his intestines bringing back the slimy reminder of pond water. He tried hard not to dwell on the memory of a greasy slick swimming around his boots where he had drunk. He had not slept properly, just dozed intermittently with his eyes snapping open at every imagined threat. A refreshing breeze came through the doorway and he raised his wobbling head to focus on the farmyard beyond the kitchen garden.

A barely perceptible shift of light outlined abandoned agricultural tools. The failure so visible out there in the unclaimed equipment was made more so by the knowledge of the farmer's suicide. Nye wondered whether there had been any relatives left to sell off all the bits and pieces. Perhaps superstition had held them at bay. Fearing that the possessions of the damned, being imbued with the same misfortune, might infect them too, they had kept their distance. Nye shuddered, asking himself what failure could be so great as to lead somebody to choke on the end of a rope voluntarily; hanging was not a quick ending. Was it his feverish imagination that produced the sound of a creaking beam? Nonsense! They had cut down the body years ago, but what about the rope, did the rope still hang there silently deputising for the horror?

He closed his eyes against the picture of the hanged man, blue, swollen, his neck distorted to one side, but the dismal notions came pad, padding around him like dust-grey wolves, pursuing him even whilst he dozed, fixing him with their level, yellow-eyed knowing. It was as if this featureless presence had a wisdom to impart, but before Nye had a chance to grasp its significance it slunk away, vanquished by the encroaching light of day.

Although he dozed, his senses remained on duty like anxious guards waiting to be hailed by a sound from the lane—an agricultural worker pedalling off to an early start, the milk float, possibly the Fox Man tramping home from his night's field studies. But no sound came; he couldn't even hear his abductor breathing, although he felt sure she could hear him. He had so convinced himself of her alien abilities that it was likely she didn't sleep as such, merely flipped off a switch in her nervous system. He was startled out of his wits therefore, when he heard a gurgling as of somebody snoring. She was actually snoring; it was that off-guard moment he had been waiting for.

He peered through the gloom. She was just about discernible propped against the opposite wall with the gun resting across her splayed legs and one hand near the trigger. He felt nervously for the reliable chunk of flint in his pocket and sized up the target. She didn't appear human somehow in the half-light, more like an unwanted rag doll slouching at the bottom of a toy chest. Loopy Lou was just the sort of name a child would give to such a doll. In fact, when he delivered the killing blow the flint wouldn't come down on skin and bone but fracture a china head

281

topping a body stuffed with beans and rags. This unnatural being had no blood in her and soon the flint resting in his palm was going to reduce this little rag-being to a heap of material scraps.

He would not take the risk of getting to his feet because the grit and debris on the bare boards would announce the attack as loudly as hobnail boots over gravel. He would move slowly toward his target on all fours, inching forward so that if she woke he would instantly curl on the floor feigning sleep.

Having covered half the distance separating them, he paused. He had not entirely convinced himself that the life-size doll in the corner of the room was not human; there were going to be grisly consequences and it would be necessary to ascertain that the job had been done properly. The last thing he wanted was a blood-stained bag of bones wriggling its way outside and into the lane to indict him with its dying breath. If the job was to be done it must be done effectively, he ordered the qualms that insisted on re-visiting the memory of an adder wriggling under Deeks's spade. It might be necessary for him too to chop and chop repeatedly through the protesting upheaval of a body. After all, she did possess such volatile energy reserves, reserves that her nervous system could draw on to rise up and take bloody revenge on him. There was only one thing worse than a corpse, something only half dead, something that had to be battered into oblivion. It was a nauseating possibility and even the dim dawn light could not smudge the scene that would later be revealed by the sharper light of day. Nevertheless to get out of this situation unscathed, her death was imperative. He drew a deep breath and told himself that he must dispose of the matter promptly. Yes, dispose of the matter, a most acceptable, objective sort of word that put a distance between himself and his victim.

The disposal of the corpse? The previous day he had noticed a large inspection cover, relating to an old cesspit, and into this he would tip both his gun and the corpse. The tale he would tell back at Ebury Hall, having limped home half dead, would be one of abduction with ransom demands. Deprived of sleep, shelter, food and clean water, he nonetheless succeeded in escaping. Nye edged forward into the final straight, a grit-grating sound travelling ahead of him as if to tell tales on his intentions. None the less vocal was the sudden creak of a floorboard and the bongo pounding of his heart. He stopped, peered again, neck outstretched with the expression of a dog assessing an unfamiliar situation.

Louise's face appeared like a pale, luminescent moon, so pale she could have been a corpse already. In sleep her skin had relaxed to take on a smooth waxiness that upset his calculation of her age since she possessed characteristics that were at once infantile and aged. Was he about to kill a child or an old woman?

She frowned as she slept, her lips pursed as they did whenever she concentrated on a task. Her right index finger rested lightly on the trigger whilst her left hand lay loosely on the barrel as if placed there by somebody else. Although her fingers sprouted nails that curled back upon themselves like ram's horns, they were fine, pretty fingers. It gave him a jolt to see that on her left hand she wore a broad, gold band. It was not conceivable that she had ever married; perhaps it had belonged to her mother. There was something about those hands that held his attention, deterred him momentarily until he decided that her head too had that same, fine porcelain quality that would shatter into fragile shards. She was only a china-headed rag doll, and soon would be no more discernible as human than a pile of old clothes swept to a corner of a room in a deserted farmstead. She quivered a little as if a short-lived epilepsy had rippled over her brain, then mumbled at one of the inhabitants who populated her land of delusions.

Nye would have turned back from the killing of Loopy Lou had his dilemma not marshalled him like a gung-ho sergeant and ordered him to proceed with his mission. What had this filthy misfit got to live for anyway? Nobody would miss her, weep for her. One, swift blow and it would be mercifully over for her. Yes, his administration of euthanasia would be a favour. He cupped his palm comfortably around the knuckle of his flint, such a comfortable, reassuring fit that it felt like an extension of his own limb. The trouble was the future. If, under some unpredictable duress, the truth should bubble to the surface of his conscience, would he find it easy to acquit himself? Would he feel comfortable with what he'd done, or would he find himself looking into the skeletal face of truth everywhere he turned?

Oh come along, come along, old chap, answered that urbane doppelganger, Lawyer Nye. Ask yourself whether, in the early stages of the abduction, had you struck her on the chin with your fist and killed her, would that have been so very different from the action you are about to take?

Conscience, the flexible friend, now satisfied, left Nye to concentrate upon the immediate disposal of the job. The command from brain to hand to rise and take the killing blow, however, never arrived. It was a battalion of microbes invading at dawn that rescued Loopy Lou from certain death. Bridging Nye's weakened defences, they entered his bowels to set about their lethal occupation. He began to sway unsteadily, his head seeming to float like a hot-air balloon and the pace of his thinking slowed alarmingly. He heard the first bird trill which, like the rapping of a baton, started up the dawn chorus.

Louise's eyes snapped open just as Nye's bowels began to bubble and send gunshot echoes through the derelict silence. A hot searing pain caused him to drop the flint and run into the garden tugging at his trousers. Squatting by the side of a former compost heap, he painfully evacuated the contaminated waters of Harmers Pond whilst baying mournfully at the rising light in the eastern sky.

The daylight that should have cheered him served only to illuminate his squalid circumstances. He had spent an hour squatting uncomfortably, rusty corrugated iron providing him with Spartan privacy. Exhausted by the heaving and contraction of his intestines, he eventually hitched up his trousers and staggered back to the sitting room where he lay down with his cheek against bare floor boards. Intermittent rodent-scuttling came to him, hinting at an intelligence operating beneath the house. Louise poked at the fire, exploding the burnt-out logs into puff balls of fine grey ash. On the hearth next to her there was an empty carton of milk cruelly underlining his captivity and her freedom to slip away whilst he suffered.

'I see the milkman's been,' he said sourly. She pulled a rats-tail strand of hair over her shoulder, inspected it, then took to picking out the nits. It was too much to bear. 'I've been up most of the night vomiting my guts up, for Christ's sake.' His abductor ignored him and continued grooming with the serious concentration of a chimpanzee. 'It's probably cholera caused by being forced to drink filthy water.'

Not a flicker of acknowledgement crossed her face.

'It's highly infectious, a killer. You'd better keep your distance.'

Whatever paranoid fears pricked her brain, death from cholera was not amongst them. Already her body housed countless parasitic organisms, what difference would one more make?

'You ignorant ape,' Nye hissed, 'I look at you and I know what they mean when they talk about bio-diversity. You're a fucking walking jungle.' Nye's big toe was beginning to throb again in hot and septic rebellion against being confined inside a dirty wellington boot. 'I hope you're not expecting me to run today, my toe's gone septic. If it's not treated it'll turn to gangrene.' His short-lived protest was overtaken by a heavy weariness and he closed his eyes.

When he woke from a shallow doze he found himself staring at a bunch of dock leaves left by his head. His abductor sat on her heels by the cold hearth staring and expressionless.

'They'm for thik toe of yourn,' she explained in an accent as thick as buttermilk.

'Dock leaves are for nettle stings, shit breath,' he snapped. He eased himself giddily into a sitting position then propped himself against the wall. He stared for a long time at the leaves on the floor and thought about a medicine cupboard at Ebury Hall with tinctures, creams, plasters, painkillers, answers to every conceivable discomfort from abrasions to hangovers. He saw it all so clearly in his mind's eye: it was here inside his head yet it was out there too, distant and receding as was the possibility of seeing the old hall again.

He was in a new world now, a world stripped of cosseting and pampering and all it had to offer in the way of medicine was a bunch of dock leaves, but at least they showed up bright green, fresh against the dusty floorboards, offering themselves as a cool bandage. He eased off the wellington boot that had become glued to the suppurating wound and sat in gloomy contemplation of his red, protuberant toe and took a grim tally of his chance of escape.

Common sense counselled him that he was better off staying put at Harmers Farm by a fire. Smoke coming from the chimney would attract attention. On the other hand, counselled long-term self-interest, if he was rescued under these circumstances the truth about his abduction would also come billowing out, as public and declaratory as smoke from the Vatican chimney—he would not be welcome back at Ebury Hall. Matilda would be forced to confront her feckless faith in him and see herself as if reflected in a hall of funfair mirrors that fattened, undulated, distorted. In short, she would see herself at last as he saw her— unattractive, foolish, boring. No, the truth would not do at all and the longer he waited to be rescued the greater the chance of its exposure. It was far better to pre-empt it by limping home with a cock-and-bull story before Sir George ordered an internal audit and Matilda went through his desk drawers.

His abductor sat on her heels by the fire, immobile and squaw-like, she who obstructed his return to a life of ease and comfort. At dawn he had raised a chunk of flint. Would he really have brought it down on her skull or had it only been a rehearsal to test certain psychological limits? It had seemed easier to conceive the act at night but the day revealed more, brightly illuminating the gory physical aspects.

Taking one of the dock leaves, he folded it into a bandage, aware of his abductor's fingers fluttering as if about to interfere and show him how to do the job properly. He bound a number of leaves around the swollen toe, then regarded the first aid with a feeling of dissociation from the green, bulbous addition to his foot. He closed his eyes and said, 'There'll be no running today, you can be sure of that.'

Although he seemed to doze, behind his hooded eyes murder rose again. He listened to the snapping of twigs as Louise constructed her nest of kindling. She struck a match and a tenuous flame took hold. The fire was a good sign, it meant that she was not expecting to move on for a while. Nye resolved to watch his 'p's and 'q's and avoid sending any sudden whim scudding across her brain. At the moment she was blessedly distracted by a beetle that clung to one of the logs stacked on the hearth. Sent into a tutting concern for its welfare, she inspected it closely, then chivvied it to safety by the side of the hearth. Nye scowled. He did not like beetles, they made him shudder. He suffered from a childhood conviction that if there was an alien invasion it was likely to appear in the form of something with a brittle shell and six legs, each independently exploring the environment by means of electronic feedback— motorised malevolence.

'A relative of yours, is it? You should have chucked it on the fire.' The remark was a mistake, it brought on a jerking anxiety which often preceded an outburst. 'It would have felt the heat and flown off,' he offered in hasty appeasement.

'Carabis Violus Ceaus don't fly.' She sighed self-right-eously and returned to a further inspection of the log. Sat-isfied that it didn't house any more beetles she committed it to the flames. 'They come in three different colours.'

'Carabis Violus,' Nye scoffed.

'That means they'm beetles,' she informed this epitome of ignorance.

'Of course it's a sodding beetle, I can see that.' Nye's mood had soured again with his guts which were beginning to bubble like sulphuric acid.

'And,' she added emphatically, 'they'm predatory.' The information did nothing to reduce his prejudice against anything that scuttled or crawled over the face of the earth.

'That doesn't surprise me.' The fire sprang into life un-der the log and fingers of heat came out to massage his in-tentions. Anchored by more immediate bodily needs, escape became secondary and Nye decided to postpone the murder for a little longer. With his head propped against the wall, he drifted back into the dream state and there en-countered a man-sized beetle that sat at a judge's bench perfunctorily waving its antenna over his protest of inno-cence. With horrid fascination, he saw the black back of the beetle merge with the black cap of ultimate judgement ...and you shall be taken from this place...

But it was not the black-backed beetle that accompanied him back into the waking state, it was the Fox Man in his black anorak and the quivering antennae of his radio receiver. 'Your Fox Man,' he asked his abductor wearily, 'does he ever go to Ebury Hall?'

'Sometimes 'er do, sometimes 'er don't,' was all she was prepared to reveal.

'That doesn't surprise me,' Nye encouraged further.

'There have always been foxes on the estate. Deeks says if you shoot one along comes another to take its place.'

'Not much good to shoot 'em then, is it since Nature do like to balance things out? I expect 'er do lose as many of they pheasants to poachers, barn owls and stoats as 'er do to any fox.'

'Jesus Christ! It speaks more than one sentence.' Thwarted by his abductor's logic, Nye fell back to dwelling on his future at Ebury Hall which was beginning to take on the impression of a distant shore from which he drifted further and further on a tide of squalid events. He had never considered the place to be home and whenever he left one of his women he would say, Ciao, must go, I'm needed at the Hall. The Hall had meant a lot of things— membership of the county's elite, status, lifestyle but it had never meant home until now. Now it was the fabled isle of food, fresh water, a clean bed, where pain and discomfort were vanquished by a warm bath and wifely concern. 'A common fox has got easier access to Ebury Hall than I have.'

His throbbing toe brought him back to face the present. It had swollen so much that it would be impossible to force it back into the wellington boot, he would need to make some space for it by cutting a hole in the toe-cap. 'I don't suppose you happen to carry a pair of scissors do you, pea-brain? I need to cut a piece out of my boot to take the pressure off my toe.'

He had expected the request to be refused, but to his surprise Louise rummaged in her pocket like an ape inspecting something in its navel. Shortly after she took out a penknife and slid it towards him. It was just a rusty old keepsake; the bolt holding the blade to the haft had corroded and the cutting edge came out reluctantly, but it was sharp enough for the job. Nye set to work on the toe-cap of the wellington by piercing a hole, then sawing toward the rim of the boot. The rubber yielded easily; it was like cutting meat without any blood. His abductor squatted, poking randomly at the fire with agitated jabs, seeming to extend his own murderous thoughts. The weapon in his hand, a mere inch of blunt, corroded metal, could hardly be described as such. Nevertheless, he set the stage for the denouement of this bizarre tragedy.

He rehearsed his snaking approach towards her under cover of night, swiftly thrusting her chin upward and slitting her throat. If necessary he would finish her off with lead shot. The trouble was, halfway through the rehearsal of his perfect plot, old Fussy Qualms strode onto the stage and began to reorganise the props and re-write the script. The scene following the murder was one in which the lice that lived upon the blood of his intended victim would drown in a surfeit of the stuff.

Shoulders back. Call yourself a soldier!? challenged Gung-Ho Sergeant Nye of the SAS. This isn't theatre, this is for real. Last night you had a chunk of flint in your hand willing to do murder, not test the parameters of your conscience.

But what about the blood? whimpered Fussy Qualms.

Yes, there's bound to be blood, but you bloodily severed a fox's brush whilst life still wriggled in its body.

She's human, Fussy Qualms had gone quite pale at the thought. She's bigger, think of the scale of the butchery: severing a human jugular with a rusty penknife is not the same as cutting off a fox's brush with a sharp knife.

His abductor was abnormally still, hunched and skeletal

under her threadbare coat by the side of the fire. Was she listening or distracted? One, two, three strides and it's over, urged Sergeant Nye.

But she's so still, so very still.

That's good, immobility makes an object out of the target. Just be quick in putting the old hag out of her misery.

Louise put her head on one side unexpectedly and listened. He'd hardly moved; surely she had not been alerted by him unless his thoughts had mysteriously broadcast themselves? If only she had kept still; in moving she became human, not merely a frustrating obstruction to his escape. Something made him look behind him toward the doorway, sensing the presence of a third party standing there staring into the room, but it was only the small grey squirrel scratching at its cache of nuts.

'Give I thik knife,' ordered his guard curtly.

'I haven't finished the job yet.' He inflected the reply with heavy meaning.

'Give I thik knife, 'tis mine.'

'I said I haven't finished with it.'

Seconds later his reprimand arrived; the gun barrel descending on his wrist with such sharp ferocity he was forced to drop the penknife with a yelp of pain. Snatching the wellington boot, he crawled to a corner of the room and cowered like a kicked dog. Her power had become ubiquitous. He watched her poke animatedly at the fire which said to him, this is what I will do to you if you don't conform. She continued to agitate the burned-out log until it was no longer recognisable. Silence fell on the room like the settling of the powdery ash in the grate. It was an hour before she deigned to speak again. 'He used to give I chocolates.'

'Who, Old Nick?' Nye snarled, still smouldering like a hot coal in a corner of the room.

'Course not.' She looked genuinely perplexed by the thought. 'The Fox Man.'

Nye looked mournfully at the grate and the grey ashes there, his dismay promoted further by the mention of somebody from another world, another time. 'What did he give you chocolate for?' he asked.

Encouraged by her silence his old arrogance returned. 'For services rendered? Ha! What could somebody like you ever give a man, it couldn't be sex? My God it would be like shagging a sewer rat.' He might be her prisoner but he was still free to hurl his insults, berate her sanity, degrade her sexuality, tell her she embodied all manner of human ugliness, and it had as much effect on her as water on oil. His spitting and hissing at his gaoler done, Nye announced, 'I'm going upstairs if I'm allowed to.'

'I int stoppin' 'e.'

Although the climb upstairs proved exhausting, it was worth it just in order to reassert the idea of independent movement. The bedrooms like the rest of the house were dirty and derelict with nothing remaining to identify the people who had once slept in them. No litter on the floor, no broken toys left behind, only faded and fly-blown wallpaper revealed a preference for those boldly coloured, geometric designs of the sixties. In the larger of the two rooms was an old iron bedstead minus its mattress and a wardrobe with a missing leg propped up on a gold-leafed, leather-bound book. A low cottage-style window faced up Long Coombe. He stooped to look out between the remaining shards of broken glass, half hoping to catch sight of the Fox Man striding toward Pikes Wood. Nye turned his back on the empty landscape in irritation to consider the room once more but felt compulsively drawn to inspect the ceiling instead.

History claimed that the farmer had hung himself in a shed, but suppose it had happened here, in the bedroom when the wallpaper was still brightly purple? He inspected the ceiling for a hook; there was none nor any dangling electric flex, no limp rope frayed where it had been cut. There were no untoward rattlings nor disturbances of the atmosphere, only the sound of the wind shunting grass and twigs from the outside through the sitting-room door below and a sense of entropy, mortality, endings.

Nye stooped to dust away some powdery mildew hiding the title of the book that supported the lopsided wardrobe and brought up some gold lettering. Holy Bible it said. Even the loftiest of man's ideals are subject to decay. In a drawer at the bottom of the wardrobe he found a brocade tablecloth with gold tassels. Clean and smelling of camphor balls it appeared to be the only item of comfort. Nye buried his nose in it. 'It's so good, it smells so clean, so good.'

Folding it into a pad for his head he lay gratefully on the bedstead and withdrew into sleep, sleep that stout comforting oak door between himself and reality, except that in that supposedly quiet realm he found himself involved in a bitter argument with a squirrel. It was as large as a man with a hyperactive and quarrelsome temperament. It glared at him with a black glass eye, although all he had done was to approach it humbly with his palm upturned in a begging gesture as it removed leaves from its cache of hazel nuts. 'Please,' he begged, watching a huge brown nut positioned in the vice of its sharp white teeth. It cracked open with the sound of splitting timber and chunks of nut meat were delivered to its bulging cheeks. With its back turned toward him it began to shuffle defensively around its soup-bowl-shaped larder in the ground. Nye was conscious of extreme anguish, although he did not give way to tears, his mouth dribbled instead. In the dream he had become a man who had lost his stature, one totally diminished by hunger. 'Please.' He advanced, whining submissively in the way he supposed he should, but the creature wheeled on him angrily. 'Piss off, Nye,' it whistled at him through its huge front teeth, causing hard chunks of nut to fly from its mouth, and Nye fell on them greedily as they landed amongst the nettles on the dung heap.

It was the sound of rain drumming on an old tin roof that woke him. It pattered with the insistent urgency of his own need for water. He made his way weakly downstairs to find Louise staring into the cold grate as if thought had departed her body. He had seen this staring vacancy before and did not intend putting it to the test by going for the gun. He touched his swollen wrist gingerly to feel again that profound loathing toward his abductor. Although not broken, it was painful to touch. Escape, formerly at the top of his hierarchy of needs, slipped to the bottom. His throbbing toe had not been calmed by the dock leaf bandage and, although it had abated, the vomiting left him with a feverish craving for water. He supported himself giddily against a wall thinking about how best to collect rainwater. 'I'm going to find water.' He tentatively probed her mood.

She did not reply so he took the risk of launching himself toward the kitchen. Like all the rooms in the house, it was mean and dirty with nothing left in it to indicate that anybody had ever cooked there, apart from an old butler sink supported on an uncertain, rough-hewn frame of wood. His feet shuffled around in the grit on the quarry-tiled floor as he looked for something to collect his water in. There was nothing left apart from the sink and three wooden shelves held to the wall by six-inch nails. The bailiffs must have swooped on anything of value, leaving the rest to insects and spiders. Strands of grass on one of the shelves suggested that a bird had entered to investigate a nesting site. The fact that the creature had rejected what would otherwise have been a safe and sheltered spot added to the dreary ambience of the room. It was a profoundly depressing place; the previous occupant had committed his last and most desperate act, then left nothing behind except a bad atmosphere. Although the act itself had been mopped up, tidied away and assigned to the coroner's records years ago, Nye's imagination still insisted on returning to the scenario. Thus, to his eyes even the white kitchen tiles were gruesomely sterile, like those in a butcher's shop, but was that a spot of blood left on the grouting between them? 'Nothing left.' He shook his head.

'Went and hung hisself didn't er,' came his abductor's voice from the sitting room. "Twas on the spot where you'm standing.'

Nye heard her verdict as if it had been inserted directly into his own thoughts. The shock sent him staggering backward into a length of old electric cable that somebody had pulled down from the ceiling.

'Foot and mouth got 'is cattle, see,' concluded his abductor.

Tears filled Nye's eyes and rolled freely down his face. 'There's nothing left, not a sodding thing left,' he sobbed. Appalled by the cable dangling like a noose from a gallows, he grabbed the only vessel available for collecting water, an old pickling jar glued to a shelf by cobwebs, and left the room to find Louise guarding the exit. 'What are you waiting for, I'm not likely to sprout wings and piss off am I? I'm going outside to get some water.'

She allowed him to pass and enter the kitchen garden. He followed a concrete path around the perimeter of the house, which ran like a narrow causeway over grass and weeds. In parts it was raised as if some local tumult in the subsoil had pushed it up and snapped it in half. In the frost-widened cracks, thistle and dandelion had taken hold. Nye inspected the guttering above his head and found a point where it had broken free of its bracket causing it to miss the downpipe and discharge rainwater in liberal amounts on the ground. Taking the jar, he aligned it beneath, his thirst dismissing any qualms about the debris that might have accumulated in the path of his drinking water. He continued his explorations stalked by two cool grey eyes which marked his movements as tenaciously as a hound's. He came to a carport resting askew on rusty poles, its guttering emptying into a plastic water-butt in steady drips. As the water inside was likely to be stagnant it could only be used to wash himself. There was a small bathroom located in an extension off the kitchen which still possessed a hand basin and miraculously a plug. The thought of engaging in such a civilised ritual as washing restored a little hope and he wandered off to find a container large enough to carry water from the butt.

Like the house, the yard and garden contained nothing of any use, only a few items discarded because they had been beyond repair. There was a polythene watering can, bleached to the shade of stretched bubble gum, with a slit near the bottom making it impossible to collect more than two pints of water at the most. He returned to the butt to find the tap at the bottom corroded, and when it failed to shift he picked up a brick and hammered at it with rising frustration. Nothing seemed to work for him anymore, neither the so-called indestructible material of the modern age, polythene, nor the time-honoured metal. In response to his blows the tap broke free of its mounting and out gushed the liberated water too fast for him to catch more than an inch. He sighed wearily over the waste and placed his watering can directly under the guttering instead. With his arms folded he stood waiting for the can to fill drip by drip whilst the countryside around him absorbed the downpour like a sponge. He became aware of Louise's obnoxious odour and turned his face away.

'They have to walk miles for water in Africa.' Her observation, conveyed on the breath of rotting teeth and poor diet, was delivered in a wheedling tone as if importuning on behalf of a moral problem.

'They, they?' he spat back irritably. 'And who might they be?'

'They who ain't got water, where 'tis dry, of course.' His ignorance was astonishing and she hunched over her answer looking up at him with a quizzical expression, elaborating further, 'Women put pots on their heads and walk miles with it.'

'Oh do they, do they indeed!' Nye breathed deeply, lungs operating like a pair of indignant bellows fanning his impatience. Drip, drip, the water dispensed itself in frugal droplets, every now and again their regularity was interrupted by chaos and the predictable pattern was shed in a minor gush of water. Drip, drip, splutter. He closed his eyes in order to shut it out. Drip, drip, he couldn't get rid of it, it was an insistent, ticking metronome that confined attention to its own tempo. Drip, drip, he found himself trying to predict when the regular beat would be disrupted by a splutter. Why, he wondered, didn't it simply continue to dispense itself in predictable quantities at even intervals?

Drip, drip, drip, Ebury Hall, drip, drip, drip splutter. Life ticking away unbroken within the regular confines of the seasons—hunting, shooting, whoring. Squeak, squeak went Mrs Deeks' buffered black court shoes that seemed to accompany her silent disapproval whenever he went to sow his oats. Trot, trot, trot, Suzanne, chin out, vulpine gaze levelled on her ageing sugar daddy. Clippety clop, clippety clop, Matilda's fat arse bobbing up and down on the back of her grey mare. Clippety clop, her predictable fortnightly demands on his body as he lay without interest or passion beneath her gung-ho urge to take the jump. He would do so, dispensing his favour with a smirk on his face. Pump, pump, the regular discharge of testosterone into Suzanne Blinney's cash box. Drip, drip, splutter! How well that word expressed the unpredictable end of it all. Splutter, flushed out, set to run half naked and hunted like a, like a...

Once upon a time his life had been divided into neat portions of pleasure, interspersed with acute bouts of boredom, and then came a dirty, wizened woman, a hedge gypsy, bringing randomness, and chaos. What had he done to deserve all this?

'Morels!' exclaimed his abductor who had hitherto been staring vacantly at the garden behind him.

It was too much and Nye's seething resentment welled to the surface. He stuck out his chin and glared at her. 'My God if I had half a chance I'd put my hands round that skinny neck of yours, give it a good twist and play football with your fucking head.'

Louise looked only mildly surprised before extending her arm stiffly and pointing in the same direction she had been staring. 'Morels!' she shouted again and marched, arm still pointing, toward a patch of blackened earth that had recently been the site of a bonfire. Nye shook his head over the improbable impression of a scarecrow leaving its crucifix in the middle of a field and walking off determinedly in the direction it pointed.

She squatted, inspecting a clump of toadstools then said to herself, 'Morels, they'm edible.' Nye looked at the fungus thinking that anything so pernicious looking with ochre-coloured phallic caps clinging to white mealy stems could not possibly be edible. Taking her index finger and thumb, Louise delicately plucked one from the ground, then presented it to her nose like a connoisseur of fine wine.

'You're not going to eat that, are you?'

'Morcella esculenta,' she said and sniffed again. 'Morcella esculenta—edible.'

'Oh I see, they come with labels on do they?'

'In the book they do,' she replied literally, then took to plucking rapidly at the rest of the harvest.

'They're poisonous, you half-wit,' but she continued to crop without reference to his opinions. 'I hope you don't expect me to eat them.' Nye returned to his own harvest to find that he had only succeeded in collecting half an inch of water in the watering can. With rainwater pit-patting on his patience he stood with his arms folded, watching Louise dart hither and thither as she plucked combustible material for kindling. 'I don't suppose you keep anything to wash with in those pockets of yours, you know, genus soapus?'

Ignoring him she continued with her task. Eyes narrowed, he speculated whether she would actually eat the toadstools, nothing would give him greater pleasure than to watch her ingest a highly toxic fungus and the best way to ensure she did would be to provoke her childish stubbornness by telling her not to. A sinister smile contorted his lips as he picked up his watering can and returned to the bathroom to empty out two inches of water. As soon as his back was turned, one of those little chaotic changes in the drip, drip pattern caused a miniature flood to splutter wastefully into the water butt beneath.

It was a good omen that a small sliver of soap, barely distinguishable as such had been left on the window sill. Delicately blowing away dust and cobwebs, he applied it to an oily rag, working up a lather, then set about his ablutions. Having dried himself on the tablecloth he'd found upstairs, he returned refreshed to the garden in order to inspect the jar that had been filling up nicely with his drinking water. Just as he arrived in the garden he found Louise emptying it and filling it instead with her crop of toadstools.

Never in his life had he felt so enraged. 'You fucking cretin!' he roared and, heedless of the danger he was in, strode toward her with his fist clenched, forgetting how swiftly she could move. In a single gesture she pushed the jar into her pocket and swung his shotgun from her shoulder. Carried forward by his own momentum, Nye took the full thrust of the blow to his ribs.

'Run' With that order all the concessions that his abductor had permitted disappeared. 'Run!' she shrieked at him, but he couldn't run whilst he was choking with the effort of filling his deflated lungs.

Nye had reached a turning point. It was that point where a prisoner ceases to hiss and spit through the bars of his cell and adapts to those laws that govern the earning of privileges and the avoidance of pain. There comes a point in all imprisoned relationships where resistance must submit to survival. It is the point where the battered wife hides her condition as if it were a crime, the abused child stops crying and the mistreated dog stops growling. He staggered from Harmers Farm with his arms outstretched as if to embrace the memory of Ebury Hall. His pursuer's rapid footsteps caught him up and turned him away from the estate. Now the way ahead, his future, was reduced to a tractor track littered with chunks of flint that gored his inflamed toe. His aching guts did not take kindly either to the rough passage toward Pikes Wood.

He felt a strange gratitude towards his abductor when she halted suddenly by the edge of Harmers Pond to point keenly at something which had plopped into the water. 'Arvicola amphibius,' she said authoritatively, but Nye just nodded his agreement and sank to the ground whilst she remained transfixed by the sight of a water vole.

He raised his wobbling head from his knees and looked blearily toward Pikes Wood, praying for the appearance of the Fox Man, but there was nobody standing there where the tractor track petered out, only rough pasture and thistle. Somewhere across the valley a dog was barking, but the sound came to him from a different world that no longer had anything to do with him. Sinking into gloom and despair Nye prayed that he wouldn't be driven up Long Coombe again. The microbe which had infected his bowels was now threatening to inhabit his throat as well. The individual aches and pains had consolidated to become a generalised feeling of illness weighing him down and he doubted that he could make it that far.

What he dreaded most was the thought of sinking to his knees; if he sank to his knees it would be the end of the run and his insane abductor would finish him off. When he checked on her whereabouts it was to see her gathering the wild narcissi that grew in clusters around the marshy edge of the pond, cradling her arm to take the blossoms tenderly like an old-fashioned maid in a country garden. Her splashing about in the water cruelly reminded him of his dilemma; he must drink from the pond or risk dehydration.

He got to his feet and waded to the centre of the pond. Projected by the westering sun, his dark silhouette floated on the surface. The spectral light over his shoulder summoned him to another night in the cold. Fear, pain, thirst, hunger, the physical immediacy of it all made ancient history out of his life at Ebury Hall. It had been a lifestyle achieved by playing the success game, a game won by diminishing his faults and polishing up the brass of his limited talents to look like gold. It was a game played in earnest, a survival game but its objective was social and psychological survival. This kind of survival game, which his abductor was rapidly winning, was raw, brutal and terrifying.

'Narcissus!'

Nye turned to find a bunch of wild flowers being shaken at him. Louise held them tightly in her fist and repeated mysteriously.

'Narcissus. Thik flowers was all that were left of un once they nymphs burned his body. He did keep looking at himself, the same as you'm doing now. Kept looking at himself in the fountain, see, then he went and fell in love with his own image. 'Tis all there in the Greek mythology,' she said as if everything that anybody ever needed to know was contained in the ancient tales. 'Run!' she ordered pertly and raised the gun. Nye looked longingly at the pond before allowing himself to be herded forward.

The green lane was one of many criss-crossing the ancient limestone hills, a former drove road cutting through a steep bank of earth held back by rock and hedgerow. Nye remembered it well. It was here, high on adrenaline, that he had waded through the clamouring hounds to claim the brush and anoint himself with fox blood. All that morning he had ridden neck and neck with Sir George, urging the lathered hunter into a performance that outstripped the rest of the field. Now he was being driven into the same lane by one of his own species, trying not to fall, fearing this place might be the end of the run for him too—finally brought down by a woman all hunched and intent on an incomprehensible purpose of her own.

When the footsteps behind him halted he too rested. Aware of her muttering to herself he turned to find out what the fuss was all about. She was squatting by a mound of leaves beneath a protruding root of hawthorn, irritably removing them one by one as if somebody had deliberately left them there. After a minute or so her efforts exposed an elaborate structure of twigs and reeds that resembled a wasp's nest, except that somebody had placed some carefully woven corn dollies on the surface, now faded and flattened by the weather. In spite of his discomfort, he found himself drawn to the structure which struck him as both alien and familiar, as would a mud hut in his own garden. An opening had been left on one side as if to admit a creature; this too had been painstakingly finished so that its edge resembled the curling rim of a woven basket. Muttering some sort of greeting, she arranged the narcissi at the miniature entrance to the structure, considering each bloom carefully before laying it down. Nye craned his neck for a better view to find something peering back at him.

There, its lip raised in a sneer by the shrinking skin over its skull, was the severed head of a fox. Nye stepped back from the ghoulish sight as if it had been invested with some unnatural influence. He stared transfixed, but it was not the morbid composition of a beheaded animal lugubriously acknowledging its floral tribute that held his attention. It was a small glossy object that reflected back the evening light, a brown plastic disc attached to a thin leather collar. 'Pansy,' explained his abductor. ''Twas what 'e called 'er, see.'

'Very beautiful,' Nye agreed, all meek and mild, his eyes fixed on the plastic disc. He recalled the morning of the hunt and the way the Fox Man had come toward them shouting and gesticulating. The vixen had evidently been one of his tagged subjects. It was just conceivable that the transmitter's miniature battery had sufficient power left to produce a signal. If the severed head stared into eternity

305

through eyeless sockets then Nye stared back, his own eyes glued to the radio collar. Louise appeared to be ready for the off again. Aiming to remain at the site for as long as possible Nye bowed his head in apparent respect for the dear departed animal.

'She ain't got no body left because they hounds took it,' Louise pointed out factually.

'Oh dear,' said Nye reverently. After a suitable lapse of time he asked, 'What's that?' apparently noticing the transmitter for the first time. 'Somebody's dropped their watch.' He had accurately predicted that Louise would claim the prize before he did.

''Tisn't yourn.' Her dirty fingers pecked it up with the speed of a bird's beak.

Nye's most sanguine hope was that the transmitter was continuing to signal and that its removal from the site would be picked up by the Fox Man. The balance of probabilities told him it was unlikely. If the equipment was still functioning then, he assumed, the Fox Man would have retrieved it. Nevertheless Nye called upon that vaguely configured dispenser of good luck and pleaded for special consideration. Now he just wanted to be off, in spite of his fatigue, in order to put his hopes to the test. The removal of the transmitter had disturbed the narcissi, sending his abductor into further tutting and fussing. Her egocentric chatter passed his ears in a intensely irritating stream of mumbo jumbo. Within inches of her transient artwork his shotgun lay ready to hand. He consoled himself with the thought that if only he had been able to fill her with lead shot then she would have already made a wreath for her own grave. He stared at it with an expression of woebegone longing.

'He used to call her Pansy,' she repeated, regarding the twiggy mausoleum with her head to one side, then waved him forward with a perfunctory gesture. This time she did not jab him in the ribs, perhaps his good manners at the vixen's tomb had bought him a little leniency. Compliantly, since compliance brought rewards, he limped in the direction indicated and turned himself sideways to pass through the gap in the hedge.

'Hurry up,' she chivvied from behind like an officious old maid. Having passed through the gap, he found himself in a field chock-a-block with rusting farm equipment. He ducked under the skeletal jaw of a ploughshare and then broke into a run across the desert of metal waste toward an ancient residential caravan and a standpipe. Let his insane pursuer take pot shots at his heels; he would happily die if he could taste fresh water on his tongue again. On reaching the tap, he gave it a desperate twist and out gushed life itself whilst behind him in the indeterminate shadows of the hedgerow two cool grey eyes watched him. What thoughts, what kind of soul they windowed, who could tell?

Nye drank deeply, confessing to himself that he had never treasured anything so sincerely in all his life. He sank pint after pint, and, once his thirst was quenched, he splashed water on his face and hair, rubbed behind his ears and washed his hands again and again.

Seated on an upturned milk crate, Nye took stock of his situation. His thirst had been slaked but another damp, cold night without food still loomed. His eyes wandered around his new prison, an acre of rusting metal sharing the same air of dereliction as Harmers Farm. His agitated imagination fancied that somebody regularly opened the gate and flung unwanted equipment into the jaws of nature that chewed and salivated leaving a digestive stain of red rust. 'If I sit here long enough,' he told himself, because the sound of his own voice reassured him of his continuing existence, 'I would see it all turn to a handful of dust.'

Such a chaotic landscape was anathema to a man who thought of industry as a well-tended urban garden. Input technical know-how, finance, organisation, weed out malcontents, dissenters, poor performers and one had economic growth. 'Not here, oh no not here in the Hedge Gypsy's domain, common sense just doesn't add up.'

As if serving time for his beliefs, industrial man sat close to tears imagining that he could hear the digestion of his rational world by some unseen force. 'Dust and rust,' he shouted across the field at his abductor who was bobbing up and down in pursuit of kindling. 'Not that you'd worry about it, pea-brain, you'd take a hammer to man's highest achievements and smash them to bits.' The damp atmosphere muffled his words to a pinched-sounding whine. 'It's a graveyard,' he concluded dismally, having in mind the hanged farmer. 'If they cut him down in the kitchen, maybe they buried him here.' Worried that his circulation might cease altogether, he got stiffly to his feet and wondered how best to use the brocade tablecloth now tied around his waist.

'Oi, shit breath, I need that penknife to make a poncho out of this.' He held it up. His abductor swung her arm like a weathervane to point at the caravan. He shuffled toward the abode that appeared to have fainted into the thorny arms of the hedgerow. When Nye put his head round the door he had the impression of a leaf-strewn, bone-littered burrow housing something with a snarling temperament. He entered to be met by a concentrated odour of urine and sweat. The filthy interior offered little protection from the elements, let alone any hope of finding food there. He would have gone outside again in order to avoid the stench had there not been another smell lurking there, the astonishing smell of chocolate. Wherever his abductor had stored her cache, it was not in a cupboard, since all the doors and shelves had long since disappeared for firewood. He traced it to a hollow bunk bed, then soundlessly lifted a mattress with stuffing that spilled out like guts. Hunger suppressed the thought of disturbing a rat's nest as his hand felt blindly in the dark under the seat. He was instantly rewarded with two bars of wrapped confectionery. Hearing Louise move outside, he snatched them and withdrew, backing away in disgust from the sight of human lice on the bedclothes negotiating their way through the debris of hair and skin cells. He had seen dogs sleep on more hygienic bedding.

Stooping, he spied on his abductor through the bramble occupying the window. Although she busied herself with the fire those eyes were more than capable of spotting the modest booty in his jacket pocket. His index finger stroked the curved surface of a compacted bar of coconut ice covered with a rippled coating of crisp dark chocolate. Hunger reared up, orgasmic, out of control, pushing him to the exquisite edge of gratification, but he knew that he would have to rein it back. Even the crinkling of a wrapper would travel through the resonant evening air and summon her.

Seventy-five hours had passed without food and those hours of deprivation had left him with the tremulous notions of a child—the woman with the shotgun was the troll, the giant, the dragon that breathed apocalyptic vengeance on anybody daring to raid its treasure trove. In terrible agitation, his finger stroked the confectionery. Common sense told him he should raid the cache again and hide the surplus. Fear, on the other hand, visualised a fly on a web; any little quiver would bring her scuttling across with arachnid speed to punish him. Instead he took a bent fork, there was no other cutlery left in the caravan, and ripped at some threads in the centre of the tablecloth until a hole the size of his head appeared. He slipped on the poncho which draped from his shoulders—a large billowing tent under which to hide his booty.

The sight of his abductor still engrossed in fire-making was only minimally reassuring with such physical and psychological odds stacked against him. Even so, he could not remain suspended indefinitely; sooner or later he would have to eat. Already his imagination was galloping ahead of his senses to taste the chocolate. Under cover of the poncho, his index finger located a neat, sharp serrated edge of plastic wrapper. He ripped experimentally at the seam and since the noise did not alert his abductor he tore further but, as soon as his finger came into contact with the chocolate, it hit him that it could be his last mouthful of food on this earth. He looked bitterly through the barbs of bramble at his abductor on all fours, bony arse turned toward him, blowing vigorously on her kindling. This woman, this abomination of a human being who had stolen his future, could decide on a whim whether he lived or died. Now all passing moments were last moments because time to him was as it might be to an animal.

He stuffed the chocolate into his mouth and chewed

ravenously; never before had he experienced such an acute gratification of his senses. His taste was so exquisitely satisfied that all other sensations were subjugated to the oral. Not only did his mouth water, but his eyes too; it was difficult not to groan and sigh. Louise, he noted, still shuffled around the fire on hands and knees, blowing from all sides. He grinned in triumph. Success making him less cautious about the noise he made, he ripped the wrapper off another bar, this time a dense nut and fruit bar. That too disappeared rapidly down his gullet. He replaced what he had eaten with two more bars from beneath the bunk bed and went outside. He sat himself nonchalantly on an old metal tractor seat at a distance where chocolate breath and constant belching wouldn't be noticed.

With thirst slaked and hunger staved off, both needs slipped in the hierarchy of needs and other sensations were in the ascendancy. The hot, stabbing pain generated by his septic toe had now found a neural pathway under the arch of his foot. The bruising to his lumbar region that had taken numerous blows from the gun barrel was indistinguishable from kidney pain and his anus itched and burned from distended veins. Nye sat hunched shabbily over his deprivation, not daring to risk his life by trying to escape. He was a prisoner, no longer master of choices. He was left with only a minuscule hope that the dead vixen's transmitter continued to signal from his abductor's wrist and its change in location would alert the Fox Man.

Louise was still pecking at combustible material along the hedgerow. The sight of her caused him so much anguish that he turned his back and hunched himself over the fire. Even here her presence continued to assert itself in the form of a neat ball of straw and twigs. Flames flickered across the surface, burning soundlessly without seeming to consume anything. Mesmerised by the idea of flickering flame fingers holding a ball of twigs and straw, her fire took on a spiritual dimension. He imagined his abductor throwing herself onto it to rise again as a ragged phoenix. With indestructible certainty a small threadbare woman with a limping mind would haunt the hedgerows for ever, dragging her poverty behind her like a broken wing.

'Run,' he muttered to himself as if to scatter the strange illusions, then curled his fist intending to smash the injustice of his imprisonment. 'Why?' he shouted across the field. 'It's not fair. It's not my fault, I didn't break your mind. I didn't turn you into a vagrant, I haven't caused your poverty. Oi!' he bawled even louder as she continued to swoop on kindling as if he didn't exist. 'Are you listening? I'm asking you why, why, why?'

The question strummed theatrically as if delivered in an avant garde setting to an audience of offbeat playgoers who gathered to listen to this absurd performance. He hadn't expected a coherent answer and received none. Her silence left him to a morbid recollection of how he had plunged his hand under those infested rags in order to find food— food which he was forced to scoff like a stray dog before it was snatched from him. He put his head in his hands, defeated. 'You've got no more concern for me than an animal.'

When Louise deigned to speak she said in a cold crisp tone of judgement, 'You killed 'er.'

The accusation was so coherent that Nye swore it had come out of the mouth of another character who had inadvertently entered the absurd drama. She sat behind the flames, her chin emphatically thrust forward, brow set in deep frowning furrows. The pert, vulpine features of Suzanne Blinney passed over her face as if stamped on celluloid. 'Piss off, just piss off, you urban vixen, go and screw Uncle George for a living. Maybe he'll remember your brats in his will, see if I fucking care. It's all gone, Ebury Hall, my job, everything, thanks to you.' Nye waved his arm at the hallucination.

'You killed 'er,' insisted his abductor.

'That's preposterous, I haven't killed anybody. It's all in your mind.'

Nye wasn't prepared for the speed and ferocity of his abductor. She leapt at him, seemingly from the fire itself and thrust the gun barrel at his shoulder, knocking him sideways off his tractor seat. Sprawled on the grass and vulnerable, he struggled to hold up his palm in surrender. Louise pointed, then gestured with the gun toward the gap in the hedge. Struggling to his knees, Nye would have been willing to confess to any crime provided he was allowed to remain still to nurse his wounds, but his appeal for clemency was denied. He was forced back through the hedge, prepared for another night at Harmers Farm without fresh water.

Halfway along the green lane, Louise overtook him and he followed behind meekly until she reached the dead vixen where she squatted, fussing reverently over her floral tribute. Once everything was to her liking she got to her feet, pointed the gun at him and said triumphantly, 'You killed 'er, I saw you do it.'

Nye gaped at the dead vixen's pointed nose peeking out from its twiggy mausoleum, then at his wellington boots, one of which had a hole cut in the toe, protruding beneath the tassels of an old-fashioned table cloth. Salvador Dali himself could not have assembled a more surreal composition. There was no need to ask further about the nature of his crime; there it lay regarding the scene through empty eye sockets. He stared at the flowers whose white, lustrous presence in the twilight possessed a more solid reality than his own. Weakness and hunger came back to him, causing him to feel detached, as if having ingested an hallucinogenic drug. He was beginning to drift away from himself into an out-of-body sensation. At all costs he must struggle back and rejoin his corporeal self where there was pain, hunger, discomfort because it was those sensations that anchored him to consciousness.

'Are you trying to tell me,' he asked, struggling through his distress, 'that I'm going to be shot for killing a fox? Are you saying that my life is as low as that...thing.' He pointed at the skull and bones that his mad abductor was making so much fuss about. A sense of outrage returned bringing a little strength with it. 'Do you know what I would do if I had the chance? I'd get hold of you and I'd shake you so hard that your eyes would fall out and what's left of your fucking brains would drip down your nose like snot. That,' he pointed at the dead vixen, 'is not a somebody, it's a thing, an animal. Animals are not people,' he added slowly. 'Not people, do you understand, you shit-wit?'

Without the stamina to sustain his anger, it drained away, leaving him to consider with disbelieving gloom that this woman was quite capable of shooting his head off then laying it to rest under a bonnet of straw and twigs. He would lie in his final resting place, the astonished expression in his dead eyes appeased by her ritual visits to his tomb carrying armfuls of wild flowers. 'Am I going to be...be—?' He said punished because he could not bring himself to say executed and at length found the courage to ask, 'When, when are you going to do it? I've got a right to know. You should have polished me off right at the beginning, it would have been kinder. Instead you set me up and forced me to run. I've been denied sleep, shelter and food. That's torture.' Bitter indignation rose in his throat constricting his words, which left his mouth like stuttered hiccups. 'When, dawn? A blindfold...some last request, a prayer, a message for my wife before you blast my brains out?'

Nye had not expected his question to be answered, let alone create the furore that followed. Louise jumped back as if she had fired the gun and taken the recoil on her shoulder. Ever since his abduction, Nye had been struck by her cool grey eyes that always looked elsewhere or were distracted by some minutia that had nothing to do with him. Now that vacancy was occupied by an expression of extreme anxiety. She rushed toward him as if charging with a fixed bayonet and passed him. She continued in this manner, looking as if she might pass out of sight. Nye gaped after her, not daring to hope that she would disappear. After thirty feet she halted and remained frozen for some seconds like a toy soldier, body stiff, shoulders square, before turning around as if poised on a mechanical pivot. She marched back towards him, seeming to have made up her mind what to do next. Instead of pointing the gun at him, she snatched a shoot of bramble and, heedless of the

315

pain, ran her hand over its dagger-sharp thorns. Watching the bright blood trickle in rivulets down her slim white fingers, Nye knew for sure that he would live.

Nye was not going to die, he was going to live and be swept along by her maniacal dictatorship like a landless, luckless refugee. Indeed, huddled under his dirty poncho on an old tractor seat, he had all the appearance of a third-world pauper squatting by the road, chewing narcotic leaves to stave off hunger and reality. He was not going to be shot, but there were a hundred other ways to die. He did not have to extrapolate greatly from his present condition to recognise that a septic toe could turn to gangrene, a chest infection to pneumonia.

The small fire had burned itself out during their absence so Louise painstakingly set about re-building her dome of kindling. He watched, teeth chattering, as she brought forth fiddly bits from her threadbare pocket. At last she put a match to it and tended to the flame on elbows and knees, her cheeks working like a pair of bellows. She huffed and puffed enthusiastically on the growing fire, whilst Nye treated himself to a malicious scenario.

'You old hag,' he muttered. 'If I had my way you'd be huffing and puffing on your funeral pyre. If I had half the chance I'd bring my boot up that skinny arse of yours and send you sprawling. I'd enjoy every minute of it, I'd stand there and watch you shrink like a quail on a spit.' He thought about her small skeletal frame, her birdish fluttering and repeated, 'A quail, that's just what you'd look like; they'd have to carry you away on a plate, there wouldn't even be enough left to give a dog a decent meal.

Oh yes, I'd sit and laugh at you burning and squealing like a witch at the stake.'

Nye's mood swung back to gloom again as he contemplated the impending night. He was mentally and physically imprisoned. Weakened by his experience he was left with nothing but the freedom to mutter ineffectual malice. He eyed the dirty jam-jar filled with the toadstools that his abductor had picked at Harmers Farm. They reminded him of slimy yellow offal slithering down the drain in an abattoir. Unbelievably her hand kept darting towards it protectively as if he were likely to snatch them from her. 'You're not going to eat them!?' Much to his amusement, she flinched, grasped the jar and held it close to her chest. 'Good God, you don't suppose I'm interested in eating that poison, do you?'

'They'm edible.'

'How do you know what's edible and what isn't?'

'It says so.'

'It, it, what it?' he yapped, impatient for her to swallow the lot and start manifesting symptoms of fungal poisoning.

'Thik book,' she answered, her own pedantic impatience equal to his.

'Oh you mean, the book,' he baited her, smirking. 'It says so in Revelations, does it? I expect God lined up all the toadstools in the world and told you specially which ones you could eat.'

'Brit...ann...ica...' Louise's reply leapt in ascending, triumphant syllables.

'Bollocks! You can only eat field mushrooms, everybody knows that,' he goaded knowing full well how her perverse nature would compel her to eat the fungi.

'They'm edible, I tell ee,' she insisted with a childish

317

menace in her tone. 'Morcella esculenta,' she pronounced, the Latin tag dignifying her defence of the fungi.

'Oh yes, morcella esculenta,' Nye pronounced in an Italian accent. He waved his arm under his tasselled tablecloth, giving him the appearance of an arrogant lampshade. 'Just because it's got a Latin name, that doesn't make it edible, pea-brain.' Only too willing to hasten Louise's end, he got to his feet and announced, 'Very well, I'll cook them for you and you can eat them, then we'll soon find out who's right won't we?'

He swept past, elated and energised by knowing that soon it would be the end of the run—for her. He flung open the caravan door and, confident of victory, looked down his nose from the imperious height of the milk-crate doorstep. 'Say your prayers, cretin.' Inside he found an old saucepan; the plastic handle had disappeared, leaving just a metal stem and returned to the fire. 'Go ahead, pea-brain, tip them in.' Rather surprisingly, she relinquished her hold on the crop and they slithered into the pot. Grinning, he shook them over the flames, accompanying his cooking with a venomous assessment of her survival chances. 'Well, if I'm condemned to die from exposure and starvation on account of a fox, then I can assure you that your cretinous stupidity is about to go on trial as well and nothing is going to give me greater pleasure.'

The metal saucepan handle had conducted heat to his hand; he wrapped his poncho around it for protection and continued, determined to serve her the toxic supper that slithered around in the bottom of the pan. 'Hah, this'll teach you to spout Latin; words aren't magic, you know,' he lectured as he muttered his own incantations over the pot like an evil apothecary willing a wicked outcome. It was not long before the juices of the fungus began to bubble. He shook it in order to hasten matters and released an earthy, not unpleasant aroma. Appetite, not always loyal to willpower, caused a traitorous memory of full English breakfast accompanied by open-cup field mushrooms.

'There, eat that, you half-wit.' He thumped the pot down beside his abductor, then returned to his own seat to smugly observe her painful end.

Steam rose like incense from the pot. Louise ignored it. When the contents cooled, she dipped in her hand and fed herself in the manner of one sliding oysters from their shells.

Nye smiled a twisted little smile as he waited. 'Don't say I didn't warn you, don't expect me to call an ambulance.'

Her supper finished, Louise sat warming herself by the fire like an old gypsy woman.

'Shall I tell your fortune, me dear?' Nye giggled in anticipation. 'Stomach cramps followed by vomiting. Just before your guts turn inside out you'll stagger around trying to hold them in. By then you'll have dropped my gun. Guess what happens next, me dear, a tall handsome man takes pity on you and finishes you off with a blast of lead shot up your arse.'

The shabby little woman continued to warm herself by the fire, seemingly unconcerned about her fortune. Time passed punctuated by her belching appreciation of the morels she had just eaten.

Spikey returned to Amwell as if the smell of early spring and the lengthening days had enticed him back to his home territory. Blinking short-sightedly in the public bar at The

Plume of Feathers he looked more than ever as if he had just woken from hibernation. He had wintered over in a warm, dusty corner of academia eking out a research grant. Help, my mind hurts! he had stencilled on his T-shirt, but, seeing the way his left eye dragged lamely after his right, Terence knew that it wasn't just his mind that hurt. Ned, who'd kept in touch since the collapse of the prosecution case against George Wentworth and Richard Nye, told him that Spikey had collapsed too. He had lost confidence and withdrawn into himself to become embittered and uncommunicative.

Terence bought two rounds as if to inject their reunion with a little of the old camaraderie and settled to discuss the final chapter of Spikey's PhD thesis. His disability was evident in the way he inclined his head toward Terence's suggestions, cruelly emphasising his loss of hearing. When the discussion tailed off, there wasn't enough left to say to each other that would fill the rest of the evening. They drank their beer as if intensely interested in its flavour and avoided the subject of the assault. It had been a wicked blow and injustice had dealt another. Terence listened to the repartee ping-ponging back and forth between the landlady and the male drinkers attempting to corner her with sexual innuendo. They would never win, Irene was far too quick for them. He found a kind of solace in her Liverpudlian patter, which had a tone of authority in it.

'Not yourselves tonight.' Suddenly she was there at the table collecting their glasses and mopping up their despondency. 'Not good news, eh, Spikey?' she tackled the subject head on.

'Have you read their press release?' Terence asked. There was no need to ask which press release since everybody assembled seemed to be depressingly familiar with it.

'Have I! The Master of the Amwell Hounds, she recited fluently, conveyed his sincere concern following an enquiry into an accident during the Ebury Hall meet. It was a most unfortunate incident. We always advise the public to keep their distance during meets, horses are very excitable animals and can be dangerous, said a spokesman... De dah de dah,' Irene concluded. 'So, it looks as if Sir George and his pink coats are going to get away with it.'

'Not entirely. Spikey's solicitor has proposed a without-prejudice discussion with their solicitor. He's looking for an out-of-court settlement that might result in compensation but no admission of guilt. Personally I think he should cut his losses...'

'Those bastards are guilty!' Spikey thumped his fist on the table. 'They're guilty, they know they're guilty and I want my day in court. I don't want them to give me money to make me shut up. What about this?' he stabbed a forefinger at his injuries. 'This isn't going to go away, is it?' Terence was about to counsel him to give it some more thought since Wentworth and Nye should be made to pay and pay dearly in settlement. The private prosecution that Spikey had been contemplating could run into thousands without any guarantee of success.

Irene leaned forward and put her hand over Spikey's fist giving it a comradely squeeze. 'If you want to go for it, Spikey I'll put a collecting box on the bar to help with the legal costs.'

Terence thought her more than capable of rattling a fighting fund from the inebriated generosity of her admirers. There were times he could have laid his head on the bosom of her humane morality, a morality that had nothing to do with law and risk, but everything to do with guts and principles. It had always been easy to signal his interest in her across the bar. Now he felt unable to deal with his feelings, whereas she seemed so adept at mopping up other people's. Terence had to confess that, at the merest flicker of intent in her dancing eyes, he would throw in his lot with the landlady at The Plume of Feathers; abandoning his vulpine studies he would sink with her into a huge and lasting embrace.

'What's the chance of winning?' she asked Spikey.

'My solicitor reckons it's less than fifty-fifty.'

'That doesn't surprise me, you're up against power and privilege.' Irene inclined her head in the direction of Ebury Hall. 'Don't worry, people like that will get their come-uppance, if not down here in the courts, then up there. Didn't I ever tell you that God's on the side of the working class, at least mine is!' she grinned.

Terence would dearly like to believe it, but the truth was they had gone to war with the sticks and stones of earnest intention to prevent a brutal kind of vandalism; now all they seem to be doing was shaking their fists at some sort of upper-class Cosa Nostra.

'And now,' Irene concluded 'we've got to do everything we can to get justice for Spikey.' She took up his hand in hers saying, 'Spikey, I'm sorry, really really sorry, but if it's any consolation Sir George has Judgement Day to face like the rest of us.'

'You think so? Excuse me,' he said abruptly and headed off in the direction of the gents. Terence also rose concerned, but found himself restrained by Irene's fingers digging into his shoulder.

'Leave him; people need to cry sometimes.' They watched Spikey's hunched shoulders, the sadness and injustice of it all had put years on him.

'So,' Irene asked, picking up their glasses, 'what are you doing tonight?'

Terence felt tempted to tell her what he would like to be doing but replied, 'Fox-watching. I've got a new woman to stalk, the Matriarch. She's a big, broad-shouldered vixen with a scowl like a feral cat.'

'I don't think I can compete with that.'

Flushed from the bright light of the bar by the clanging of a ship's bell, Terence strode along the narrow street of nineteenth-century cottages. The orange glow of a street lamp de-marked the village boundary, thereafter a frost-powdered drystone wall reflected light from a full moon and marked the way. Now he was the Fox Man again, the night throwing a cloak around the persona so that he could travel incognito, at one with the subjects he studied. Out in the fresh winter night he felt free for a while from the problems of his fellow kind, their conflicts, their politics.

There had been two drinkers at the table, and a third presence—injustice. It had joined them for the evening like an unwelcome guest and there it remained, squat, ugly and persistent. With his breath creating a head of steam in the cold air and the accoutrements of his trade rattling on his back like a tinker's pots and pans, he left the village and headed off to Pikes Wood to monitor the progress of his new vulpine family. On passing the entrance to the green lane where Pansy had been hounded to her death, he was reminded of the vagrant woman and her ramshackle caravan in a nearby field. Loopy Lou they called her in the village, but he would always think of her as Robin Redbreast, the name she had selected for herself, and so she was with her bossy, staccato chirruping.

He switched on his receiver and, in the course of tuning into the Matriarch's frequency, picked up the signal still pulsing from Pansy's transmitter. It appeared to have shifted a few degrees eastward from its normal location under her coracle-shaped mausoleum. There was only one creature he knew who would be unable to resist the little keepsake and he imagined Louise wearing it on her old brown coat like a badge of office. He walked to Pansy's grave to confirm that it had been removed, to find Louise's offering of wild narcissi. It was a sadly innocent tribute, sincere but short-lived, like the sand monuments children leave behind on the beach for the tide to take.

It bothered him to think of Louise alone by her fire, withdrawing to sleep under damp and filthy rags when it went out. She could die there, her frail corpse withering: who would know, who would care? Perhaps he should show a little kindness by abandoning his night's study in order to sit and talk to her. Perhaps he could persuade her to seek help, ask a social worker to find better accommodation. He pictured her all scrubbed, smartly dressed tucking into a plate of good food in a hostel where she would have company. It was when he thought of her sharing human company he abandoned his worthy intentions. Robin Redbreast, like her namesake, did not need the company of others. Her world was out here in the fields and the hedgerow. She didn't need rescuing; she had adapted, survived. Her lifestyle was inoffensive, made little demand on resources and on the people around her. She was, he concluded, happy enough practising her strange and inexplicable rituals.

People need to cry sometimes. Others, he thought, looking at the white flowers, need to scream. Perhaps madness is just another way of curling the fist and yowling at the world. He turned his back and returned along the green lane.

Louise did not die from fungal poisoning; on the contrary she ate a healthy portion of protein and lived. For dessert she dipped into her cache of chocolate. Nye's own hunger, no longer a snapping yapping cur appeased by scraps, had grown monstrous. It rose in waves from his stomach like an opiate undermining his will until concentration abdicated in favour of euphoria. He was a falling man losing his grip on reality.

Did he dream or was he actually riding on the back of a landslide, flailing wildly in red mud? He saw himself cling to an outcrop of limestone but even that immovable substance broke free and rolled down Long Coombe. Pikes Wood came careering past as he turned and tumbled to a halt at the feet of the Fox Man who had been regarding his fall with a knowing look. The large, benign man threw back his head laughing. 'The descent of man, I see,' he said and beckoned to him to follow. In the green lane, where the mad woman joined them, they paid their respects to the vixen's skull. Nye was shown the nature of his offence, then led back to complete his sentence seated on a tractor seat. 'Whose law have I offended?' he mumbled weakly. He looked for Louise, but she had disappeared with the Fox Man so he addressed the vague presence at the other side of her fire. Like the Reaper whose face is never seen, Louise's judgement took on form without identity.

'Tell me,' he asked in a reasonable enough tone, 'do you think that a man's life should be rated the same as a fox's, because if it is, then where does he fit in with the natural scheme of things? Must he stay at the bottom of the pile, crawl into caves for shelter, scratch the earth for a living, is that his place on this planet, do you think?'

'You did it on purpose, 'twas cruel.' Louise's indictment leapt out from the tarantella dance of flames.

'But nature's cruel too,' he addressed the disembodied accusation. 'But you don't try a lion for eating a lamb.'

'But nature isn't cruel, is 'er, not like you. You meant it, you meant to be cruel.' She made her point slowly so that he would understand and then continued, 'It took an hour for Pansy to die. You set 'er up, she got away. You set 'er up again, she got away again and so on. Thik vixen died of fear, she were dead on 'er feet and still runnin'. She were carryin' cubs an' all. 'Twere a wicked thing to do.'

Nye was too weak to argue and his attention drifted away like an untethered balloon. He did not see, therefore, the tears that ran down Louise's cheeks nor hear her sigh. 'She were carrying young 'uns. I shan't never have none of me own.'

Sensing another presence beyond the shifting patterns of firelight, Nye focussed on the spot where he'd last seen his abductor's face vaguely dancing. He did not see her through the juggling yellow and orange flames but found a circle of beings gathered there. Each were perched upon makeshift seats of discarded bits and pieces they had selected from the strange museum of rusting farm equipment. Seated in their various and unique ways, they stared at him with the same wary curiosity he regarded them. 'Who are you?' He was genuinely puzzled by them, although not disturbed, having been aware of them ever since dusk fell. They had been out there, configured by mist and ambiguous hedge shadows. Once they had judged the moment to be propitious, they elected to approach and show themselves to him. They did not answer his question directly but preferred to address one another, consulting and commentating amongst themselves. 'I wish you would answer because you see, you see, I need to know what you are.'

Orchestrated by the question they all shuffled forward in unison, bringing their seats with them. 'Shouldn't we be asking who he is?' they tittered. It had become impossible for the assembled beings to disguise their animal characteristics. Some, he noticed, had excessive hair that sprouted comically and unpredictably from ears or over the tops of stiffly starched collars. Others had jaws that extruded themselves into muzzles. One lady, dressed for an evening at the opera, possessed a wolf's ear that twitched quizzically in his direction whenever he spoke.

'Chocolate,' he told them. 'If I am to be tried, then I will need a little chocolate.' Chocolate, a surfeit of the stuff, came cascading out of the night landing in a heap on the grass at his feet followed shortly by a bottle of whisky. He saw Louise's face floating just above the level of the flames, yellow and disembodied as if severed from a corpse. 'Who are they?'

'Huminals,' she mouthed without sound and went away, taking the gathering of strange jurors with her. He had rather taken to them and hoped they had just withdrawn to debate his case. Their vaporous disappearance left him a little sad, a little stranded.

'You see, you see…it's…' he swayed on his tractor seat by the fire trying to grasp a word that might enhance his understanding, '…elemental, that's it, elemental.' He addressed the space where he'd last seen Louise's face. 'I have air, I have water, fire,' he pointed, 'and earth. It's what we're made of, you know and it's what we all go back to.' Nye found his observation so profound that its gravity kept him glued to the earth. He knew that he was facing the possibility of his own death through starvation. It was with a surprisingly pleasant feeling of detachment that he looked forward to breaking through the physical illusions of life. 'Fire, water, earth and air,' he concluded dreamily.

His concentration waned and his voice trailed off as if he had been trying to pursue a half-remembered tune. He began to fall again, avalanching, arms flailing, hands grasping not rock, earth and trees but the values upon which his former life had been built. He was scrabbling around amongst the remains of a shattered self, trying to reconstruct Richard Nye of Ebury Hall as events continued to tumble past him out of control. Everything was falling, collapsing.

He got to his feet in order to provide a counter-movement to his falling feeling and noticed chocolate bars and a bottle of whisky peeping out of Louise's pockets. He stared until giddiness and the tingling return of circulation forced him to sit again. The sight of food tethered his attention once more within the stockade of physical survival. Nye pointed and slobbered. 'If I say I'm sorry,' his eyes bulged and watered, 'would you give me some chocolate and a little whisky? A drop of whisky would make everything more bearable you see...If perhaps I confess...would you like me to confess? That chocolate, may I?'

His pleading, which had the obeisant appeal of a soft-muzzled dog, brought results. Louise placed a generous helping of confectionery on the grass. 'I int stoppin' 'e,' she said righteously as Nye fell to his knees beside it. He snatched a bar and stuffed it into his mouth with groaning pleasure. Two others followed in the same fashion. Having satisfied his immediate hunger, he grabbed the whisky before the concession was removed. He took off the cap and swigged the equivalent of a wine-glassful. Nye revelled in the way the spirit hit his guts and went coursing along his arteries.

The consumption of such a large volume of alcohol catapulted him into instant drunkenness. He giggled and held out the bottle to the woman who only moments before had been his archenemy. He addressed her as if they had been fellow travellers sharing the same dossing culture for years.

'Have a drink.'

''Tis poison.'

'Oh no, no, it's not poison. I wouldn't drink it if it was poison. Maltella Highlandii—edible. You should have some, it puts blood in an anaemic soul.' He drank again, then remembered what it was he had offered in return for the goods and leant forward to make his confession.

Nye had meant to talk about fox hunting, but he was so drunk the subject slithered beyond his mental grasp. Even the reason for his going hunting in the first place eluded him. He supposed there had been a reason for it, although he was damned if he could remember. 'The unspeakable in pursuit of the uneatable,' he managed to slur. 'That's what he said, didn't he, you know what's his name, you know?'

'Oscar Wilde,' Louise supplied promptly.

'That's the man...fine man...fine brain. He's right, there's not much point hunting something you don't eat.'

'People don't eat foxes, do 'em?'

'Quite right...quite right...people don't eat foxes.'

'So 'tis a waste then, ain't it?' ran his abductor's logic.

'Absolutely...a waste.' Nye slipped away into a nodding reverie of agreement from which he was jolted unexpectedly by the memory of his wife. 'Matilda...Matilda Amelia Wentworth.' Chin on chest, he accompanied her name with a maudlin hiccup. 'Matilda Amelia Wentworth Went-with-the-job...' he giggled. 'It's true, you know, she went with the job. Sir George, Sir George Wentworth, Master of the Hounds, whipped me in and brought me to heel with the promise of a place on the board, then led me to cover his favourite bitch. Hah!'

Nye fell to silence for a while, staring into the fire, contemplating the memory of himself dressed in a black evening suit, counting himself amongst the gentry. 'Illusion,' he confessed, 'there wasn't anything solid about any of it, not like this.' His foot thumped the ground: 'This is solid, this is the only reality, the earth under our feet. You see...you see...' He stumbled after words, as if chasing bubbles. 'Sir George knew she wasn't top-drawer when it came to the county marriage stakes, had to offer a job on the board, bride price you see. Everybody knew, except for her.' He swallowed more whisky causing another explosion of peppered peat. 'Love,' he ejected the preposterous notion from his mouth, 'there was no love in any of it. Oh yes, she loved me all right, worshipped the proverbial ground and all I ever did was to stick pins in her. If you stick pins in a balloon it usually goes off pop, but my wife just refused to go off pop. I was lured, of course, lured by a fortune and walked straight into the trap. Snap! A man can get very angry with himself in those circumstances. So, I put her in the trap too. Her cage was love for a man who didn't love her, didn't even like her. Do you know something, shall I tell you, you fucking Mother Confessor...? I took a great deal of pleasure in poking my fingers through the bars...but she never learned. Peck, peck, peck, fooled every time. Peck, peck at every scrap of praise. She never saw me sneering. I'd feed insults and she'd gobble them up thinking they were compliments. Trapped, both of us, me by ambition and she because she wanted a husband at any price. I don't suppose I've been a very nice man really. I expect she's found out about Suzanne, that's why they haven't sent anybody to look for me. My best bet is to sit here and wait for the Fox Man...'

The huminals had become interested again and returned to the fireside with their relatives and children in order to witness Nye's confession. Their strange disfigurements were becoming increasingly apparent with ears and tails and paws displaying irrepressible evidence of an emergent species.

'You see,' he addressed them, 'I was looking for a place at the top of the tree, it's what drives us men, the thought of a place at the top. Oh yes, I have to admit that in climbing there a man might trample on other men, but that's nature for you. You'll understand how it is with us, being partly human yourselves. Hunting...' He took up the subject that had been abandoned by his wandering attention. 'That's why a man goes hunting; it confirms his position at the top of the animal tree. King of all the animals. It's simple.' Nye brought the speech for his own defence to a close, noticing how the jury had shuffled with their seats into a circle.

They conferred amongst themselves for a while then came to the collective conclusion that they disagreed with him, that his views were offensive to them and insufficient to vindicate him. He caught sight of Suzanne Blinney among them, posed like Cleopatra on a pallet of straw, her little pointed chin resting lightly on a paw. The pale, grey silk gown she had worn to the hunt ball was hanging from her in shreds that intermingled with a reddish fur coat. It was either a metamorphosis or a revelation taking place. The dress fabric suppurated as if composed of decaying cells pushed aside by the emergent beast. He searched her form for a feature to identify the woman he used to know. He sought out her manicured fingernails only to find claws tapping impatiently on a disused oil drum. She was making an appraisal of him. Although there was no expression of recognition in her green animal eyes there was a waiting patience in her posture which condemned him.

Clearly she had established a queenly presence amongst the huminals who deferred to her superior opinion. The babble of their voices rose as if in final summary, at which point she left her pallet and they parted to let her pass. Without a backward glance she trotted off into the dark, her fox brush waving from the place where human buttocks should rightly be. As she left, she released a contact call that wow-wowed ahead of her. Unable to see her any more, Nye followed, guided by the scent of urine which she sprinkled lavishly on the ground. Soon he found himself trotting easily over the tussocks of grass and thistle, his muzzle close to the ground. The sky had become a dome across which time passed rapidly, days congealing into seconds; the crescent moon whooshed perilously close, then re-presented itself as a bright orb in a different aspect of the heavens.

When the world stilled again Suzanne and the huminals had returned to the numinous substance from which they had been created. There was only Nye left, weak and drunk on a tractor seat, the fire and the sound of his mad abductor sighing periodically. He was dwelling on the past when a memory came careering out of his childhood. 'Somebody gave me a jigsaw puzzle one Christmas. I must have been about ten I suppose. It was a huge picture. *The Ascent of Man*. That was it, the ascent of man from ape to astronaut. It took the whole of Christmas to finish it but I was left with two pieces. One had the lower jaw of the ape, the other the lower jaw of the spaceman and each...this is the clever bit,' Nye giggled, 'each was supposed to fit into the face of the other one.'

'That were because 'twere all about evolution, see.'

'Thanks for that, pea-brain, but I had noticed.'

''Tis all there in the book.'

'The jaw of an ape in an astronaut and vice...vice...' Nye's available vocabulary was slithering out of reach of his tongue again.

'Vice versa, I expect you meant,' supplied Louise.

'Do you know something, pea-brain...I could fit the jaw of modern man in the ape's face, no problem, but I just couldn't fit the lower jaw of the ape in the face of the spaceman.'

"Twas supposed to fit there, 'tis where we do come from, apes.'

'I know, but I couldn't do it, it seemed like mutilating modern man.'

'So what did thee do?'

'I made a template of the piece on some card and coloured in the astronaut's jaw.'

'Did that work all right for 'e?'

'Not really—it didn't fit and the colour didn't match.'

'So thee never finished thik jigsaw.'

'No,' agreed Nye, growing maudlin over the memory, 'never finished because I threw away the proper solution, but I could never throw away the conundrum. Never threw away the conundrum,' he repeated drunkenly and toppled from his tractor seat to lie on the grass, comatose.

At dawn a barn owl returned along its silent flight path to roost on a branch above Terence's head. As its unblinking presence forbade any disturbance of its roosting habits, he continued to dictate his field notes in the barest whisper.

'Daisy and the Matriarch are asleep under a holly bush. The Matriarch has her paws around Daisy's neck as if she had leapt on her in play then fallen asleep. I would estimate that she's within a fortnight of giving birth. Certainly tension accompanies the two vixens' comings and goings. Daisy spent a great deal of time grooming her pregnant comrade this evening. She received a little complementary grooming in return which sent her into ecstatic quivering with her eyes closed and her ears folded back. Paintbrush's increasing presence and his creation of several caches of food confirms that he has fathered the Matriarch's cubs and that the birth is imminent. If Pansy was dainty and querulous, the Matriarch is arrogant and disdainful. As she stalks her territory with her characteristic scowl, I am inclined to think of her as more feline than vulpine. She frequently barges and nudges poor, compliant Daisy into submission or chucks her belligerently under the chin to elicit grooming. I have great hopes for the survival of the cubs of this tough and assertive new subject. The vixens have hunted, played, groomed and now they sleep. It's unlikely they'll wake again before dusk. Time for me to pack up and be off.'

Terence took a look at the barn owl through his field glasses: the creature stared back with round-eyed patience at the human intruder. 'All right, I'm going,' he whispered humorously. He got to his feet and stretched with a feeling of satisfaction and fulfilment. The long frozen hours of observation had passed in what seemed to have been minutes. He quietly packed away his equipment to avoid disturbing the vixens, although they seemed to tolerate his presence in the wood, unlike the owl who stood sentry to his departure from it. He followed a furrowed footpath, scooped by his nightly tramping.

Halfway down Long Coombe his attention was caught by a small brown-coated figure walking rapidly towards Harmers Farm. He imagined Pansy's transmitter pinned amongst all the keepsakes that vied for space amongst the bare threads of Louise's coat. She soon disappeared behind a tangle of woody shrubs by the entrance to the deserted farmyard. She remained there, perfectly camouflaged, whilst a milk float approached from the direction of the village. Terence was about to witness a little petty thieving and focussed his glasses on the proceedings. If Louise was unaware of his surveillance, then the milkman was equally ignorant of her astute eye on the back of his float. She peeped from the bush briefly then withdrew.

There was something in her stance which reminded him of Old Rogue's outstretched neck as he watched Peter Deeks scraping his supper plate onto the compost heap. As soon as his back was turned, Old Rogue lost no time in helping himself. The milkman reversed into the yard in order to turn, placing the float precisely in front of the bush where Louise hid with her hand raised in readiness like a tentative paw. One hand darted out to nick a pint of milk, the other claimed a pack of fruit yogurts. The booty disappeared into her pockets, leaving the milkman none the wiser. 'So, you're a thief, Robin Redbreast, a naughty little thief.'

The Fox Man raised his field glasses again and unashamedly tracked her along the green lane. What he saw as he focussed on her scuttling retreat wiped the grin from his face and turned his mouth dry. There was a shotgun slung across her shoulder and around her hips; dwarfing and weighing her down, was a belt of ammunition. He had always taken her pert condemnation of violence and love of nature for granted. Having adapted to her quaint incorrigibility, he hadn't perceived that it hid a devilish fury until the day Pansy died. If that fury was provoked and sighted along a gun barrel then tragedy would ensue. Concern for public safety demanded that he report her to the police. The trouble was, in addition to possessing a gun without a licence, she would be charged with theft of a firearm. The thought of such a free spirit locked behind bars, even for a short period pending psychiatric reports, was intolerable to him.

Deciding to take the risk on his own shoulders by negotiating for the surrender of the gun, he felt in his pockets for something with which to barter. There were a few sweet biscuits left over from the night's supply and some cigarettes. In addition, he would put one of his spare transmitters and his wristwatch on the negotiating table. As soon as Louise agreed to exchange the gun he would hand it in at the nearest police station as lost property and hopefully nothing more would be said about it.

Still rehearsing the opening gambit, he approached cautiously and hid behind the hedge in order to take stock of the situation. He focussed his glasses on the old caravan listing on its brick piers, and then on a brass standpipe that had collapsed onto a piece of rotten wood. In a patch of muddy red earth, created by the relentless trickle of water from the leaking tap, lay a bedraggled man. His cheek was pressed flat to the ground; one hand clutched an empty whisky bottle, the top of which rested within an inch of his parted lips. He was curled like an infant that had fallen asleep on its feeding bottle. Over his cadaverous, ashen face crept a layer of stubble and filth. He lay so still in a pool of vomit that Terence assumed him dead, having perhaps choked himself. It was the most pitiable portrait of degradation he had ever seen. Louise sat rocking back and forth on an upturned milk crate, her agitation concentrated in bright flushes on her cheekbones, as florid as two red poppies.

Like a spring uncoiled, she jumped to her feet and

rushed to the side of the prone man. She placed the carton of milk by his head as if he would rise from the dead to drink it. When he didn't stir, she knelt beside him, ritually wringing her hands until some other matter sent her anxiously pacing. The evident guilt and anxiety revealed by this frenetic toing and froing set Terence's heart thumping. It was one thing to focus his field glasses on a corpse, another to witness the abhorrent spectacle of Louise shovelling earth over it in order to bury her guilt. A sweating panic broke out in beads of perspiration and dripped from his temples. His whole body was tensed ready for flight, yet he felt so transfixed by the horror of the scene he became incapable of a decision.

The so-called corpse stirred, bringing tears of relief to Terence's eyes. The man's revival summoned Louise to his side again, not to help him to his feet but to prod at him experimentally with the gun barrel. Although he was in obvious pain and discomfort, the man managed to raise his head from the ground a little, then sank back closing his eyes as if he just wished to be left alone to die in peace. Louise looked up suspiciously as if sensing the presence of somebody else. Terence remained as still as he possibly could, conscious that anything could trigger the paranoia that presided over her present state of mind. Her eyes darted hither and thither along the hedgerow before turning her attention to the man by the standpipe who had now rolled onto his side. This time she prodded him in his back and the poor emaciated fellow didn't even bother raising his head. The hand that had been grasping the whisky bottle waved feebly to fend off further blows. The action produced an involuntary movement in his leg giving the appearance of a wounded horse unable to rise. Terence gawped in horrid fascination unable to fathom nor take his eyes off the absurd spectacle.

As to the nature of the relationship between this ragged pair he couldn't even begin to speculate. After a while Louise returned to sit on the milk crate where her tuts and sighs were audible enough to be heard across the field. With hunched shoulders, she grumbled at the circle of grey ash where her fire had been, accompanying her inexplicable monologue with gestures that suggested she was snatching at ghosts. Whatever aggravated her surely floated in the thin air, invisible to all eyes bar her own psyche. The odd behaviour disappeared abruptly, at which point she dipped into her pocket for a bar of chocolate and took to nibbling at it. Terence shook his head in disbelief: how she could even think about food whilst her friend lay there like that was beyond him, she who valued anything that lived more than her own life. Her brief breakfast over, she looked up and stared suspiciously at the hedge as if sensing his presence.

What occurred next forced him to jettison his original plan entirely and flee. Quite what it was that startled the fox some thirty metres away he had no idea. A sudden alarm call ricocheted through the early morning air. Louise got to her feet, threw back her head and answered. Wow, wow, wow came from her parted lips like the ululation of departed souls. She could not possibly have seen him hidden by the thickly woven hawthorn yet she stared straight at him with a cool, animal authority more vulpine than human. Not only had she learned the language of the creatures she loved, she had become one of them. It was not a woman he focussed his glasses upon but a vixen with a shotgun in her hands. Discarding any claim to bravery, the Fox Man fled across the field with one clear answer to something that had puzzled him about the identity of the man who lay prone by the standpipe.

Something in the hedgerow stirred and a dew-heavy spider's web quivered. Two brown eyes studied its intricate weft, stretched over a hawthorn loom, then settled on a hazel twig with a shrivelled nut that had hung on tenaciously through the winter. The strong bright morning sun had already mopped up pockets of resistant frost at the base of the drystone wall that tumbled down the length of Long Coombe. From pasture land to the east came the tenuous bleating of a lamb answered reassuringly by a ewe. Something close to the hedge issued a whining complaint and was suppressed by a sharply-hissed order. The dog stood to attention, its perky Alsatian ears and black button nose innocently at odds with its potential aggression. Ordered to sit, it fidgeted under the restraint of discipline, its keenness to be up and doing rippling from its shoulders to its haunches. The Fox Man kept an eye on the restless shifting of its huge paws in the mud which disconcertingly expressed his own unease.

Everything foreshadowed risk and catastrophe. Like the shrivelled nut trembling on the twig, the vulnerable bleating of the lamb, it all seemed to be clinging to chance. He lowered his bearded chin onto his chest and regarded the scene from beneath his bushy brow, a tall and glowering posture which hid the anxieties of a gentle man. His trepidations were not helped by the convulsive swallowing of a police marksman. With neck-craning concentration, he sighted his whole body along the length of a rifle, a posture reminiscent of an eager lurcher. Impatience rose again in the throat of the Alsatian and a quick smack on the nose sent it to the ground where it remained, chin on paws, with disgruntled exhalations of breath.

Louise's social worker clasped a plastic carrier bag with both hands in the way grannies clasp their knitting, although she was only in her thirties. She had brought crisps, biscuits, chocolate and cigarettes to the scene. Her strategy was as distinct from that of the police as an anthropologist, come to parley on native terms, compared to that of an imperialist who had come to conquer territory. It was a difference confirmed by the way she regarded the marksman through owl-eyed specs. She and the Fox Man stood together, natural allies, on one side of the gap in the hedge whilst the dog handler and marksman stood on the other. Both sides were co-ordinated by a senior uniformed officer who held a megaphone like a bugler about to sound reveille. A police car with a fourth officer was parked out of sight at the end of the green lane.

The Fox Man and the social worker had pleaded for a low-profile operation. It had taken even longer to persuade the police to allow them both to approach Louise and negotiate for the release of her hostage. Five people and a dog had been waiting for thirty minutes, their nerves tethered by professional training.

Richard Nye had managed to seat himself at last and was now propped against the plank of wood which in turn propped up the standpipe. His head lolled, sadly comical, from a hole in a colourful brocade tablecloth. From time to time he opened his eyes and made an effort to focus. He had vomited disgracefully and not bothered cleaning himself. Louise's social worker monitored the situation through the Fox Man's field glasses whispering her observations. 'He's very hung-over...he's obviously eaten something in the last four days, but I doubt he would have had more than chocolate, and not much of that—she doesn't share easily...'

She did not convey her disquiet over the cool, dissociated set of her client's eyes. That cold schizophrenic stare bored through immediate reality into an alien world to which nobody else had access. It was a domain peopled by devils and demons that constantly taunted and threatened her.

'She doesn't take her drugs I'm afraid. The hallucinations, visual and auditory, come and go. She's very dissociated at the moment, but her mood can easily swing to extreme anxiety. She can be very unpredictable under pressure but I don't believe that Richard Nye is in any immediate danger, other than from an accident...she's far more likely to turn the gun on herself than him. I think we should be patient and wait for her to calm down before approaching.'

As if by way of demonstration, Louise leapt suddenly to her feet, raised two tiny fists and began to shake them at the scudding clouds. 'Cunt, cunt, cunt!' she chanted.

The senior police officer, taking the maniacal outburst to prelude an attack on the hostage, raised the megaphone to his lips. The social worker's arm shot out in order to restrain him from any intervention that might increase her client's anxiety. The dog whimpered. Louise swung round and began to prod thin air with the gun barrel.

'Louise!' boomed the megaphone without restraint. Nye's expression of helplessness turned to radiant relief.

The social worker stretched out her arm again in warning. 'Wait! You'll only make her worse.' The police dog, misinterpreting the signal, leapt eagerly forward through the gap in the hedge, dragging its startled handler behind it. He stumbled ignominiously at the end of the dog's lead into the field where his foot caught under an old ploughshare. Louise stared in abject terror at what appeared to her to be a large grey wolf bearing down upon a fallen man. She raised the gun to take aim and a second later turned the barrel on herself. She opened her mouth and placed the end inside.

Nye, weak and desperately hung-over did his best to stand, but only succeeded in landing on all fours. Hampered by the poncho, he crawled forward with his arm waving at Louise poised as if to swallow the gun. 'You cretin!' He saw her finger twitching spasmodically on the trigger and the last four days of his brutal hounding came back, not in the form of pain and discomfort, but as a strange kind of revelation. All he could think of was a little wizened woman stooping by the hedgerow for her firewood, pointing to where a circle of edible fungi grew on the site of an old bonfire, who chattered over the names of wild plants and their legends. 'You can't blow it all to smithereens, pea-brain. It's the end of the run, you've won, it's over.'

The dog, by now utterly confused by the ambiguity of the situation, was, by turns, leaping forward at the end of its leash then pouncing on its handler seeming to have lost all control of itself. Louise went rigid with fear. Nye swayed giddily on all fours, his only thought was that matters must not be allowed to end this way. He crawled level with Louise, raised his hand to the belt of ammunition and used it to steady himself whilst getting to his feet. He took hold of her skinny shoulders as if to rattle some common sense into her. 'Listen to me, you shit brain, you can't do it,' he shouted, now more passionately devoted to saving her life than he had ever been to killing her.

'Louise!' boomed the megaphone from the other side of the hedge and shortly after a gunshot rang out. Louise and Richard Nye fell together. The dog handler, having succeeded in getting to his feet, lifted the dog by the scruff of the neck and shook it until he felt it submit. The senior police officer strode across the field still clutching his megaphone, followed shortly by the marksman still sighting his rifle. The danger was over. Three police officers and their dog, now as compliant as a lamb, formed a semicircle around the fallen figures. They stood respectfully to one side when the social worker arrived. She fell to her knees by the side of her dead client, still clutching her bag of goodies like a gift brought too late.

Terence was the last to arrive. Nye could taste the warm metallic flavour of blood and knew that he was dying; he could see the Fox Man coming and raised his hand in a vague gesture of greeting. 'So you've come at last,' he tried to say, but heard only bubbles of sound like his own breath rising to the surface of water. He looked into the kindly, generous brown eyes and would liked to have lived long enough to tell the Fox Man about the chase. He looked at Louise who lay dead beside him and paid his last respects with a consoling pat on her shoulder, which, in his weakening state, was no more than a flutter of movement.

At the moment of death, that demonic disease seemed to have leapt out of her, leaving her still and silent, a little porcelain figurine. Insane, ugly, filthy she might have been in life, now at the end of the run Nye saw her as a human being, the first he had ever held any respect for, and recognised in her love of the fox a passionate embrace of life itself. His strength was ebbing and he barely had enough to turn his head.

The Fox Man followed the dying man's gaze upward where something was taking place in the huge dome of the sky. A buzzard hovered there, its huge wings taking the shape of thermals. The bird dived suddenly, falling from the bright blue summit down upon its prey, a true hunter. Nye closed his eyes and, with his last breath, clasped his hand around something. It was the memory of a small piece of jigsaw puzzle.

—END—

St. Julians

1/12/05

# THE EPIC VOYAGE OF THE
## *SEVEN LITTLE SISTERS*

THIS edition, issued in 1957, is for members of The Companion Book Club, 8 Long Acre, London, W.C.2, from which address particulars of membership may be obtained. The book is published by arrangement with the original publishers, Hutchinson & Co. Ltd.

*"A blessed companion is a book"*—JERROLD

# THE EPIC VOYAGE
## OF THE
## *SEVEN LITTLE SISTERS*

A 6,700-MILE VOYAGE
ALONE ACROSS THE PACIFIC

*

# WILLIAM WILLIS

THE COMPANION BOOK CLUB
LONDON

*Made and printed in Great Britain
for The Companion Book Club (Odhams Press Ltd.)
by Odhams (Watford) Limited
Watford, Herts
S.557.ZSA*

## TOILERS OF THE SEA

The stars on countless thrones are keeping
    Eternal court in silent night,
While deep below where seas are sleeping
    The sailors praise the august sight.

The stars in endless drifts are bringing
    Their caravans thru time and space,
While deep below where winds are singing
    The sailors watch with lifted face.

The tempest smites with crashing thunder,
    The night is black with flame and wind—
On seas aroused to slay and plunder
    The sailors to their vessels cling.

The sun her light is skyward sending,
    Flooding the spheres with golden day,
While deep in depths, dark and unending,
    The dead drift silently away.

# ACKNOWLEDGMENTS OF ASSISTANCE

In addition to those mentioned in the text of this book, I desire to express my gratitude to the following: D. W. Onan and Sons, Inc., Minneapolis, Minn.; The National Company, Inc. (Radio), Malden, Mass.; Charles Ulmer, Inc., Sailmakers, City Island, N.Y.; Columbian Rope Company, Auburn, N.Y.; San Mateo Water Company of Lima, Peru; Establecimiento Molinero "Los Andes S.A.", Lima, Peru; Goodyear Rubber Company of Lima, Peru; Sterling Drug Company of Lima, Peru.

National Maritime Union of America, New York, N.Y.; American Radio Association, New York, N.Y.; Union of American Ship Radio Operators; The American Radio Relay League, West Hartford, Conn.; U.S. Navy Hydrographic Office, Division of Maritime Security, Washington, D.C.; U.S. Navy Provisions Supply Office, Washington, D.C.

Vice-Admiral Roque Saldias, Sr , Minister of the Navy Peru; Admiral Guillermo Tirado, Chief of Staff, Peruvian Navy; Commandante Alejandro Martinez, Jefe del Arsenal Naval, Peru; Captain Abraham Woll Davila, Peruvian Navy; Captain Mario Rivadeneira Bedoya, Peruvian Navy; Captain Roque Saldias, Jr., Peruvian Navy; all the officers and men of the Peruvian Navy; Captain A. Wriedt, Senior Captain, Peruvian Merchant Marine.

Congressman Sidney R. Yates, Washington, D.C.; P. C. Hutton, U.S. Consul General, Guayaquil, Ecuador; Roy Kerr, Guayaquil, Ecuador—Standard Fruit Company of New Orleans; Victor J. Dolezal, Guayaquil, Ecuador.

Compania Ecuatoriana de Balsa (C.E.B ), Guayaquil, Ecuador, site on which my raft was built; Jacques Kohn and Jean Kohn, sons of the owner, Henri Kohn; Gonzala Guevara, manager of the balsa mill; A. Puga, consulting engineer; A. Castano, plant engineer; office staff and men of the C.E.B.

Hotel Bolivar of Lima, Peru; Customs of the Port of Callao, Peru.

# CONTENTS

7

# THE PHOTOGRAPHS

8

*All photographs property of William Willis
except as otherwise credited in captions*

## CHARTS AND SKETCHES

THE ADVENTURERS CLUB

HONORARY LIFE MEMBERSHIP

AWARDED TO

WILLIAM WILLIS

IN RECOGNITION OF HIS REMARKABLE
6700-MILE TRIP ON THE RAFT "SEVEN
LITTLE SISTERS," FROM THE RUGGED
SHORES OF PERU TO THE SUN-BAKED
SANDS OF SAMOA, ONE MAN AGAINST
THE SEA. WE HAIL THIS EPIC DRIFT
AS THE GREATEST SOLO JOURNEY
SINCE LINDBERGH'S OCEAN FLIGHT.

NEW YORK CITY · OCTOBER 28, 1954

THE ADVENTURERS CLUB OF NEW YORK

# ★ I ★

## VOYAGE OF THE SPIRIT

I AM engulfed by the crashing of the seas as the raft plunges through the night. I look at the compass—west-by-north—but can hardly make it out because the light from the lantern is dim. The lantern stands inside an old apple box as protection against the wind; the box is tied to the bamboo deck.

I am sitting beside the lashed wheel, my eyes staring into the darkness. I watch the big mainsail driving the raft through the night. It looks like a wind-plough or like a high-arched gateway to the Pacific. Except for a cat and a parrot I am alone. . . . I am one month out from Callao.

The seas rise up beside me one after the other. Some smash into the ends of the logs and bury the rudder in foam. Now and then a high sea almost leaps on board. For a while I listen to the wind in the rigging, wondering if it is blowing up more. I go forward. The ropes stand as tight as iron bars. I slack a little on the sheet. We are on the starboard tack. Everything looks shipshape, and I work my way back aft again, never letting go with one hand until I have a firm hold on something with the other, for the raft is rolling, pitching and sliding—moving incessantly. I have no life-lines stretched across the deck; they would be in the way; it's speed above all that counts in working the raft single-handed. I have only one line running from the right leg of the mainmast to the right afterstay—that's for a last-ditch hang-on. I generally keep well inside it, towards the middle of the raft.

I sit down again by the wheel and watch the course. The few inches I slacked on the sheet bring her up more and make a better course. I have a hard time keeping my eyes open. I'm worn out but long past thinking about it. Since leaving Callao I have been getting about two or three hours sleep a day. I sleep in catnaps—ten to fifteen minutes at the time, whenever there is a chance.

How the raft is driving through! I watch the foam from the bow drifting back. Then my eyes go to the sail standing steady and solid, like a wall. It's a well-cut sail and a joy to look at, day or night.

To my left, in the south, the Southern Cross lies low above the horizon, like a blazing lance-head tipped towards the west—towards my course; behind it, in mountain-high masses reaching to the zenith of the sky, stand galaxies of stars in all degrees of brilliance. Almost ahead of the raft, a point or two to the right, hangs a planet, burning a soft, yellow light. It is the brightest light in the sky and shining in front of me like a lantern. Every night I think so and watch for it to come out of the dusk. I often talk to it. To my right, almost due north, where the night seems blackest, I can see the first three stars of the handle of the Big Dipper. The other stars of the big northern constellation are below the horizon, for I am over four degrees south of the equator. I am about fifteen hundred miles out from Callao.

A big sea has sneaked up behind me and stands house-high above the stern, ready to smash down. I leap up and grasp the wheel. But my raft, the *Seven Little Sisters*, is no longer there to be buried by the hundred-ton avalanche—it has lifted its skirts high and got away in the last split second, sailing above the roaring, snarling foam, letting it thunder and rage and rush among the logs, racing forward towards the bow to spout up in geysers through the split-bamboo deck.

12

I am always conscious of the sounds below me, of the seas attacking the logs with roar and fury, hitting hard, solid blows like sledges. Day and night the roar goes on but at night becomes an endless symphony of disaster. One wonders how the lashings can hold. How can ropes stand up under such strain, hour after hour, day after day, with seas coming up and smashing down in endless procession?

But my logs stay bound together. Perhaps they know they have far to go. Occasionally, when the weather permits, I lift up a section of the bamboo deck and check the lashings. None has given a fraction—they are holding like steel cables. The raft acts like one solid mass and rides the seas like a gull.

Far to go—far to go! But why? Why have I built this raft and why am I sailing it deeper and deeper into the Pacific where ships have seldom sailed?

This is not a stunt—not merely an adventure. And I did not want to prove any scientific theory, or discover and set up my new course of any kind for others to follow. To me, this voyage was something much more—it was a pilgrimage to the shrine of my philosophy. Call it an adventure of the spirit. On this voyage I wanted to prove —had to prove to myself—that I had followed the right start throughout my life. It sounds like strange talk, a pilgrimage on a raft. . . . . But so it was!

I was born with a strong faith in Nature and a conviction that by living a vigorous, natural life, in accordance with what I considered Nature's laws, I could get still closer to her and so partake of her strength. This to me was the path to happiness; I had followed it since I was a child, and the long years had made me feel that I had done right. And now, while I was still in the full strength of body and mind, I wanted to put myself to the great test, the test to which each man must put himself some time. I would test myself in endless labour and sleeplessness, on primitive, scanty food, in exposure to the elements that I loved, in the terrors of loneliness and, like a soldier in battle, living under continual threat of death. And this thought also inspired me· I would perhaps contribute some knowledge about survival at sea.

My nature had always driven me to the most vigorous existence and I had been well trained since childhood for what I could expect on a raft voyage. I had stood on all the sweat-drenched frontiers of America, from Alaska to Mexico and beyond, from California to the Atlantic seaboard—a toiler, stripped to the loins, wielding shovel or axe, loading a thousand ships, cutting the giant forests of the Northwest, harvesting endless wheat fields from Kansas to the Dakotas, and building derricks when Texas first went wild with oil. Many times I had crossed the continent, labouring. . . . *By the sweat of your brow* . . . it is written. It was written on my soul.

The big planet ahead of my raft has sunk into the haze of the horizon. The Southern Cross has long disappeared. The dampness of the night grips to the bone. The pounding of the seas on the logs is a rude lullaby. The darkness looks cold and distant and the fresh brilliance of the stars has gone. I look at the compass and then bring the wheel over a spoke, watch for a while how she steers, and put the lashings on again. Then I sit down once more.

Dreaming my dream. Sixty-one years old—the calendar tells me. I wipe the spray from my face and smile. Sixty-one years old . . . I know Nature, my big partner, has not let me down. I feel she never will. The years have been kind. Since I was fifteen I have stood shoulder to shoulder with the world's toughest men, the world's toughest breeds, on land and on sea, and up to this minute I have been able to hold my own.

14

I have followed the path I chose. Often in the midst of writing and drawing and dreaming, when not engaged in physical labour, I have feared that I might deteriorate physically and especially spiritually, in such a life of ease, and so would be cut off from that deep communion with Nature which mean happiness. Whenever this fear gripped me I would get up and once again go among the toilers. . . .

I can tell by the smash of the seas against the logs that the wind has shifted. The whole feel of the raft is different, her rolling and pitching and sliding follows a different rhythm. I bend over and peer at the compass—almost west-northwest. The wind has hauled more to the south—it occasionally does before dawn. I pull my jacket closer around me. The seas are pounding the raft fiercely, like a wrecking crew working beneath the deck. Meekie, my slim black cat, opens her eyes, gets up and stretches, looks at me seriously, and then curls up again on my old grey sweater.

Teddy, my wife, had knitted that sweater for me in 1950. I first wore it on a freighter running to Europe in midwinter. What was Teddy doing now? Waiting, as she had done so often before? She had faith. My mind went back to the time when I first had the idea of building a raft and sailing it across the Pacific. . . .

# A DREAM OF THE SEA

THE plan to build a raft and sail it singlehanded across an ocean first came to me when I was an able seaman on the S.S. *Charleston*, a collier belonging to the Mystic Steamship Line of Boston and running between Norfolk and New York. The year was 1951. I always shipped as able seaman.

We let go the anchor off Brooklyn, and when the collier had swung around to the tide the mate standing on the forecastle-head beside me said: "We'll be here six hours before we can go up the river, Bill. That ought to give you enough time to get to the hospital and back. I hope your wife is getting along all right. Beat it and don't worry about the ship."

I dashed to the forecastle, took a quick shower, and changed clothes while the other sailor on my watch blew the whistle for a launch to come out from the shore. I was out of the launch and on the dock before it was tied up. From the bus I ran to the subway and finally took a taxi to the hospital.

"Mrs. Willis is still on the critical list but go right up," the nurse at the desk said quietly, handing me a special pass, since it was long past regular visiting hours. I did not wait for the elevator but ran up the five flights of stairs to my wife's room. She lay still and white on the narrow, high bed. She had just been through six days in an oxygen tent.

I had wanted to tell her about an idea I had just had on the trip coming up from Norfolk—about a raft I intended to build and sail across the Pacific singlehanded, but I thought better of it seeing how weak she still was. I had to wait for another time. We talked for a little while, and then I had to rush back to my ship to take her up Newtown Creek to Brooklyn where we unloaded.

On that collier on the Norfolk–New York run my decision to build a raft was made. We were sitting in the mess-room one night when the talk drifted to lifeboats and life rafts and emergency rations and what a man had to go through when he was adrift at sea. We talked about what it would be like in another war, when ships would be torpedoed or sunk with the new super-weapons they were perfecting, and the ships' crews, or what was left of them, were adrift again all over the oceans. Some old-timers on the *Charleston* had been through a lot and there was one whom we considered still raft-crazy. This was a term used by seamen to denote a man mentally impaired by his experience while adrift on a raft.

That's how it started, but the original idea was much older, going back to the early days of my childhood when as a tot of four I had stood on the edge of a muddy little pond and tried to put a few pieces of wood together into some sort of raft. I managed it somehow, as kids always manage to do things, and proudly but apprehensively—and no doubt quite shaky—shoved off, standing on the contraption. What a thrill . . . floating! Only a few feet away from the bank but floating! Then the thing came apart and I splashed around to keep from drowning and got a good ducking and later a spanking at home. But a few days later I was back trying again—dreaming a little boy's dream. Many years passed, but the dream remained.

The *Charleston* had a radio telephone through which I could be reached at any time. My wife was improving rapidly. I never would have been on a ship at this time but she insisted on it when I brought her for a thyroid operation to New York from Miami, where we had lived for some time.

"The city will get you, Bill," she said, "running around and not knowing what to do with yourself. I know you couldn't bear coming up here to the hospital every day and looking at me. I'll be all right—I have all my people here to look after me. A thyroid operation is not serious anyhow." She was more concerned about me than herself. "You are so helpless," she said. "Get yourself a ship— that'll take your mind off all this. You've been working too hard at your writing and need some physical exercise." She had been getting along fine till she had that setback due to a cold. After two more trips I thought it was time to tell my wife about my idea.

"You know, Teddy," I began, "I had an idea a few trips ago—I've really had it on and off since I was a kid. I'm going to build a raft and sail it across the Pacific singlehanded."

"A raft—singlehanded? What are you talking about?"

"Yes, I'm going to build a raft and sail it—single-handed—across the Pacific. I'm going to find out how much I really can go through in the way of hardships—I mean living on starvation rations and working around the clock—working day after day without sleep and exposing myself to everything the sea and sky have in the way of bad weather."

"The things you get in your head! . . . ."

"Teddy, you know I've been living along those lines all my life—going the limit in what a man can do. I should be all ready for it. I got you to live the same way, you know that very well—otherwise you wouldn't have made such a quick come-back from your operation."

Teddy stared at me, speechless, and then shook her head. "Bill . . ." she said.

"Yes, Teddy, I'm going to put myself to the test, the big test—take everything that's coming my way on the sea." I was watching her eagerly. "You understand, don't you?"

"I understand, yes, I understand. You have another one of your ideas. You bet I understand. Forget it, Bill— a raft across the Pacific? Forget it! One man! . . . Please don't let me hear anything about it again. You are not going on any raft—not alone and not with me."

A month later, as the *Charleston* was entering Hampton Roads on the way to Norfolk, I was called to the bridge to answer the phone. Teddy was at last ready to go home. I was paid off as soon as we were alongside the dock. I took a plane and flew to New York. Just before Christmas, 1951, we went back to Miami to spend the winter in a warm climate. I had a boat in Miami, a 31-foot, native-built sloop which I had bought in the British West Indies and sailed to Florida three years previously.

The next summer I shipped again, this time on a tanker. We carried crude oil to the Northern refineries from Venezuela and the Texas fields. For two months I sailed the Gulf of Mexico and the Caribbean and then north past Hatteras, through squalls and calms, dodging hurricanes and lying hove-to. And always, in fair weather and foul, I saw the raft I was going to build beside me at sea—watched how she took it, how she laboured and rolled and pitched, how she came up after taking it over green and solid, glistening in the sun and streaming with crystal torrents, how she pushed through the white foam of breaking crests, climbed to the top of long seas like a queen and came down again ready for another dip and struggle. I would build a raft that could take it, And all the time I was talking to my shipmates of lifeboats and life rafts and starvation rations and slow death staring over the gunwale.

19

Labour and hardships and short rations I had known since I was a youngster on a square-rigger. . . . Labour till the flesh of fingers and palms split open and white bones showed through—from pulling on the ropes. Square-rigger days! Beating it around the Horn on the British four-masted bark *Bermuda*. Had I forgotten? High aloft on the topgallant yard-arm, swinging in tremendous arcs through the howling sky, I had struggled, fingers frozen, with sails standing hard like sheet iron, while deep below me the deck swam beneath the raging sea and I wondered whether the ship was under me or I was adrift on a mast in chaos—wondered whether I had somewhere to climb down to when the last sail was furled. Months of such toil I'd had, with forecastle and galley under water, with rations getting lower and lower till maggots were a good part of our grub, and the drinking water going down in the tanks till it was thick enough to pick up with a fork.

I remembered another big square-rigger, the four-masted bark *Henriette* out of Hamburg, lying off the Horn, fighting to get westward. The sails were torn and we were forced south into the Antarctic ice with mutiny and starvation, madness and death on board. Hardships? I thought I could handle myself if ever I got my raft into the sea.

On the *Bermuda* we lay for months in Antafogasta and Mejillones, loading nitrate for Europe, and here I heard from the Chileans of rafts that sailed and drifted up the coast like ships, had done so for centuries.

They came up one after the other—the scattered years on the Old Debbil sea—while standing the lonely look-outs on the forecastle-head of the tanker. Yet I never considered myself a professional seaman. The land had claimed me, too, even more than the sea. One period for almost twenty years and another for nine years I had not been a sailor. But the sea played its big part in my inner life always, seen or not seen, more than the mountains and plains and the dark forests stretching their beauty across my horizon. The sea was written into my soul. Its vast endlessness under the free-sailing clouds, the free-roaming winds had a mystical significance for me—it was my carpet to the infinite. For that was the order given to me when I was set on my path through life—to live in the infinite as much as on the earth. The sea was the stairway on which I could kneel and worship.

I never mentioned the raft again to my wife till the autumn of that year. She had fully recovered by now and we were taking a long vacation in our boat, sailing lazily along the Florida keys, sometimes running across to the Bahamas or to Cuba.

"You still have that raft idea!" she exclaimed. "No, I'll never allow it. One man on a raft! That's ridiculous. The *Kon-Tiki* had six men and in bad weather they had their hands full. You will never get me to agree to that!"

I argued in vain that mine was to be an endurance test—endurance of body and mind, and that only by going alone could I prove anything.

Teddy knew something about the sea, though born and raised in New York City. Until she met me she had never had any contact with a storm except through the windows of her office high up in Radio City.

On this same 31-foot-long sloop in which we now lay snugly at anchor behind the reef near Sombrero Light, while the moon turned the sea into a dream, Teddy had been baptized in salt-water right up to the neck with a hurricane handling the ceremonies. And she had proved herself. She knew something about the sea though she seldom talked about it.

21

In 1948 we had left the West Indies in the hurricane season with neither motor nor radio. We had bad weather from the start, weeks of squalls when hurricanes were trying to make up. Then we got caught, off Yucatan. For three days we lay hove-to, drifting to the dinghy we had thrown overboard for a sea-anchor while the hurricane wore itself out. Then we started to leak. We dumped about two tons of iron to bring her up and pumped and baled, lying in a glassy, windless sea. After two days the S.S. *Bonito*, of the Suwanee Steamship Company of Jacksonville, saw our distress signal and came up. She looked as big as a warehouse lying alongside us. The captain wanted to take us off but I wouldn't abandon my ship and lose it. Then he offered to take Teddy off and bring her to Havana. I climbed back down the pilot's ladder to our boat.

"Teddy, you're getting off—you're going to Havana." Five feet one, weak and in salt-encrusted dungarees, she stood up very straight and faced me. "After five weeks of what I've been through on our boat—abandon it and leave you behind?" she asked quietly. "Not me—I can stick it out if you can. I'm not getting off and you can't make me." Threats didn't help.

During the worst of the hurricane she had insisted on being lashed to me, saying in the matter-of-fact way of an office girl making a long-distance call: "I am not afraid to die, Bill. Don't you worry about me. But I want to be tied to you when the end comes. I would like to go just a minute or two before you—I don't want to be left alone with the sharks."

And then the *Bonito* was gone, heading for Cuba and one of the northern sugar ports. We were alone again on our sinking boat. It was getting dark and the sea was coming up and the glass was falling, as the captain of the *Bonito* had warned us. We were about thirty miles south of Dry Tortugas and out of the shipping lanes. The captain was sending an S O S—that was our only hope.

The hurricane had left us with only one lantern which we used to light our compass. The sidelights had been smashed. We pumped and baled but seas started to come on deck. About two o'clock in the morning I saw the lights of a ship bearing down on us. The sky was heavily overcast. I grasped our lantern and went forward and, hanging on to the forestay, swung it to attract attention and keep from getting run down. But the ship, Gulf bound, kept on her course, her green and red sidelights surprisingly big and clear, staring balefully out of the darkness.

"Get ready to jump, Teddy."

"Okay, Bill, I'm ready—hang on to me. I have all our papers."

She meant our passports and ship's papers which we had in a watertight wrap. We were almost awash. Just when we thought we would be ploughed under, the ship swung off to our starboard. Against the dark sky as it passed about a hundred yards abeam, I could see that it was a man-o'-war. We were saved. The S O S had been picked up by the U.S.A. Navy in Key West and the destroyer escort *Robinson*, one of three ships despatched at once, had found us with her radar. We were towed into Key West.

For a few days Teddy and I walked as if we had made a long trip on a mean horse without getting off, but otherwise we were all right. But to me the significance of the trip was that Teddy had proved herself a full-fledged partner of the Willis team. She had seen the sky crashing down on us with all it had and the depths coming up to take us more than once and she had never complained or weakened. So now, years later, in this

23

matter of building a raft and sailing it off into nowhere she had the right to approve of it or not.

After our vacation trip along the Florida keys, I continued with my writing and drawing. About six months later I shipped on a tanker again. We had a hectic trip, almost getting rammed by a Staten Island ferry leaving New York harbour and, at sea, ran into heavy weather from the start. I almost got killed by gear coming down from the foremast as I was going to the forecastle-head to secure a boom that had been torn loose by mountainous seas. In the same wild night drums of Diesel oil got loose on the boat deck and two sailors broke arms and legs trying to secure them. Coming into Baltimore harbour in a fog with 250,000 barrels of high-octane gas, we missed by inches a supertanker loaded with the same kind of cargo. I was at the wheel at the time and wondered where I would come down if we blew up or if I would just keep right on going through the sky.

When I told Teddy about the narrow escapes on the trip and brought up the subject of the raft again, she said: "Go ahead with your raft—I am tired of trying to keep you from it. As I see, it's a toss-up between the frying-pan and the fire, with the Old Debbil sea all around you no matter what you do. I know you'll go anyway, regardless of me," she said, breaking away from my joyful grasp. "I know you—you would go on a single log. All right—but don't blame me. I don't see how you can make it."

We moved back to New York shortly after this and I spent some time in the big public library on 42nd Street studying charts and maps of the winds and currents that I was likely to meet on a trip across the Pacific.

In the autumn of 1953 I wanted one more ship for a final test of fitness and hardening up. I went to our union hall, picked the S.S. *Kettlecreek*, a Calso tanker sailing out of east coast ports, passed with the doctor, and then took the train to Barber, New Jersey, where the ship lay. A big, young fellow with about a square yard of shoulders stood by the gangway when I came on board. I recognized him as a shipmate of a few years ago and put down my suitcases.

I asked the age-old seaman's question: "How's the ship?"

"She's all right," the young fellow replied and added: "And she is a feeder."

"How about overtime?" I questioned him further.

"You can get it on this wagon—day and night if you can take it."

Day and night I took it. My shipmates, not knowing what I was after, thought I wanted to break the Atlantic record for putting in long hours at hard labour and they shook their heads. After two months I got off.

Physically I was now ready to tackle the raft.

# ★ 3 ★

## PREPARATIONS

It was already late in October, 1953, and the end of the year was the latest I should be in Ecuador, the land of balsa trees, to cut the logs for my raft and start putting it together. And I had no backer yet.

I saw a number of men, the kind of men who back Broadway shows, rich men, men eager for publicity, men in the theatrical business. But I found no one to back a man for a solo voyage on a raft across the Pacific.

One Saturday Teddy and I went to Milford, Connecticut, to spend a week-end with a friend I had not seen for years, Werner Woehlk. "How are you doing?" he asked when we were settled and talking.

I told him about my project and that I was looking for a backer, knowing that financially he would not be interested. He was a manufacturer and very conservative and his mind was on machinery and hard facts. He listened to me and said nothing.

About an hour later he remarked quietly: "I'll back you, Bill—that is, if Teddy allows you to go."

He called Teddy aside and I heard her answer him: "I can't stop him—I've tried it for two years. . . ."

"All right, Bill—I'll back you," he said, joining me again. "On one condition. . . ."

I looked at him.

"On the condition that you come back. I want no money back—no percentage, no account of how you spend it—just come back. When do you want my cheque?"

We shook hands and then squared off for the first toast to my solo trip across the Pacific.

"Come back, Bill . . ." he said, as we boarded the train the next evening to return to New York.

It was Teddy who talked me into planning to take a radio along. I knew nothing about radio or the International code used in transmitting and so enrolled at the Y.M.C.A. Trade School for a course. A full course required many months of hard study and I had hardly any time left. I knew it was almost useless but tried to please Teddy. For two weeks I attended the afternoon classes in code practice; then I had to quit. All my time had to be given to other preparations. There were endless things to take care of and Teddy and I both were so busy we hardly had any time to sleep.

I decided to make the voyage without a radio, that is without a transmitter, but I did intend to take a receiver to get time signals for a check on my chronometer. This was quite a blow to Teddy. "How will I know where you are or if something happened to you?" she asked almost timidly. She never was one to show her emotions but I knew how she felt.

I tried to convince her that a transmitter was not needed. "Teddy, for thousands of years men have crossed oceans without radio. They did so only fifty years ago."

"But we have radio now."

"Listen, if I have to depend on a transmitter to give me courage I have no business going. I am depending on myself. I would like to have one for your sake, for you have to sit here and wait—wait and wait—I know. But you see it can't be done; there just is no time. And rather than take a radio along and not be able to operate it or repair it in case of trouble—no, that would be worse."

During all the hectic weeks while I was getting ready,

27

Teddy was by my side doing as much as I. At night, and often into early morning, we would sit in our apartment near the New York Botanical Garden and lay out plans for the next day.

There were endless details and our apartment was strewn with notes to help us remember. There were cameras. I had bought a 16-mm. movie camera, and since I had never taken movies I went round to a number of people to get information. When I had a few spare moments I took practice pictures in the nearby Zoological Garden. I also bought a camera for still pictures. Then I needed watertight bags and containers, tape, two kerosene stoves, fishing lines and hooks, storm lamps and flashlights —a seemingly ever-mounting number of things.

One night, Teddy brought up a new question: What if disaster struck; what if the raft broke up in a storm somewhere in the emptiness of space, or if the lashings parted under the constant strain, or the logs, weary of the long drift, filled with water beneath me and sank? Even if I had a radio it might not work or there might be no time to operate it; and besides, even if I got a message across, who would ever find me, drifting on a log somewhere beyond the range of planes with the sharks having their fun with me?

Teddy suggested taking a rubber life raft. Being more primitive, I decided to take along a canoe, an Indian-built dugout. That would be my lifeboat. It should be a seagoing canoe of the kind used by Indian fishermen off the coasts of northern South America. I had seen such canoes and knew them to be seaworthy. With a little extra work they could be improved so that they could ride out heavy weather. If there was time I would put a keel on it, raise the sides and deck it over. If not I would fit it out with a bamboo outrigger. It would carry masts and sails, of course.

28

This made Teddy feel better but I had to do a lot of explaining how a 26- to 28-foot canoe could be made safe for the middle of the Pacific and sail perhaps thousands of miles.

I reminded her of the boats used by the Cha-cha fishermen in St. Thomas, Virgin Islands, who use canoes imported from other parts of the West Indies, fit them out with keels, and stay out in very rough weather. We had been around St. Thomas for months when we had our sloop. She also recalled the Indian turtle fishermen we had seen far out at sea off the coast of Venezuela and British Guiana. That was back in 1938 on the little Norwegian freighter *Ingrid* where Teddy and I had first met. Teddy had booked passage in New York for a round-trip cruise through the Caribbean while I, travelling as a mining engineer, was going down to Paramiribo, Dutch Guiana, in an attempt to get into Devil's Island to help an innocent Frenchman escape from the prison. I was successful, and after my return to New York Teddy and I were married.

I had originally set December, 1953, as the deadline for my departure from New York but could not quite manage it. There was just too much to take care of.

I had been to Washington and received some cartons of survival, or disaster, rations from the U.S. Navy to try out on my trip. I had also seen the Ecuadorian Ambassador, Dr. Jose Chiriboga, and he had given me some letters of introduction to important officials in Ecuador.

Back in New York I went to the U.S. Hydrographic office and picked out my charts. I took small-scale charts, just three to cover the vast space from the west coast of South America to Australia. I also had my sextant and compass checked. These were the same instruments that had made the West Indies trip with me and Teddy on the native sloop and brought us through the hurricane.

The compass had a five-inch dial and was magnetic and the sextant, a Plath, had a micrometer scale and was both a beautiful and serviceable instrument. My sails were to be made by a famous sailmaker in City Island, New York. He intended to use Orlon, a light but tough synthetic fabric.

The success of my voyage would depend to a great extent on the rope used for lashing my logs together. I got in touch with a rope manufacturer and made arrangements for the best grade of manila to be sent down to me in Ecuador. For tying the main carrier logs I intended to use 1½-inch rope.

Finally came the day to leave New York—January 6, 1954. It was snowing when we came out of the house and drove the long distance to the Idlewild Airport. The following day, at noon, I stepped off the plane into the scorching heat of Guayaquil, Ecuador, 3,000 miles from New York and about a hundred and twenty miles south of the equator.

# ★ 4 ★

## SEARCH FOR LOGS

THE Ecuadorian planter turned around and pointed to
a spot on the chart he held in his hand, then gestured
through the window of the small, single-motored plane
to the jungle beneath. He said something but I could not
hear above the roar of the engine. He looked at the chart
again and then folded it up, shouting something in the
pilot's ear, who nodded. We were flying at an altitude of
about fifteen hundred feet. Below us and to each side
as far as the eye could see lay the green mass of the
Ecuadorian jungle, stretching away on the left to the
foothills of the Andes and broken underneath us by a
wide, forking river and a maze of waterways dotted with
wooded islands. We were flying south to the plantation of
my companion.

It was now March 2. Almost two months had passed
since I had left New York and though I had covered
thousands of miles of jungle by air, searching for the right
size balsa logs for my raft, I could not find them.

Time was running out. I had to be at sea and in the
Humboldt Current by the end of April in order to make
the voyage before hurricanes began tearing up the western
Pacific.

For two months I had been flying over the Ecuadorian
jungles in small private and commercial planes, sitting
beside Ecuadorian pilots, following rumours and
promises of big balsa trees, through equatorial rains and
squalls and fog drifts and lightning, sometimes of atomic

31

fury. I had had enough narrow escapes for a stunt-flyer, dodging tree-tops and coming down on water-soaked and often flooded landing strips that were hardly visible among rows of banana trees.

I had seen thousands of balsas but few that were more than eighteen or twenty inches in diameter. That was the size the mills wanted. It made the best lumber and also was easiest to handle by the woodsmen who never had more than a single yoke of oxen to drag them to the roads or to the nearest creek. For that reason no trees were left to grow to larger size. I had originally wanted logs three feet in diameter; now I would settle for 2½-foot logs if it were possible to get them.

I had been told that big balsa trees were plentiful in the interior towards the Andes, but there was no way of bringing them out. There was no way of even getting to them except by rivers and creeks which would require a journey of weeks. Besides, unless a tree stood directly on the bank and could be cut and dropped into the river, it could not be moved since there were no oxen in those wild and isolated regions.

At first it was the weather that worked against me—the rainy season was a full four weeks late. "How can you expect to get your logs to the nearest creek to float them to a river?" I was asked. "Impossible—you must wait for the rains. You can do nothing before the rains come."

Finally the rains had come, smashing down in such torrents on the jungles that everything was flooded. I was told a different story now. You could not get oxen into the woods now; they would sink up to their necks. "You have to wait, Don Bill, wait till the water runs off."

"But it keeps on raining," I said, "and may keep on for another two or three months."

There were shrugs of the shoulder, sympathetic faces. "Don Bill, you have to wait." Time means nothing here.

32

The author working on his raft.

The raft floats on the Guayaquil River.

And the rains continued to rattle down on the vast stretches of primeval forest, on the semi-darkness in which the balsa trees fought with other giants for light, reaching up to fantastic heights to pierce the shield of leaves, to catch the light and the air with their two-foot-wide leaves. In three to four years they raced from the earth into the sky, to over 100 feet high if necessary, depending on the height of the surrounding trees. But light and air they must have to live.

"Don Bill, you must have patience." This is what they kept telling me in Ecuador. Wait—while time was ticking off the hours and the days that meant success or failure.

I kept moving about continually, following each trail. I was known to most of the pilots of the small, single-motored planes that crossed the jungles from Guayaquil to different haciendas and settlements. We had become like comrades, had shared many a thrill while almost crashing into giant treetops, into hillsides or steeples when the landscape was blotted out by fog or rain or darkness.

The plane started to bank sharply and come down. The hacienda owner in front of me turned around again and pointed excitedly to the ground. We continued to bank, spiralling down sharply, lying almost on the side. I had found the Ecuadorian pilots to be first-class flyers over their jungles and was accustomed to their breath-taking manoeuvres.

The landing strip was directly beneath us, a narrow stretch of grass on the edge of a field of bananas. We kept on circling, dropping fast. A few natives stood beside the field looking up at us. Down and down till we were among the trees and then bump—bump—bump, ploughing through the water, standing on the landing strip.

My companion had a passion for efficiency: the

manager of the hacienda had been notified by radio and was waiting for us with horses and a guide. A few minutes later we were on our horses and jogging along single file.

After a few miles through bananas and jungle we came to a wide creek, swollen from rains. Without a stop our horses went into the water. We pulled up our legs to the saddle-horns to keep from getting wet while the horses struggled in the racing current. I was worried about the cameras in the knapsack on my back. If I had known this I would have had them in a watertight bag. My horse almost fell over backwards getting up on the other bank, which was steep and slippery.

For two hours we went through jungle and bananas and cocoa trees before we reached the hacienda. We ate our lunch and the horses were brought out again and we went back into the jungle. It was virgin forest with many big trees, some strangely formed, fantastic, like houses in fairyland in their covering of aerial roots. Finally we dismounted.

We walked a short distance through the brush and then stood before a big balsa in a smooth, grey coat. It looked rather small for my purpose and was also crooked and tapered quickly.

"What do you think of it?" my host asked in his nervous, insistent manner. He was married to an American woman and spoke good English. "What do you think of it, Mr. Willis? Shall we cut it?"

There stood the men with their axes and machetes, ready to chop it down—eight men with axes poised. My host had a passion for speed and efficiency.

I had to make a decision. I thought the tree was too small though I had seen nothing larger during my long search. It wouldn't measure two feet at the base with the bark off. I knew that the coast trees had thick bark. I looked up again at the crooked trunk, at the quick taper of it. Originally I had wanted seven trunks for my raft. It would take nine of these or even ten, and they would lie in the water like a mat, sluggish—a dead, wobbly raft. Speed would be out of the question, and speed I would need with the sun cooking the Pacific to dish up the hurricanes. In my mind's eye I could see them making up out there in the far reaches of the ocean.

I had written to my wife only the night before that if my logs got any smaller I'd soon be able to take nothing along but a can of water and myself. "But, Ted, I'm going even if it is in the middle of the hurricane season."

I walked around the tree once more, my eyes still envisioning the Pacific. With trees of this size, I would have to change the rigging and my whole raft design. The men were looking at me, eager to begin. "Cut it," I said.

They went at it, taking turns chopping, and in a few minutes the tree fell.

I was busy with my camera while the men started prying off the bark. The white flesh of the tree began to show. I didn't like the tree—even less now that it was down. The small end did not measure fifteen inches. I walked back to the stump from which the sap ran in streams and noticed that the centre of the trunk was red and mushy-looking. I poked in it and it gave way under my fingers like a sponge. I pulled out chunks of the red spongy mass. A wood chopper stood near me, a veteran of the woods. "What's this?" I asked.

"*Corazón de agua, señor.*" (Water-heart.)

"How far does it go inside?"

He looked carefully at the cut. "Maybe halfway up the trunk, maybe more."

"That will soak up water like a sponge."

"*Si, señor.*"

"And the log will sink, or almost sink?"

"Si, señor."

I stopped them from stripping.

They cut eight more trees and all had water-heart. I found out that the large balsa trees in this whole region were infected with it. The next morning I flew 150 miles back to Guayaquil.

# ★ 5 ★

## SEVEN JUNGLE TREES

TIME was running out. Another eight days had passed and it was March 10. Would I be lucky on this hacienda, would I find my logs today?

We were riding single file through the jungle twilight, dodging vines and ferns and branches, pushing them away and bending low, almost double, to stay in the saddle. Our horses were sweat-drenched, fly-tortured and muddy, stumbling over roots and splashing through pools, skirting windfalls and struggling through swamps. But they kept going, sure-footed and tireless.

The first four hours we had been in the open, trotting briskly on a road, and then had followed a trail towards the far border of the big Swedish-owned Clementina Hacienda. The day had started with a rain that slackened a little while we mounted our horses but then had settled down to a steady, smashing downpour that had only now let up. Nobody wore rain gear on account of the heat, and we were drenched, sitting stiff and hunched and silent on our horses while the wet branches showered raindrops over us.

Light began to show ahead and we came to the banks of a river. For a moment I thought I was in Alaska—seeing the white, foaming mass of water rushing through countless channels against the boulders. White water—like Alaska. Chilled as I was from the long drenching of the rain, it was easy to imagine.

We got off our horses, the three of us—the assistant

37

manager of the Clementina, the Ecuadorian guide, and I
—checked saddles and bridles and cut whips for the
crossing. Then we followed the native who knew the ford
into the stream. We went slowly, picking our way carefully, guiding our horses at an angle to the current to
keep them from being swept off their feet. There
were holes in the river bed dug up by the rushing
water and sometimes our horses sank down to their
bellies.

We followed the other bank upstream, skirting
tremendous thickets of bamboo that reached high and
green into the now sunny sky, bamboo almost a foot thick
at the bottom and giving the wild, river-chained country
a strange, almost prehistoric look.

A few miles upstream we crossed back over the river,
going through the same nip-and-tuck struggle to make
it through the roaring, boulder-strewn waters. Then we
entered the dense jungle again. This time the ground
was broken by ravines and gullies. We continued as far
as we could on horseback and then dismounted, tying
up our horses. Our guide kept ahead a little, occasionally
shouting to us. He had scouted this area a few days before
when the Clementina knew that I was coming.

After about two miles we stood before the first balsa.
I took out my tape and measured. It was about the same
size as the balsas we had cut at Balao on the coast, the
ones that were rotten with *corazón de agua*.

"Do your trees have water-heart around here?" I asked
the manager.

He shook his head. "Never saw it on any of our
trees."

We picked out twelve trees. They were rather small and
not too straight but I had already lost too much time. I
had to build my raft and get into the sea if I wanted to
sail this season. I decided to take them and look no

further. After the Balao trip I had cabled my wife: "Tell the sailmaker to hold back on the sails—may have to change design of raft."

I had even considered building a raft with a double layer of main logs and that way get enough body and carrying power for the rigging which, with only one layer of small logs, would be impossible. But no matter what I would build, my raft would have to be seaworthy, be worthy of a seaman and the sea. I would go on three logs if they were big enough, so long as they were lashed and rigged into something that could sail and stand up to anything that blew. I would build a "hurricane" raft or no raft. I intended to follow no ancient design, evolved and proven by the masters of past centuries, much and profoundly as I admired them, for I had studied them and the way they were handled. I would build a raft that one man could sail and that would not come apart. Such a raft I knew had not yet been built.

"How are you going to get the logs out of here?" I asked.

"With oxen—can't get in here with a tractor," the Swede said. He spoke perfect English as did all the other Swedes on this big, efficient and modernly equipped hacienda which had opened its doors to me and treated me as one of its own.

"And then down the river . . . ?"

"That's the only way out of here," he replied. "There's only one question—the river. Can the logs take it?"

"Not get smashed up, you mean?"

He nodded apprehensively.

I must get started, I must take a chance, I was thinking as I visualized the boulder-strewn, raging river—long miles of it with bends and gorges. "We'll take a chance," I said. "I have to get the logs."

"Okay, then we'll start Monday." He was a quiet man,

39

capable and energetic. "I'll come in with the oxen Monday morning and we'll start cutting."

This was Thursday. We rode back to the hacienda and I sent a radio message to the Standard Fruit Company office in Guayaquil, asking for a plane. They had flown me to the hacienda and been very helpful throughout my search. While I waited for the plane one of the Swedish overseers offered me a thousand dollars, his life's savings, to put into my venture.

Back in Guayaquil I telephoned an American business man who was interested in my expedition and told him that I had found my logs on the Clementina and would start cutting the following Monday. I told him that the trees were rather small but that I had decided to take them.

"Hold off, Bill," he said. "I may have bigger logs for you. Call me at the office later. I'll be here till six; after six, call me at home. And keep checking with your hotel in case I should call you."

I did not go out again that evening.

The next morning my friend flew me to Quevedo in his private plane. With us on the plane was an Ecuadorian who owned a hacienda and a number of banana plantations besides. Quevedo is perhaps the largest balsa region of Ecuador and in the last years had become one of the banana-growing centres of the world. The ground around Quevedo is very rich, the richest in all South America, according to some experts. It is well drained and the climate is perfect for growing bananas—that fantastic plant of the tropics requiring only eight months to grow from a thin slip of a plant a foot high to a stalk with a marketable bunch. Stalks grew to tremendous size here, some requiring two men to carry them.

The Ecuadorian, a swarthy, heavy-set and easy-going man who made yearly trips to the Mayo Clinic for a physical check-up, had recently cleared a large acreage of jungle for bananas. He said that he had left a number of big balsas standing and cut others that were still on the ground and could be got out easily. They were, he said, a full three feet in diameter.

The flight to Quevedo, which lies on the Palanque River on the Guayaquil–Quito highway, required about forty minutes. Three or four commercial airlines with daily schedules connect this important town with the coast.

We had to cross the Pelanque coming from the airstrip. It was a full half-mile wide and swollen from weeks of rain. With a crowd of natives, we crossed the racing current in a motorless iron boat held bow upstream by a line running along an overhead cable and, strange to see, propelled swiftly just by the current and the angle of the rudder.

Quevedo was full of jeeps and banana trucks hauling stalks to the banks of the river. There, fleets of Diesel barges loaded the fruit for the trip down the river to Guayaquil and waiting steamers from Europe and the United States.

We drove about thirty kilometres beyond Quevedo in a jeep, over roads flanked solidly by bananas. The tall plants, bending under the weight of big stalks, were held up by bamboo props.

Finally we took a side road and after a while got out to walk a short distance. There lay the balsas in a pile, rolled to one side in a vast clearing dotted with young banana plants. The logs were dark brown and old. Some were partly burned and all of them had split from lying unprotected in the sun. They seemed to have been cut many months ago. Others lay scattered over the partly cleared jungle, also brown and weatherbeaten and entirely useless. Not a tree had been left standing. Another false alarm. . . .

"Stick around Quevedo for a while, Bill," my friend counselled me. "You see they do have big trees around here, the kind you want for your raft. You waited so long, you can wait another week or two. You can always go back to the Clementina. By that time the river may be down more."

I stayed in Quevedo.

After a few weeks everybody in that thriving and peaceful little river town knew me. "That's Don Bill, looking for logs for a raft to cross the ocean," they would say. The natives were proud that I had come to Quevedo for my logs. I was greeted by the men loading banana barges, by truck drivers bringing in the stalks, and by the children. Even the dogs got to know me and let me pass without a bark. I learned to know the country around Quevedo better than many natives for I followed up every rumour of big balsa trees. In many a lonely ranch house almost hidden in the shade of cocoa trees, I was made welcome, given the best bed to sleep in and the choicest food to eat, and in the morning was provided with guides to scout the forests.

One day a native took me into the woods many miles from Quevedo. He said he knew of some very large balsas. We travelled for hours through an almost impassable jungle, slashing and cutting every foot of the way through bushes, ferns and thorny vines. We waded for miles, climbing over fallen trees lying across dangerous waterways and swamps. Finally, after struggling up a steep slope, we came into a forest of tall trees with hardly any underbush. Only the long, thin vine of the *beiuca* hung down like rope from the great heights of the tree-tops. This is the vine which has been used since ancient times for tying the rafts together for the rivers and the sea.

The forest looked almost like a park. After travelling a short distance we came to a giant balsa. It was the first

42

really big tree I had seen. It was a beauty—smooth, mouse-grey bark, almost bluish in the half-light, standing straight and even all around like a column, with no branches except those near its spreading top. It was well over a hundred feet high and tapered only slightly, measuring a full three feet in diameter a good part of its length. I figured I could cut two logs for my raft out of it.

"Can we get it out of here?" I asked my companion.

"*Si, señor.*"

"Then let's look for the others."

Balsa trees generally grow in groups of three or four within an acre or two; while similar groups may be found four to five hundred yards away. In less than an hour we had found eight perfect trees.

We made our way back over the same difficult trail, got on the road, and caught a banana truck to Quevedo. I looked up the owner of the forest at once, a young Chinese.

He listened to me and then shook his head. "I am sorry, Don Bill. I knew about those trees all the time; there is no way of getting them out. I would gladly give them to you but there is no road or creek near. There is no tractor around Quevedo and oxen couldn't do the job— it's too far and the ground is too bad."

Years ago, big tractors had disappeared from Quevedo because of difficulties involved in getting them repaired.

The man saw my disappointment and added: "To prove to you how anxious I am to help you I will send my men in the morning and start cutting the trees."

I shook my head. Another trail had ended.

Everybody in Quevedo was becoming interested in my expedition and in the big money I offered for three-foot-wide logs; and the rivermen, or balseros, who brought thousands of balsa logs to Quevedo every week from the upper country for reshipment to the mills in Guayaquil, spread the news far and wide.

About a week later I stood before another grey giant standing in the stillness and shade of a high-ceilinged forest. We were near the Hacienda Tierra Nueva on the Guayaquil-Quito highway.

"Is it a *macho* [male tree]?" I asked the Ecuadorian who was with me.

*"Si, señor, es un macho."*

I measured it with my eyes. It was a beautiful tree and I knew I wanted it for the centre log of my raft. I had been told that seven or eight big trees could be found on the hacienda and that they could be got out without too much difficulty.

I walked around it looking up the trunk. I put my hand on the smooth bark; it felt good—cool and strong. "We'll make it, old-timer," I said under my breath, "we'll make it." My eyes saw the wide levels of the Pacific.

The native was busy with a piece of vine measuring the circumference.

"Mark it, *amigo*—it is big enough."

He picked up his machete and cut two deep slashes into the bark.

Then we went on till we had found and marked seven more trees. I wanted an extra one in case one should get damaged or lost on the river. My long search for logs for my raft was at last over. The next morning I signed a contract with a Quevedo man to cut the logs I had marked and to deliver them on the banks of the Palanque in the town of Quevedo within ten days, for the sum of 1,000 sucres (about $55) each.

That same day the contractor sent his *macheteros* into the jungle to cut a road to the trees for his oxen.

A few days later three wood choppers stood with their axes beside the first tree we had marked. A big white

44

cockatoo screamed in the top and then flew away, the white wings shining high above in the sun.

"A bad sign," remarked one of the cutters.

"All signs are good," I said, and took his axe. The steel bit into the soft wood to the hilt and I had to wrench hard to get it out. Then the woodsmen took over, chopping away from two sides.

Soon the tree was cut clean through. It did not fall at once, retaining its balance. The choppers walked away to be in the clear, waiting for a breath of wind high up in the leaves to topple it. Sap was flowing from the cuts.

"There she goes."

There was a slight, barely noticeable movement. At the same moment I thought I heard a groan, strange and heartrending, from the roots of the stricken tree.

Then it began to fall, picking up speed, in a far-reaching arc, breaking smaller trees, with a long-drawn, frightening sound tearing the last fibres that held it to the stump and then crashing to the earth amid a shower of leaves and twigs. It bounced once and lay still.

Seven noble trees had to fall to make a chariot for a dream. It was no wanton dream that inspired me. A tree is sacred to some men. Can I ever forget the years in New York when I walked miles each day amid the canyons to see a tree or two struggling to live in that wilderness; and farther uptown, in Central Park, where I came to know every tree that grew there?

The Seven Little Sisters were hard to get out—full of sap and enormously heavy. Three yoke of oxen failed again and again, lying on their heaving bellies, their legs dangling limp in the loose mud, panting desperately. But up again! Man's will—a chariot for the Pacific. We cut saplings for levers to roll the logs into better positions while the oxen lay like dead. We cut other saplings to cover low spots, saplings for the logs to slide over, through

45

the dark green tunnel we had slashed through the jungle.

This was no novel work for me. I had been a logger in the Brazos Bottom of Texas long before I had begun to shave. An Irishman was my partner. We cleared land; so much an acre and so much for a cord of wood. We lived in the woods and life sang all day long as we worked with axe and saw and peavey. We cut live oak, pecan, water elm, ash, white oak, hickory, and gum. Longhorn cattle were standing in a mute circle around the tree as axe and saw bit into it. The tree stood as if doomed beneath its sombre festoons of Spanish moss. The longhorns were waiting for the crash to get a feed from the moss. We burned limbs, leaves, branches and logs, living in the incense smell of burning wood, in the crackling of fires that rarely went out. In the early morning we would bury our iron pot, filled with beans and salt pork, in hot ashes —also a big pan of biscuits, and at noon find everything piping hot and just right. Then began the feast of hot biscuits, beans and pork, soaked and swimming in molasses that we got by the gallon from a nearby mill.

Some men must have trees to live. Later, I worked in Washington and in Oregon, in the giant forests flanking the Columbia River, and in California, where the big ones never die. There were times when we picked up the dead—when a tree struck back.

In Alaska, in 1925, I had worked a whole summer on a raft, boom man for a pile-driver rig that was building salmon traps for the Quadra cannery. All day long I stood on the loosely chained logs on the open coast, dancing a jig in my long caulked logging boots to keep my feet on the churning, smashing logs. Any fall or slip meant injury, perhaps a snapped bone. And the water was like ice from the snow-laden gullies of the shore and I was wet to neck all day long, cutting the logs out of the chains and hooking them on, to be hoisted under the hammer and driven into the sea. And when the pilings were down, hanging crews came with wire netting to string it from pile to pile, from top down to the bottom of the sea, and no salmon could get away once it got into the trap.

Yes, I had handled logs and trees before.

A truck brought my balsas one by one to Quevedo where they were rolled down the bank into the river and tied together. With a little palm-thatched bamboo hut on top of the logs, such as all rafts had for protection of the rivermen against sun and rain since ancient times, and with 500 stalks of bananas to keep the logs low in the water and the sun from splitting them, my three balseros started down the river on the 200-mile trip to Guayaquil. They steered the raft with two big sweeps, one in front and one in the stern—not an easy job on a waterway full of bends and narrows and shallow spots. It would require four to five days.

As soon as I saw them off I took a plane to Guayaquil.

At the time when I was planning my expedition in New York, I had become acquainted with the Ecuadorian Consul General, Mr. Duran-Ballen, and through him had obtained an introduction to Mr. Henri Kohn, the "balsa king" of Ecuador, who had offices in New York. He had given me permission to build my raft on his property and to use other facilities of his plant. And so my logs were floated to his sawmill in Guayaquil, the largest one in the world for balsas, and hauled ashore. At last I could start building a raft.

47

# ★ 6 ★

## SQUARE KNOTS

IT was now April 2, nearly three months after my arrival in Ecuador.

"Let us begin, *amigos*," I said to the three Ecuadorians I had picked to help me. We walked amid house-high stacks of kiln-dried balsa lumber to the corner of the mill where my seven logs lay. I had cut only *machos*, male balsas, which are considered much stronger though less buoyant than the lighter and more fragile *hembres*, or female trees. We had hauled them out of the river and erected a bamboo cover to keep the sun from splitting them. It would also protect us during the construction.

"Look—blood!" one of the Ecuadorians exclaimed as we came near. We stopped in our tracks, consternation on our faces. The logs were spattered with red, some parts almost solidly covered.

"*Los gallinazos . . .*" one of the natives remarked.

The cattle pens of the municipal slaughter house of Guayaquil bordered on the mill, within a few feet of my logs. Hundreds of vultures were living on the refuse and, when they were not busy gorging themselves, sat on surrounding roofs and trees, almost breaking them down with their weight.

On the previous evening they had had an unusually big feast. A steer had died in the pen and fallen to their beaks, and after doing away with it to the last shred many of the birds had spent the night in the trees and the shelter above my logs, leaving their droppings.

"*Señor* Willis, that blood is not a good sign," said one of my workers, a serious, grave-faced fellow.

"All signs are good," I replied. "Better blood now than later—when I'm alone on the sea. Let us begin, *amigos.*"

And the echo of my words, ". . . . when I'm alone on the sea," kept ringing within me. I knew I could not stand alone, and under my breath I muttered: "Let my hands be like iron to bind the ropes around the logs and tie the knots—let my judgment be both quick and accurate, for time is short."

I had made no blueprint or a model of the raft but I knew what I wanted.

We started aft with the centre log, rolled the next one from the right to it, and commenced. No grooves for the ropes were cut into the trunks because, in contrast to other woods, balsas are hardest on the outside. I wanted to preserve all their strength and also prevent saturation by sea water; besides, cutting grooves would require time and, also, the lashings would not grip the round logs as evenly and firmly as I desired. I used 1½-inch manila rope.

Each lashing bound just two logs together in one place, forming a figure eight. This meant that each lashing was independent of any other and that if it should come apart or be cut for any reason, such as scraping over a coral reef, no other lashing would be directly involved. I used square knots, tightening each half of this simplest and most ancient of knots with a tackle. Nowhere did I follow a rigid pattern in the distance of the lashings from each other but worked according to the logs. I tied them as they had lain in the water when they drifted down the Palanque and the Guayas, to make them feel at ease on the voyage, for I wanted to be on the best of terms with my *Seven Little Sisters*. Since they were by no means

49

straight but rather on the crooked side it meant that there were gaps between them. These gaps were from a few inches to 14 inches wide. The big gaps, one right in the bow and seeming almost to split the raft, caused many of the spectators who were always around during the construction, sitting on the wall of the slaughter house to watch the *navegante solitario*, as I had been called by the Press all over South America, to shake their heads dubiously and whisper their disapproval. But, straight or crooked, I lashed the logs as they lay till they groaned and creaked and were welded into one mass under the pressure of tackles and mangrove levers. Knowing the strength of the rope I used, I knew that they would not come apart even in a hurricane—even though everything else on her, house, rigging, deck, and myself were battered to bits and swept into the sea.

My helpers — I generally used four — were regular employees of Henri Kohn, on whose property I built the raft, and were loaned to me for the job. Two were carpenters and the other two handymen. They had little experience with lashing rope but learned quickly. One of the carpenters especially was a capable man though weighing perhaps less than 110 pounds. He was a master at working with mangrove wood. After the main logs were tied I had a stroke of good luck in getting a Swiss, J. Buhlmann-Koch, to work for me as foreman. He had lived for years in Ecuador, spoke Spanish fluently and knew how to handle men. He also had never used rope before or even been near a ship, being a mechanic by trade, but caught on almost miraculously and was as steady and dependable as the mountains from which he had come.

The raft now measured 33 feet long in the middle, that is, its greatest length was at the centre log; it tapered to the log on each side to 28 feet, and was 20 feet wide aft and 18 feet forward. Across the seven carrier logs, the raft proper, I lashed three mangrove beams to strengthen them, one on each end and one in the middle. Mangrove wood is extremely strong and so heavy that it sinks in water. Next came six crosslogs of balsa, reaching from side to side of the raft, each from 12 to 18 inches in diameter. On these crosslogs I put, in sections that could be lifted up by one man, a deck of split bamboo lashed to bamboo crosspieces and strongly constructed.

We next cut two sockets into the forward mangrove, one on each side of the raft, and set a mangrove beam in each, 16 feet long. These two beams, one on each side, pointed up a little and forward and were joined in the centre 8 feet beyond the middle log of the raft. They formed the jib-boom or bowsprit. They were as carefully lashed and secured as the seven main logs.

The mainmast was next in the order of construction. It was a double mast, consisting of twin, or shear legs that were stepped, one on each side of the raft, in the same mangrove crossbeam as the twin-legged bowsprit and joined 30 feet above the deck in the centre of the raft. This was in the ancient pattern of all seagoing Ecuadorian and Peruvian rafts. We secured the mast with three stays of steel cable, two running aft to each corner of the raft, and a third one forward to the end of the jib-boom. The forestay, besides the mainmast, would also carry a jib or foresail which I intended to use in heavy weather when it would not be safe to carry the big mainsail, or if for any reason the mainsail was out of commission.

The construction of a double-legged or shear-legged jib-boom was the outcome of much thought during the years following my resolution to build the raft. It was something entirely new in naval design. The principle here was the same as with a twin mast—to distribute strain evenly over the whole raft surface without letting anything touch the comparatively frail balsa logs themselves.

Did I need a jib-boom and a jib? When weighing my chances against the sea which might bring down on me at any time the terrible calms that infest regions near the equator, when ships rolled from beam to beam till they were dismasted, or else met with the titanic fury of Pacific hurricanes, I considered every possibility of design that would enable me to make a successful lone voyage. With a jib, I knew I could manoeuvre more freely if the need arose; and a jib-boom would enable me to set the foremast farther forward than on the ancient rafts, due to the forestay running far beyond the length of the centre log. This gave me a chance to put up an aftermast, the next original feature of my raft. The aftermast with its big triangular sail I considered very important.

The third new feature that I worked out for my raft was the steering apparatus. The ancient Indians, on rivers and along the coasts of South America and all voyages they may have made, used only sweeps, or steering oars—round blades of tough wood cut from a certain tree at points where the roots rise like folds out of the earth to blend with the trunk. These blades were lashed to long poles. This method of steering requires a man on duty at all times and was therefore impossible for me to follow. I needed a regular ship's wheel connected with a regular rudder. This proved the hardest nut to crack, even after designs were worked out—but at last the job was accomplished and, in spite of dire prophecies of many seagoing men that following seas would smash it within a week, the apparatus proved on every occasion that it could take all the pressure coming its way.

After the rudder was finished we built a hut, 6 by 8 feet and $4\frac{1}{2}$ feet high. This was to house my instruments, clothes and food, and everything else that had to be protected from the weather and the sea. We first erected a frame of 5-inch-thick bamboos and lashed it to the main and crosslogs. It was set a little to the left of the centre of the raft to allow more space on the right, away from the onslaught of the south-east tradewinds to which I would be exposed on the trip. The hut was lined on the inside with 3-inch-thick kiln-dried balsa boards, a very good insulating material. On the roof we first put galvanized iron, then a double layer of split bamboos, and topped it off with the usual palm leaves with which each hut, house, and raft shanty have been covered since immemorial times in this section of the world. The outside was sheathed with split bamboos, used extensively in Ecuador for the walls of houses. I also put iron rings on the outside corners to use for cable in heavy weather.

I continued to have visitors from near and far, men from the coasts and the balseros who brought logs for the mill from the forest territories of Ecuador—men with Indian blood in their veins and sailors by heredity. Many were steeped in the wisdom learned from long lines of forefathers who had sailed in their rafts to the Galapagos, to Colombia and Panama and south to Peru. The first Spaniards coming to the west coast had seen them in their strange crafts and marvelled at their skill. But these ancients had sailed long before any Spaniards had come, ever since the first balsa had tumbled into the water and lain there floating like a cork. Now their rafts and sails had dropped beneath the horizon of time, leaving no written record of their voyages, only the record in the blood and eyes of their descendants, in their quiet manner and proud bearing. They came and saw and sometimes they talked, and I always found time to listen and to learn. And the men from the coasts always asked: "From where do you intend to sail, *Señor* Willis?"

"From here, from Guayaquil Gulf, *amigo.*"

Then they would shake their heads. Some said out-right that it could not be done.

Since I first had the idea of building a raft I intended to sail from Ecuador, the country where it was to be built. I knew it meant beating to westward against current and wind from the moment I struck the open coast, in order to clear the Galapagos archipelago, 700 to 800 miles due west. I meant to accomplish this by means of centreboards acting like a keel. It was quite clear, after studying current and wind charts, that it would be a formidable task and perhaps impossible, but I thought I could do it. It would fit in well with the spirit of my voyage, to test myself in endless labour against almost hopeless odds; it would be a test of my seamanship and of the unique construction of my raft as well. And I would see right from the start whether I had chosen my rations right: roasted barley flour and sugar, to be supplemented by the fish I hoped to catch.

This plan demanded that I sail at the latest before the end of April, the beginning of winter south of the equator. But I had been delayed for two months getting logs and now it was May already and I was far from being ready. The great Humboldt Current, coming out of the Antarctic and sweeping north along the west coast of South America, strikes Cape Blanco and is deflected to the north-west till it clears the Galapagos Islands, after which it takes a westerly course across the Pacific, finally mingling with the South Equatorial Current, also a westerly drift. Cape Blanco lies 150 miles south of the Bay of Guayaquil.

I knew that ancient raftsmen, when trying to reach the Galapagos, always sailed south along the coast first, south beyond Cape Blanco to Paita, 200 miles from Guayaquil, to be sure to be in the full current before it swung to the north-west. That also was the reason the

54

*Kon-Tiki* expedition had sailed from Callao, a full 700 miles south of Guayaquil. I knew this but thought that with my new type of raft I could set my own course.

Now both current and winds were against me, for during the winter months the Humboldt Current continued to flow north along the coast for a considerable distance after rounding Cape Blanco. Could I expect to cross this tremendous flow of water, pushed northward by now prevailing southerly winds, and maintain a straight westerly course to get past the Galapagos?

"When are you going to be ready?" I was asked every day. And at night the same question was repeated at the little restaurant where I had my meals and which was the hang-out for a handful of American and European adventurers who happened to be in Guayaquil. Most of them had spent years along the Ecuadorian coasts as well as in the Galapagos, fishing and beachcombing and looking for buried treasure. They lived strange, Robinson Crusoe lives in this out-of-this-world archipelago.

I spoke to seamen and fishermen, men who had been born on the coasts and had spent their lives on coastal vessels and schooners running to the Galapagos, to Colombia and Panama, and they all said the same thing—that it would be impossible to get westward on a raft at this time of the year. They considered it doubtful at any time but only a boat with a powerful engine could do it now.

I spoke to the son of a man who owned one of the Galapagos Islands, a man immensely rich with plantation holdings and Galapagos fisheries. This son had made many trips between Guayaquil and the islands and flatly prophesied that my voyage would end in disaster if I sailed from the Bay of Guayaquil. He gave me numerous examples of the swift northerly drifts that he had encountered during the winter months.

One night a sunburnt man dropped in at the restaurant and was introduced to me. He was a Swiss and sort of a scholar with special interest in archaeology. He had just come from the Galapagos, intending to break his lonely life on the islands with a month or two in Guayaquil. He became greatly interested in my trip.

"You can't make it," he said like all the others. "You'll be caught in the Current as soon as you are outside and carried to Colombia. That's the ancient raft route. What —tack single-handed against the Humboldt for a distance of eight hundred miles?" He looked at me with his blue, sun-beaten eyes starved for human companionship.

"It can't be done, Bill. What good are your centre-boards if you have no wind? You will drift where the Current takes you. And it will take you fast. There is a powerful set to the north during the winter. And even if you managed to get near the Galapagos—let's say you could—you could not get past. Take that from me. There are strong northerly currents running through the islands —running as much as six and eight miles an hour and more. I make my living there, fishing—I should know. I've been around there for eighteen years. We sell to American boats coming down from San Pedro, California. We can't even fish from a sailboat on account of the Current. And once you are carried north it doesn't stop till you are in the Equatorial Counter Current that takes you straight east into the Bay of Panama."

After the restaurant closed we walked to the river and sat down on a bench in the park. "How about if I get myself towed down to Cape Blanco and start from there?"

He shook his head. "No, it's too late for that, too. You have to get farther south than Cape Blanco. The Indians went down to Paita, a little port about half-way between Guayaquil and Callao. That's where they started from to get to the Galapagos. And they knew just when and how to sail. They knew the seasons and the moon and the wind, things we don't know any more. And they had crews to handle the rafts. Nobody went alone."

I had already written my wife about the difficulty of getting straight west after leaving the Bay of Guayaquil. "Let the whole thing go and wait till next year," she had replied. "It's too much for one man; everybody can see that. Better give it up and we'll take our loss."

Wait till next year and let my beautiful raft sink into the mud of the river or rot and split ashore—after all the work and all the dreaming?

I paced my room in the hotel until morning. It was a large room with a high ceiling and a stone floor to keep it cool, exactly 20 × 33 feet, the size of my raft.

Up and down, up and down, I paced till it became light and the city awoke. At eight o'clock I went to the cable office and sent a cable to my wife:

"GET IN TOUCH WITH GRACE LINE TO CARRY RAFT TO CALLAO. WEIGHT ABOUT 10 TON. 33 × 20 LENGTH. MAST 30 FEET BUT CAN BE TAKEN DOWN."

The answer came shortly:

"GRACE LINE TIED UP IN NEW YORK BY STRIKES. BOATS SHIFTED TO NEW ORLEANS. CARGO SPACE NOT AVAILABLE. SCHEDULES UPSET. NO BOAT WITH HEAVY LIFTING GEAR BOOKED FOR PUNA. HOPELESS. GIVE IT UP."

Puna was the port thirty miles below Guayaquil where the Grace Line boats stopped.

I went to the local steamship agents but here the outlook was just as bad. No ship with heavy-cargo gear, such as was needed to lift my raft out of the water, was due for two months. Besides, it was doubtful if space would be available. I was told that letters would be sent to Europe to find out. Letters to Europe!

57

"KEEP AFTER THE GRACE LINE," I cabled back to New York. "ALSO SEE MR. BERCKEMEYER, THE PERUVIAN AMBASSADOR TO WASHINGTON, ABOUT FREE ENTRY OF MY RAFT AND ALL EQUIPMENT."

I was hoping to use the great Peruvian Navy Base in Callao, but dared not mention it at this time. A short while later I received my wife's letter about what had happened in Washington:

"What—alone—he wants to cross the Pacific on a raft alone?" Mr. Berckemeyer, the Ambassador, had asked her.

"Unfortunately," Teddy had replied. "I tried for two years to keep him from it."

The Ambassador thought it over. "I think it is foolish, very foolish. I am frank, Mrs. Willis. But brave men must be helped, even to the utmost. I will do my share and I am sure you will not find Peru wanting. Go back to New York and do not worry—you will hear from me."

A few days later a mud-stained, lumbering truck made its way to the mill, bringing a seagoing fishermen's canoe for me from the village of Manglaralto. It was obviously a veteran of years of fishing in heavy surf and open sea, and built by Indians. The dugout was of red cedar, 26 feet in length with a 3-foot beam, and sides $1\frac{1}{4}$ inches thick.

And then came a news flash that the strike in New York was settled and shortly after a cable from Teddy that the Grace boat *Santa Cecilia* would pick up my raft in Puna. More good news! Peru had granted my request for free entry of my raft and all equipment.

I cabled Teddy:

"TAKE THE NEXT PLANE TO GUAYAQUIL."

A few days later my wife stepped from the plane, weary but radiant, glad to get away from endless chores in New

58

York, glad that many months of anxiety were at last over.

"Oh, Bill, what you've been through! How thin you are! I've never seen you like this," she cried on seeing me.

"I'm okay. But what you've been through! But you look fine, Teddy—wonderful. Did you bring everything?"

"Everything."

The customs officers were considerate and we had no trouble with our two sextants, a chronometer and a watch, films, compasses, navigation books and charts.

Then we drove to the hotel. We sat up all night talking —there was so much to tell.

"I knew I should have been down here taking care of you," Teddy kept saying.

The next day I took her to see the raft.

"It's beautiful, Bill. Oh, it's beautiful! Oh, I wish I could go along!" she exclaimed.

We put out a ladder from the little dock and Teddy went on board. I introduced my helpers and then showed her around the raft, explaining its parts. She touched everything—the smooth masts, the lashings, the bamboo cabin, the fluttering leaves of the roof.

"How wonderful, Bill—how wonderful! But there is no railing, Bill . . . you will fall overboard! You're in a little pond here but you are going out on the ocean!"

"I don't think I need a railing, Teddy," I said.

"You do—you do too! You can't go without a railing. What's the matter with you? You're going on the open sea. You must have a railing of some sort. You must, Bill!"

"Okay, Teddy, I'll rig up something."

"Rig up something. . . ." She gave me one of her disapproving looks. "I want you to put up something you can depend on, something solid."

"I will, Teddy, I will. I don't see how, just now, but I'll put up something. I'll find a way."

A few days later a Grace Line launch towed my raft

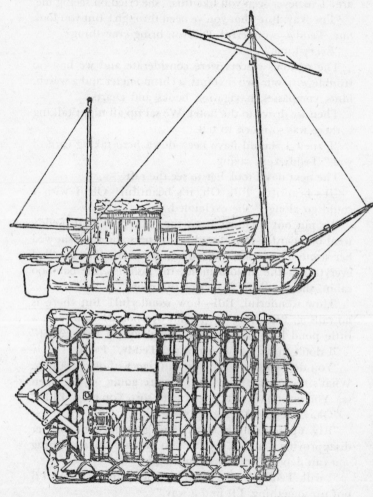

**PLANS SHOWING CONSTRUCTION OF RAFT**

Pacific Raft
*Seven Little Sisters*

| | | |
|---|---|---|
| LENGTH | 33 | FEET |
| BEAM | 20 | " |
| MAINMAST | 30 | " |
| AFTERMAST | 20 | " |
| YARD | 17 | " |

down the river to Puna. Teddy was to follow later in a fast and luxurious passenger launch. After an all-night tow we arrived in Puna in the morning and tied up to wait for the Grace boat. My Swiss foreman was with me.

During the afternoon a motor-driven petrol barge lying near us left the dock. I was watching and saw that it swung back in again after clearing the dock and came straight at the stern of my raft. It moved slowly but there was a strong tide and it was an iron ship about seventy feet long, loaded with perhaps a hundred tons of petrol and was bound to damage me if it struck.

I shouted to the captain to reverse his engine. He was looking at me out of the pilot-house but kept on coming, his hands grasping his steering wheel. Did he think my frail balsa raft was of iron? Was he blind? A crash was imminent and I jumped out on the stern, to the very edge of the logs, and threw myself against the iron stem of the oncoming vessel.

I knew that the lines which held my raft to the dock had a few feet of slack, which would let it go back a little and, as they say in the prize ring, ride with the punch. This is what happened but my body had to take the first shock, I strained with all I had and felt my insides tear.

The captain came at me twice more, though with less momentum, as if he were playing a game. Each time I stopped the barge. Then he backed up and swung out. I could find no explanation for the man's action. Perhaps he tried to show off, as some natives are apt to do, but did not have enough control of his engine.

I went into the cabin and examined myself. I was ruptured.

I decided not to tell my wife or anybody else—nothing should stop me now. Common sense told me to do something, that I would perhaps regret my decision. 'No,' I thought, 'I'll wrap myself up in rope if it comes to the worst—out on the ocean. Nobody is going to know about this. I've come through with worse. Nothing is going to stop me now.'

The Grace liner was not ready to take us on board till long after dark. Two heavy mangrove beams had been lashed underneath the raft while I was beside the dock, one across each end, for the lifting cables to be fastened to. Finally a tug brought us alongside into the glare of the floodlights of the anchored ship. The raft was going to be set down on Number 3 hatch, right in front of the white-painted bridge. Passengers and crew lined the rails, staring down at my strange-looking craft, the *Seven Little Sisters*, this jungle-thatched thing that wanted to throw its tiny gauntlet at the Pacific.

I was worried about the heavy lift. Anything could happen with the lifting gear, to the winch or to the man handling it. The chief mate of the *Santa Cecilia*, a serious man who obviously knew his job, had boarded a launch in the afternoon and come to the raft, inspected it and then returned, reporting to the captain. He had assured me that every possible precaution would be taken.

Slowly the electric winch, handled by an able seaman, lowered the big jumbo boom, used only for heavy hoists, with its 5-foot-long blocks and four sheaves of 1½-inch-thick steel cables, over the side of the ship, directly above the centre of the raft. From the enormous hook of the lower block hung four steel cables—strops, as seamen call them—with an eye spliced in each end. Lower and lower came block and boom. All the lights of the big ship seemed focused on the raft, making it appear a garish white. A few feet above the cabin top, the block stopped. Long-shoremen took the free ends of the strops and fastened one to each corner of the raft, slipping the eye over the protruding end of the mangrove beams that were lashed beneath.

I checked each corner, left a man to hold each strop in place, and then jumped on the cabin roof and signalled to the mate who was watching from the rail.

"Take up the slack!" The mate relayed my order to the winchman who was not visible from the raft.

I heard the drone and whine of the powerful winch as it took hold. Slowly, almost imperceptibly, the cables and strops tightened as the boom came up. I could see that a master was handling the winch. I had inquired about him in the afternoon: he was a Panamanian. Finally the four cables encircling the raft stood like bars of iron. There had been no jerk, not the slightest sign of any strain. I jumped from the cabin roof to the deck and then to the tug that had brought us out.

The *Seven Little Sisters* came up like a dream. It was almost uncanny. Not a sound or creak from a cable or block, from a lashing or a log. Silence had fallen over the big ship. The crew lined the lower rails and, above, the promenade decks were black with passengers. The captain looked down from the bridge.

Higher and higher rose the raft. When it was clear of the rail it stopped. There was a pause as a different winch was put into operation and then the mighty boom with its blocks and the yellow balsa raft hanging down from it swung slowly inboard.

The tug raced around the stern of the ship and brought me to the gangway. I sprinted up the ladder and came just in time to see the raft lowered down on the hatch. A masterly job—it came down as gently as a babe put in a cradle. I congratulated the mate and winchman while sailors got busy securing the raft with cables, ropes and timbers to keep it from sliding off the hatch in the extremely heavy coastal swells usually encountered on the 700-mile trip down to Callao.

The pilot was on board and the ship's whistle had

The canoe in place on the deck.

The author tests his craft on the Guayaquil River; (*below*) his wife, Teddy, visits the raft.

blown for the departure. I accompanied my foreman to the gangway and said goodbye to him. He intended to go to Quito, the capital, where he had been offered a job by a Swiss firm that was installing a hydro-electric plant in the Sierras.

Within a few minutes the floodlights on masts and superstructure went out one by one and the big ship lay in darkness. Looking up at the bridge from the hatch I saw the glow of the pilot's cigarette. From the forecastle-head came a rumbling, knocking sound as the anchor chain was heaved in. We were ready to go. I put my hand on the outside log, thinking, 'Soon we'll be on our own, little raft.'

The rapid ringing of the ship's bell on the forecastle-head told me that the anchor was up. The red and green running lights flashed on and the ship started to swing around. She was on her way south to Callao.

I went up the ladder to the promenade deck. Teddy, who had boarded the liner in the afternoon, was surrounded by passengers. She introduced me to them. There were Americans from all sections of the United States; people on vacation, business men, teachers, and officers with their families joining military missions. It was quite a while before Teddy and I could get away to the dining-room. I was hungry—I had hardly eaten all day.

It was long past the dinner hour, but a steward set a table for us and piled up everything the kitchen had. The night chef sent word to us to go the limit. (I had told the mate in the afternoon that I belonged to the National Maritime Union, the seaman's union whose members were on the ship, and the news had spread. I knew that Teddy and I would be treated like kings on the way down.) She was sitting beside me and we talked while I ate. Afterwards we went back on deck and mixed with the passengers. Everybody seemed thrilled, and I had to answer endless questions. I was a little bewildered by this attention which almost seemed homage. Perhaps it was only deference to a man they thought insane.

We spent three glorious days on the trip to Callao. For the first time since coming to South America on January 7, I was free from worry and could relax. Between loafing and posing for endless photographs I had talks with Captain Tierney, a veteran of this run. We discussed charts, weather, currents, and other navigational factors and problems I would have to contend with on my voyage.

The *Seven Little Sisters* took it easy, too. Lashed across the hatch, right in front of the high, white-painted bridge, the raft looked out on the blue Pacific as though getting acquainted, letting the wind tousle the leaves on the cabin roof and sing an ancient sea song in the rigging. She seemed to like the Pacific.

On the morning of May 10 we arrived in Callao. It was a beautiful day. As we came slowly to the dock I could see a group of photographers ready to rush on board as soon as the gangway was down. The pilot, after bringing us alongside, came quickly from the bridge and greeted me on behalf of the captain of the port, the Peruvian Navy and the Ministry of the Interior. Then came the Press for an interview. Later, pictures were taken of Teddy and me. In the meantime the raft was lowered over the side and put back in the water.

A representative of the Grace Line helped us through the customs and all the formalities of our entry. Our goods, including the raft, had been on the ship's manifest as 'accompanied baggage'. Everything had been prepared for our coming, and instead of requiring hours and perhaps days, was settled within a few minutes. Callao, Lima—all Peru was opening its arms wide.

From the dock a car took us to the Peruvian Navy base and I was introduced to one of the commanding officers. I was offered full use of the base for finishing my raft. This was the very thing I had hoped for and I accepted gladly. A tug was at once dispatched to bring the *Seven Little Sisters* from the Grace Line pier to the base.

Then we drove to Lima. It is a large, beautiful city where old Spain and the Inca empire mingled with the ultra modern of American civilization amid evergreen gardens and flowers of breathtaking beauty, looking out upon the calm, blue endlessness of the Pacific.

At last we were alone in our rooms in a stately, palatial hotel. The day had been kind. We were quite over-whelmed. Such welcome, such kindness and considera-tion we had never dreamed of. We, complete strangers, were being treated like favourite children returned to the fold.

The day following our arrival we paid our respects to Mr. Harold Tittmann, the American Ambassador in Lima, and to Mr. Bernard Heiler, the Consul, and became acquainted with different members of the Embassy staff. Among them was Mr. T. T. Driver, the Public Affairs Officer, a man who knew the sea and took great interest in my project. In the weeks that followed he gave us valuable assistance and advice.

From the Embassy we went to the American Navy and Army Missions. I explained my plans and they offered to help in every possible way with their technical knowledge of radio and coastal currents. I later contacted them frequently and a day seldom passed when at least one member of the staff did not come out to the raft to see how I was getting along.

After one day of meeting people and getting acquainted with Lima, I began to work. There was a lot to be done yet.

The body of the raft was finished, also the house and masts, the rudder and wheel, but the sails had to be fastened, the running gear reeved, the radio and generator installed, and provisions procured.

Every morning an officer of the Navy base came to the raft where I was working and asked me what I needed that day in men, skilled or unskilled, and in material. In a short while the men came, helpers and technical experts both, and the material also was brought. My work became pleasant.

About a week after my arrival I was standing on the dock beside the raft when three persons who looked like business men came up, accompanied by an officer who introduced us. One of the visitors was Sir George Nelson, British tycoon, chairman of the English Electric Company and of the Marconi Company and a member of the Royal Thames Yacht Club. Sir George, being on a tour of South America, had driven out from Lima to look at my raft. After taking some snapshots he asked me what kind of transmitter I had.

"None—I decided to go without one."

"Without a transmitter, in this day and age? What if something should happen to you? You are going alone, I understand?"

I explained that I had started a code course but had become so busy that I had to stop. And rather than take the transmitter I could not operate, I would go without one. I said I regretted it only on account of my wife.

We shook hands again and the party left. A few days later I received word that Sir George had cabled to London for a Marconi emergency transmitter, the Salvita III, which is used extensively in the British Merchant Marine, to be flown to Callao. It arrived within a week and in a ceremony attended by notables the transmitter was presented to me.

When coming to Callao I had thought that I would be ready to sail in about two weeks but the finishing up proved to be endless. Week followed week, and then a month had passed and I was still working on the raft, busy with details. "You will run smack into the hurricanes," officers warned me. Probably none of them thought that I had a chance.

At last I was ready for a trial run. A tug took us out about ten miles and let go. Teddy, accompanied by a couple with whom we had become acquainted, and three Peruvian sailors were on the raft with me. There was little wind but the raft looked good to me. She rolled but took the swells much better than the big tug.

We were only out about two hours. I merely took the trial to give Teddy an idea of the seaworthiness of the raft and to give her a ride.

After our return in the evening the Press and everybody else were anxious to know how the raft had stood up. I had nothing but praise for her and said that nothing had to be changed. But I later told Teddy that it would probably be five or six weeks before I really knew the raft.

I set the date for my departure four days after the trial run.

## GOOD-BYE

JUNE 22. The phone beside my bed rang and I opened my eyes, picking up the receiver.

"*Señor* Willis, it is seven o'clock."

It was the day. Today a minesweeper of the Peruvian Navy, the *San Martin*, would fasten a towline to the *Seven Little Sisters*, take it sixty miles offshore and let go. My voyage across the Pacific would begin.

We dressed and were ready to go down to the dining-room for breakfast.

"Bill." My wife looked up at me.

"Teddy."

It was a little while before she could say, "You said you would make it, Bill. . . ."

"I will make it, Teddy."

"I think I should come along and help you. I could do so much. . . ."

"Not this time, Teddy. I have to go alone."

"You are so sure of yourself."

"I'll make it, Teddy. I'll be on the raft when she comes ashore."

"Perhaps dead."

"Ted, I'll make it."

"I feel, myself, that you will. But I don't want you to go to Australia—that's too far. Please, promise me not to go to Australia; it's too late in the season. Promise, please. You talked so much about it lately. I know you— once you get started you don't want to stop. You must promise, Bill. Samoa is far enough. Please, promise."

"I promise. I'll stop in Samoa."

"Oh, Bill, I am so glad—so glad. That will make it a little easier waiting for you." She bent her head. "Oh, why do women always have to wait. . . ."

My wife had good nerves but she had been through a lot, the last six months.

"I'll clear for Samoa, Teddy."

"Oh, Bill, that makes me happy. It will make it easier."

We took our leave of each other now, in the gilded, high-ceilinged room of the hotel. The rest of the time we were together we would merely be posing, smiling and looking happy, and speaking brave words into microphones.

Before long I had her smiling again, this little woman who in 1948 had said on our sinking ship: "If you stay, I will," and had refused to be taken off. We went down to the dining-room for breakfast.

An hour later I walked into the office of the harbourmaster of Callao. He held the rank of captain in the Peruvian Navy and we had become friendly during my stay.

"So this is the day," he said. Like most officers in the navy he spoke English.

"This is it, Captain Mathey. My papers are ready?"

"Here they are, all signed and ready." A serious, old-time seaman, he smiled. "I marked down Polynesia as your destination."

"I am clearing for Samoa, Captain Mathey."

"You can't expect that, Mr. Willis. . . ." He smiled. "You have no ship, you have a raft."

"Put down Samoa, please, Captain. That's my destination." I handed back the clearance papers. "The raft, *Seven Little Sisters*, is clearing from Callao for Samoa like a regular ship."

"If you say so." He gave the papers back to the clerk to type in Samoa.

"I'm not shooting in the dark; I am going to sail once I am out there, Captain," I said.

"You are confident, Mr. Willis," he said as we shook hands. "I'll watch from the window when they tow you out. I'll have my glasses right on you. The very best of luck!"

Back to the Arsenal Naval. Hundreds of people had gathered to see me off—business men and tradesmen and workers of the navy yard, men, women and children, all the curious of Lima and Callao with time to spare. Among them stood naval officers and men from the embassies and consulates and attachés of military missions. Newspapers, magazines and wire services had sent reporters and representatives; all were asking questions, trying to get a last bit of information to flash around the world. Photographers clustered around Teddy and me, moving in and out, shooting pictures from all angles.

Everything was ready but they always kept pleading for another shot. It started to get Teddy, these repetitions of the final embrace. "This is about all I can take, Bill," she said trying hard to keep her eyes dry.

"Okay, Teddy—this is it, then. Remember, I'll make it. Don't you worry too much, little one. Four months or six months, maybe—but I'll make it."

"I believe you." For a moment she strained against me as if she would hold me or come with me, telling me all a woman can feel in one overpowering moment what her lips did not dare to say under the barrage of curious eyes and cameras.

I climbed down to the raft. Somebody handed me Meekie, the black cat which the officers of the submarine base had just given me. Eekie, my green parrot, was already on board in his cage.

72

The three sailors who were to stay on the raft till they let me go the following morning, sixty miles offshore, fastened the towline while photographers swarmed down from the dock into waiting launches and started to take pictures. Yachts lined up in a wide circle to accompany us out to sea.

"Time to go, little raft—time to start."

I took another look around—everything was clear on deck and the towline was ready. Eekie was in his cage hanging from the ladder beside a bunch of green bananas, last gift of the naval base. The little green fellow was working on an ear of corn as if he had not eaten for a week.

The shore, the pier, the surrounding warships were lined solid with people. Thousands had come for the take-off. Every officer and man of the big navy base was there.

My eyes went up to Teddy standing at the edge of the pier almost directly above me—just a few feet away.

"Teddy!"

"Bill!"

"Don't forget—I'll make it."

What a smile!—it struggled to stay on top, to stay big, to give me the last lift. . . .

"Let go on the dock," I said to the sailors standing by on the crowded pier. There was a scramble and the raft was untied. We hauled in the lines.

Slowly we started to move away from the dock. Foot by foot the gap widened. One, two, three yards of open water already. The voyage had begun.

We hauled the raft with ropes and by hand along a group of destroyers tied up abreast, slowly and carefully, in order not to hit anything with the bowsprit and bring down our rigging. I was kept busy but now and then I jumped to the edge of the raft and waved. My eyes were on Teddy against a background of the colourful, cheering multitude. Friendly Peru!

Then it got me a little, I think, for we started to swing around the destroyers and would soon be lost to view—I would see little Teddy no more. And my two arms came up, and with hands clasped above my head I gave the fighter's salute. This was for Teddy. She knew my past, knew that I had faced men in combat. Now I was to face the Pacific. But hers would be the harder lot.

Steamers blew their whistles as the *Seven Little Sisters* moved through the harbour, out through the breakwater and then into the open sea, followed by a procession of yachts and launches blowing horns and sirens. It was just twelve o'clock noon. The sky was grey and solidly overcast, the sea grey from horizon to horizon with whitecaps whipped up by the southeast wind.

"*Mucho viento* [plenty wind], *Señor* Willis," the sailor at the wheel said to me, buttoning up his pea-jacket and looking cold.

"That's what I want. Plenty of wind."

The last yacht and the launch with photographers had dropped astern. A big swell rose high beneath the *Seven Little Sisters* and lifted her. She took it as though born to the sea. The sailors looked at me and we grinned. Hour after hour we were pulled deeper into the sea.

The minesweeper was rolling ahead of me through the night. A powerful light lay on her afterdeck. A lantern was swinging from my forestay. Two of the Peruvian sailors lay on the bamboo deck, rolled up tight in a blanket, asleep. The third sat propped up against the cabin. The wheel was lashed. I was sitting beside the open door of the cabin, my eyes staring at the light of the minesweeper, ready to grab the wheel if she stopped suddenly for any reason. I watched all night long, hour after hour, till my eyes got sore. I did not want anything to happen

74

now: running into the stern of the *San Martin* could bring down my mast. Finally the darkness turned into grey and after a while the minesweeper swung off and the captain shouted through the megaphone to let go the towline.

Sixty miles offshore, *Seven Little Sisters*. Put on your sea boots!

We let go the hawser and hoisted the mizzen and mainsail.

"I'll come 'longside and take the men off," the captain shouted.

"If you come 'longside in this sea you will smash my raft, Captain," I shouted back. "I hold you responsible."

I told the sailors to grab boat-hooks and poles and hold the raft off from the approaching, heavily labouring ship. Then the captain changed his mind and shouted he would lower a life raft and take the men off that way.

I went into the cabin and wrote a last message to my wife and gave it to one of the men.

*Hello, Ted! Everything is going fine. Sailing along for about an hour on our own. Still have three sailors with me—tug standing by to take them off. Tell Amateur Radio Relay League of America I am transmitting 11 a.m. and 6 p.m. EST. Love. Bill.*

One of the sailors said to me: "If you make it, *Señor* Willis, you will come back with your chest full of ribbons, like an admiral."

I sensed a doubt, a grave uncertainty in his words and asked: "Do you think I will make it?"

He remained silent. I looked from him to the other two seamen, obviously descendants of men who had put out during past centuries from these same shores and in similar rafts, who had sailed from Peru up the coast to Panama and to the Galapagos, and in some instances had

75

been driven helplessly by storms or, to avoid extermination by enemies ashore, had sailed westward into space, taking the same trail that lay before me now.

Their chiselled Indian faces were like stone, their jet-black eyes blank, devoid of expression. None answered my question. I smiled. Then their eyes became alive again, glittering and sharp, watching me curiously, watching the gringo—searching him for a sign of weakness. They were the last men to see me—they wanted to probe me.

Shortly afterwards I stood on my yellow bamboo deck and saw the men on the tug pull in the life raft with the three sailors. As soon as it was on board, the tug swung around, gave a long blast, and headed east, back to Callao.

June 23. . . . 7.50 a.m., EST, Lat. 11° 38′ South; Long. 78° 11′ West, appr. 60 miles west of Callao.

*Seven Little Sisters*—let's go!

Now I had to learn raft sailing. I knew time would teach me. I had told Teddy I expected it to take many weeks. But I knew I would learn. For this the sea had taught me long ago: never to think that she was mastered or ever could be—the sea and the sky both, since they always work together—but that the best one could do was to study them and while obeying the laws of their terrible strength find a way to survive. With this in mind I had built my raft, humbly and utterly serious, and now I hoped to learn how to handle it in the emptiness that lay ahead.

# ★ 8 ★

## ALONE

I STEERED for about an hour, watching the compass closely. Then I looked up and all around—at the sky and the sea and the horizon, and realized more clearly that I was alone. I watched the seas rising and falling around me beneath the unbroken greyness of the sky. I saw them crash into the logs in foaming torrents, heard them rumble and roar beneath me. The raft rolled and pitched and laboured as it made its way through the seas. I was alone. Again my eyes peered into the greyness. Everything was as it had been out there, as it had always been; nothing had changed, except for this little bit of of a man, Willis, who had his way at last—he was alone on the raft he had built and was sailing westward.

My eyes returned to the compass, and hour after hour went by. I was getting used to the realization of being alone. "Bill," I said to myself, "it's you, nothing else, just you—you are it. *You* have to get through—and that's got nothing to do with the raft or the sea."

I looked at my watch. It was now almost noon. I had steered continuously since the *San Martin* had turned her back on me. I was steering west-northwest to get farther offshore so that no freak or westerly gale could take me back to land. I would head northwest later.

I cut two lengths of three-quarter-inch rope and made lashings for the wheel. Then I watched the course. The raft did not do so well without me at the wheel, swinging back and forth considerably, and I could see that I had

77

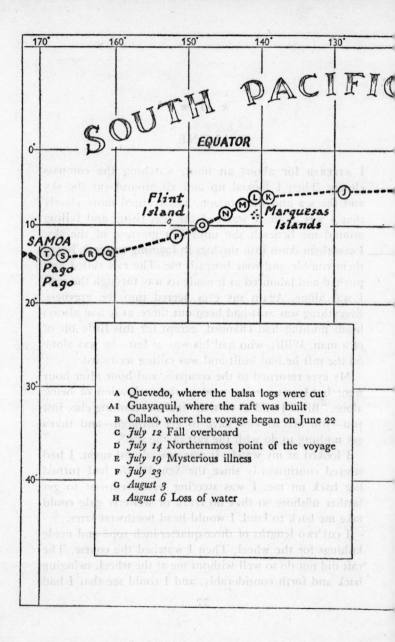

| | | |
|---|---|---|
| 170° | 160° | 150° | 140° | 130° |

**SOUTH PACIFIC**

**EQUATOR** — 0°

*Flint Island* ○

Ⓙ

Ⓚ Ⓛ Ⓜ Ⓝ Ⓞ

*Marquesas Islands* — 10°

Ⓟ

**SAMOA**
Ⓣ Ⓢ Ⓡ Ⓠ

*Pago Pago* — 20°

30°

40°

A  Quevedo, where the balsa logs were cut
A1 Guayaquil, where the raft was built
B  Callao, where the voyage began on June 22
C  *July 12* Fall overboard
D  *July 14* Northernmost point of the voyage
E  *July 19* Mysterious illness
F  *July 23*
G  *August 3*
H  *August 6* Loss of water

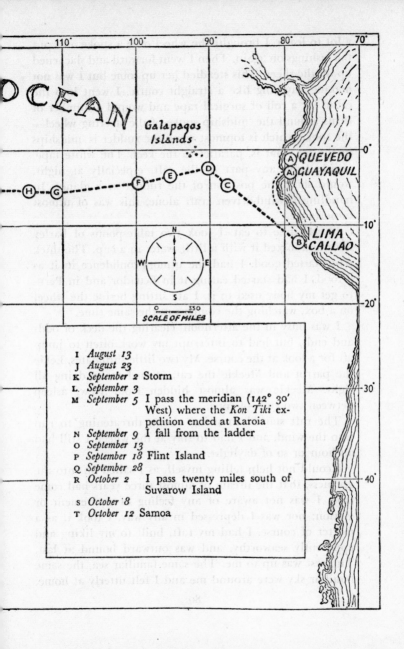

OCEAN

Galapagos
Islands

Ⓐ QUEVEDO
Ⓐ₁ GUAYAQUIL

Ⓗ ◦ ◦ ◦ Ⓖ ◦ ◦ ◦ ◦ Ⓕ ◦ ◦ ◦ ◦ Ⓔ ◦ ◦ Ⓓ
Ⓒ

LIMA
Ⓑ CALLAO

N
W ⊕ E
S

0 ———— 350
SCALE OF MILES

I   *August 13*
J   *August 23*
K   *September 2* Storm
L   *September 3*
M   *September 5* I pass the meridian (142° 30'
West) where the *Kon Tiki* ex-
pedition ended at Raroia
N   *September 9* I fall from the ladder
O   *September 13*
P   *September 18* Flint Island
Q   *September 28*
R   *October 2* I pass twenty miles south of
Suvarow Island
S   *October 8*
T   *October 12* Samoa

a lot to learn. I brought the wheel over a spoke and put the lashings on again. Then I went forward and slackened up on the sheet. This steadied her up some but I was not making anything like a straight course. I went into the cabin for a roll of surgical tape and wound a number of turns around the 'midship spoke of the steering wheel— the spoke which is topmost when the rudder is 'midships in the sea, that is, parallel to the keel. The white tape, visible from any part of the raft, especially at night, would show the position of the rudder at a glance. In handling a wind-driven craft alone, this was of utmost importance.

It was time to eat. I took two tablespoons of barley flour and mixed it with a little water in a cup. The thick paste tasted good. I had the utmost confidence in it as a food. I had started eating it in Ecuador and in Peru, to get my body used to it. I ate sitting beside the wheel on a box, watching the compass at the same time.

I was busy in the afternoon, clearing the deck of odds and ends, but had to interrupt my work often to jump aft for a look at the course. My two little shipmates, Eekie the parrot and Meekie the cat, seemed to be doing all right. Meekie was almost hidden from view, asleep between two coils of rope.

The raft started to swing about, threatening to run into the wind, and I had to stay at the wheel. I still had an hour or so of daylight.

I could not help telling myself, as I sailed on into the greyness, that the dream of almost three years had come true. I was not aware of any feeling of excitement or elation; nor was I depressed in any way. I took it as a matter of course. I had my raft, built to my liking and apparently seaworthy, and was outward bound at last. The rest was up to me. The same familiar sea, the same familiar sky were around me and I felt utterly at home.

The author at the helm.

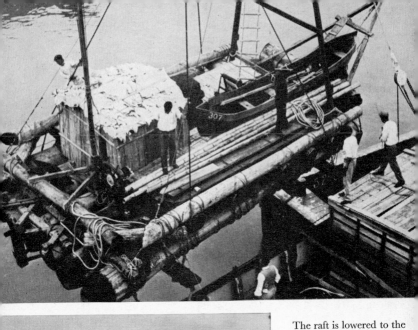

The raft is lowered to the water at Callao, Peru, after a 700-mile trip from Ecuador.

*Courtesy of the Grace Line*

Sails hoisted for the first time in the dock at Callao.

Under sail on trial run, the author at the wheel.

With the commander of the Navy Base at Callao.

*Courtesy of Ultimo Hora, Lima, Peru*

Eekie and Meekie (*right*) sign up as shipmates.

I was glad that the trying days of preparations were over.

I had started on my voyage. "Six to seven thousand miles of open sea lie ahead of you, Bill. Don't take it lightly; seven thousand miles, maybe more. Have you really thought of what that means? It hasn't sunk in yet, has it?"

A sea crashed into the stern and the wheel almost got away from me. I had to smile, seeing how the raft took it; she certainly was built to take it.

Now, about the distance I had to go—six to seven thousand miles—and the long months ahead . . . four or six or even more—I must forget all that, forget all time and distance, utterly. "One day after the other; take them as they come. No time and no distance—get them out of your mind. You know something, Bill: you are on trial, you alone. You're out in no man's land now."

I scanned the seas. I understood how they would rise in a gale and flatten out in the calms; they were like old friends that had run beside me many times during my life.

I leaned over the side and dipped my hand into the sea and sprinkled the water over my head and face and chest. I had done it on impulse, not thinking what I was doing, and then I realized that it was a sort of baptism, a consecration.

A little later the raft ran more steady and I went up on the mast to check the gear, to be sure everything was shipshape for the night. The ladder swung quite a bit, as I knew it would from my trial run. Everything looked secure aloft but I thought some of the blocks could have a better lead. I would attend to that soon enough.

Coming down again, I rigged up my transmitter and sent out my first message, saying that everything was going well and that I was steering west-northwest. Teddy, I knew, would be waiting in the hotel for a telephone call

SOUTH PACIFIC OCEAN

BRITISH SAMOA

UPOLU ISLAND

Manua Islands

Tau

Ofu

Tutuila Island

Pago Pago

A  October 9
B  October 10
C  October 11
D  October 12   I sight Tau at 6 PM
E  October 13   Tau, Olosega, Ofu
                I sight Tutuila at 9 AM and send last message
F  October 14   At 2 AM I set my course for British Samoa
G  October 14   The Manua-tele starts tow to Pago Pago, arriving October 15 at 1:30 AM

THE APPROACH TO SAMOA

from the Peruvian Naval Station reporting my message. Perhaps the *San Martin* was already back in Callao and had given her my last message. She had originally planned to stay on in Peru for a week or two and visit some of the Inca ruins, but then had decided to return to New York as soon as she knew that I was well on my way. "I couldn't enjoy anything till you came back," she had said.

As darkness began to fall I took Eekie's cage, wrapped an oilskin coat around it, and put him in the cabin. Teddy had told me that the night air and flying spray would be bad for the parrot. On leaving Callao I had the cage swinging from the ladder, but later in the day I gave it a permanent place on top of the yellow-painted box that housed my little generator, which was lashed against the forepart of the cabin. Eekie had been in good spirits all day but squawked angrily when I wrapped the coat around the cage and carried it inside.

Meekie was tied to the little hand-winch at the foot of the ladder and had not moved so much as an inch from the place where she had hidden herself in fright after being put on board the raft. I couldn't tell whether she was seasick or not but she looked pitifully disconsolate and refused to eat. I was sure she had never been tied up before.

I had lighted one of my three lanterns, put it in a box to shield it from the wind, and adjusted it so that its light fell on the compass. The box and the compass both were lashed to the deck for the raft was having a rough time in the seas. I had decided against carrying running lights. I might encounter ships in this coastal area, I knew, but since I didn't dare to sleep I would see any lights that appeared on the horizon, and if a ship approached me I would flash my searchlight to keep from being run down.

83

I was sitting on a little wooden box beside the wheel, steering. West-northwest! Hour after hour the raft sailed, on through the night. The darkness was almost solid around me. No stars stood in the sky. I probably wouldn't see the sun or stars for a week or so. The Humboldt Current, carrying cold water from the Antarctic into the tropics, was the cause of this haze. I could sail out of it by heading due west for a few days and still be in the southeast wind but I would lose the push of the current.

The seas broke white beside me in the night. They smashed ceaselessly over the stern, making a terrific, deafening noise. A ship's bottom is built round and streamlined, like a fish, and so offers little resistance to the seas and suffers little pounding, but my raft had a large, square surface for a bottom, something solid for the waves to get hold of and to strike at.

It was wet and cold. I put on more clothes. I ate raw sugar, spooning out the nearly black, paste-like stuff from a jar. It tasted good and gave me a quick lift. Now and then I got up, lashed the wheel, and went forward with my flashlight to check the rope and sail and rigging. Forward, I always took a look at little Meekie. She was in exactly the same spot, looking very small, her little black face all screwed up, her eyes tightly closed. She seemed lost to the world in her misery from grief, at having been torn away from the life she had known, to be put on a jolting, thundering thing that hurled itself through raging water, and finally at being tied up like a prisoner with a collar around her neck. I checked up on Eekie, too, lifting the corner of the coat now and then and flashing my light at him. He growled every time. At frequent intervals I flashed my light on my rudder, to see how it was taking the smashing seas.

I had removed the lashings from the spokes. No stars, no sun—I would have to run by dead reckoning for some

84

time. What lay ahead?—I could not help wondering. "Forget time and space, Bill. Somewhere far away lies Samoa—or call it China or the end of the earth. Day by day—that's your only course. After a few months you can begin to relax, look around you, and say you are on the way." And so passed the night with the ceaseless pounding of the seas and the distant moaning of the wind—passed while I dozed and nodded and dreamed.

At daybreak, I put Eekie's cage back on the yellow box and he squawked with joy. I tried to tempt Meekie with some milk but she refused it, shrinking farther into her little space where she sought security and peace.

I tried to boil some water for my coffee but could not get the stove started, and drank it cold. I used instant coffee.

There was no sun. In the afternoon I threw a piece of balsa wood over the side and by its speed, as it drifted past the raft, computed that I was making about two miles an hour.

I had let Eekie out of his cage to give him a little freedom. He climbed about a bit, then settled on the ladder about ten feet above the deck. I was watching him from the wheel. Suddenly he gave a squawk and flew out beyond the raft. His wings were clipped short and he came down almost at once, just clearing the deck in his descent, and plopped into the sea. In a flash he turned and started to swim towards the raft by working his wing stumps frantically. I grasped a stick and held it out towards him. He clutched the end of it with his break and scrambled on to it. The next moment I had him aboard.

I dried him off and put him in the cabin. As soon as he was inside he became violently seasick and vomited profusely. He had eaten bananas during the day. He was now a spectacle of utmost misery. I never realized a bird could show such suffering. Within a few hours, however, he recovered somewhat, and when I wrapped him up in his cage for the night he gave me his customary growl of disapproval.

After I had lit my compass lantern and the raft was foaming through the darkness I went forward to see what I could do with little Meekie. She had not eaten since we left Callao and she hadn't budged from her refuge.

I had quite a time getting her out and taking her aft, though she was obviously a gentle little creature.

I put her down on a sweater and tied the end of her leash to the handle of the transmitter, talking to her and stroking her all the while. Presently she perked up a little. At last she seemed to understand that I meant no harm, and opened her golden eyes wide and gazed wistfully at me. She even appeared ready to talk.

"Are you a little seasick, Meekie?" I asked her.

"No," she seemed to answer, "I am not seasick, but I am sick right down to my little soul. I don't like it here."

"I can see that," I said, talking to her as I would have done with any shipmate, "but you will be all right soon. Everything will come out all right, little Meekie. We'll all get along together, the three of us, Eekie and you and I."

I went over her black fur with a flashlight. "Meekie," I said, surprised, "you had at least fifteen million fleas on you when I got you in Callao. What became of them all?"

"I was loaded with them all right," Meekie replied, scratching herself a bit. "Some of them must have drowned trying to jump on the rubber raft with the three sailors, getting back to Peru. I saw them jump. I would have jumped too if I hadn't been tied up. Most of the fleas got washed off me by the seas. I was drenched many times, you know. I still got a couple left though, I think."

I stroked her and talked to her in a low voice till she closed her eyes.

86

I had dozed on and off during the day and managed to come through the boisterous night without actually falling asleep at the wheel. When it became almost impossible to keep my eyes open I ate sugar and made myself coffee a number of times. I kept water and coffee and a cup always near the wheel.

Still no sun.

My stove gave me trouble again but I finally managed to bring water to a boil and had hot coffee. I sent out a message at 11 a.m., Eastern Standard Time, giving my course and reporting that all was well.

In the afternoon I let Eekie out of his cage for some exercise but this time fastened a line to his foot. Meekie sat near the wheel, half asleep. She had eaten a little and seemed to be content. Then she became aware of Eekie, who sat beside his cage, forward, his back towards us. Meekie, eyeing the heedless bird, took a sudden leap towards Eekie. I cried out but Meekie paid no heed. I grabbed a tennis shoe lying near me and threw it at her just in time. That startled her and she flashed down to the main logs through an opening in the bamboo deck. I didn't see Meekie again till late at night when she came aft and snuggled up to me as if we were old, old friends and nothing had happened between us. I was sure she had forgotten all about the incident.

The night was one long struggle to keep awake. It grew light at last but again without sun. The wind was steady and strong and the raft laboured quite a bit, taking seas and spray. I was still steering west-northwest. I figured I was now well off the coast. I was quite used to being alone by this time. Deep down, there was still a gnawing uncertainty within me, mainly concerned with the raft—what she would do in a storm, how the rigging would stand up, and whether or not the lashings would hold—but I was much calmer already. I was taking root

87

in my new life—the sky, the sea, and the *Seven Little Sisters*.

The fourth day out, I noticed a frayed piece of rope trailing astern from the right aftercorner of the raft where my anchor was lashed. I thought it was a piece of old dock line that had been caught underneath the raft and now had worked itself free. No sailor would allow such an unsightly thing to remain. I got out on the end of the log, which was still slimy from the waste oil that had floated around in the harbour, and, holding on to the mainmast stay with my left hand, tried to clear the rope.

I had put a marlin spike and a knife within reach before venturing out on the log. It proved a harder job than I thought and I had to work with my right arm deep in the water, groping beneath the thick log to cut or disentangle the rope. Several times I was forced to rest. Finally I cut the line and was clearing the ends to let it drift astern when my right knee slipped on the greasy log and my leg went into the sea. I had a good hold on the stay; my life depended on it. Quickly I pulled myself back up. I thought nothing of it, but later, looking back over the side I noticed a huge brown shadow in the depths. It was shapeless and I thought that my eyes had played me a trick. I looked again, and the brown colouring became more defined in the dark-grey waters. Could it be a fish? After I had changed to dry pants I had another look and this time I plainly saw a good-sized shark swimming just where my leg had dangled in the water.

The knowledge gave me a shock. I was not quite so alone as I had thought. The sea beneath me was undoubtedly alive with sharks. I also realized that I should have had a lifeline around me, for if my hand had failed by a mere second I would have dropped into the sea with nothing to cling to—and that would have been the end.

The following day, towards evening, I saw a school of whales about a mile to windward. I also saw some tuna near the raft. They were all big fellows, swimming deep down. I did not try to catch any. Next day I saw my first dolphins and schools of flying fish. During the same day I saw the sea sparkling far off where, for a moment, the sun had broken through.

# * 9 *

## RAW SUGAR AND BARLEY FLOUR

TODAY, June 30, I had been out a week and saw blue sky for the first time, a little patch no larger than a fingernail. That meant I had not been able to take a sight and so could only guess at my position. By dead reckoning I put myself at Lat. 8° 17′ South and Long. 82° 20′ West, 400 miles from Callao. But there was no question about being in the Humboldt Current. It was cold. I had to wear two sweaters, a flannel shirt and a pea-jacket to keep warm, also two pairs of woollen socks Teddy knitted for me. It had been cold since the day I left Callao towed by the *San Martin*.

How strangely everything drifted out of my mind, as if I had had no real contact with the world of men, no real hold on its existence. I could hardly remember anything and details not at all. It disturbed me. My sense of time had disappeared also.

As the day waned I filled my lantern with kerosene to light up the compass and got ready for the night. The old oilskin coat went around Eekie's cage to keep out the penetrating cold. Meekie was all snug underneath the winch on an old sweater. After a short twilight it was dark, as is the way of the tropics.

I jumped up and stared into the night. Was something coming loose aloft? I had dozed at the wheel. I picked up the flashlight lying beside the compass that was dimly lighted by the lantern and flashed it over the mainsail.

Everything was all right—just the usual sounds, the knocking of endless seas.

I was still getting used to the raft. I listened to the wind and the sea. Now and then a big wave hit and rolled underneath. The rudder got the shock first and the wheel kicked hard trying to go over. After a while another one would come with a crash and roar, lift the raft, go churning underneath and move on.

I felt the steady straining of the sails, the straining of the whole, solidly bound raft as it pushed ahead, driving, smashing through. She was steering pretty well tonight but needed watching. I let her have her way quite a bit, I had learned that. I did not try for a beeline; there could be no straight course on a raft handled by one man. Off she went ten degrees to leeward off the course. And then back again. That was good enough for me—no beeline on the raft. I wouldn't wear myself out juggling the spokes, staring at the compass till my eyes came out. I probably lost from ten to twenty per cent of my mileage every day that way but it could not be helped.

She acted like a ship; there was not a loose inch on her. And the seas liked her. Those logs just lay in the water like part of the sea, like they were born for it. I wished at times that some of the ancient Indians could see me making my way through the night on one of their balsa rafts.

The thousand noises of the sea surrounded me, seemingly filled all my body. Into the darkness, into the heart of the sea—this was sailing! There came a big one, bruising the raft with its shock. Then it sounded like the swishing of countless brooms, showering drops over me. White manes were all around me, above the black, tumultuous muscles of the sea.

Was I really a seaman to have gone on this voyage? I had known real seamen in my life, knew what the term

91

implied. I could see them now, men of many nations, grim-faced warriors of grey seas. Perhaps they were the faceless ones, as one puts it now, the men who did not speak, but they were the true ones. They had come from all over—from the Finnish coasts to Portugal and every place between, to the north and south. And from America came the Grand Banks schooner men who put their dories over, loaded down with cod gear, when steamers ran out extra lines to hold them to the dock. I had sailed with them all and at no time did I think I could beat them in their silent strength.

*What are you doing here, Willis—on this thing, and all alone?* they asked me now, a host of sunken shipmates, the crippled, broken men in the harbours of the world, their dim eyes gazing emptily at forgotten seas.

"Not to show you up, boys. I'm sailing on what I learned from you, old-timers; I'm merely carrying on. This is a voyage of the spirit. I'm half spirit now, standing half in the sea and half in the sky and outward bound, just starting. You did not know, sailing with me, that I was half spirit even then. That's why I left you time and again to wander over the earth, too, and see the rest of creation, to see all its people and sit in silence among them. I had to live that way too."

I felt hungry and, putting the lashings on the wheel, went to the cabin. Working almost twenty-four hours a day with little or no sleep, one lost a lot of energy and had to make up for it with extra food.

A meal was quickly prepared: a tablespoonful of flour put in a tin cup and mixed with just enough cold water to make a thick paste. I ate it slowly but in a minute was finished. It was roasted and ground *cañihua*, a cereal growing in the Andes above the 12,000-foot level. Someone had told me about it and I had been lucky to get fifty pounds for my trip. It did not grow in large ears like

92

most of our grains and also was hard to gather, and so there was not much of it around. It was well known to the High Sierras Indians. The Incas also knew its great sustaining and nourishing powers and fed it to their best warriors before battle. It certainly agreed with me. I also used barley flour, of which I had about seventy pounds, roasted and ground like the *cañihua*.

Eating made me think of Quevedo where my logs came from and an evening when I sat with some adventurers in a little restaurant. We were talking about what kind of food I would take along on my trip. These men were all veterans of the jungles and Sierras and had been over every inch of the country as prospectors, surveyors, scientists, and ranch managers. I said I would take only primitive food along to keep in spirit with my venture but had not yet decided on what. This was in true keeping with my usual philosophy that at the right time the right idea will come. Let things develop of themselves, give them time to grow, from the outside towards you, and then from within you reach out and recognize them when they come.

"I've been thinking about something for you," said a veteran recently returned from a long stay among the Jibaros, the fantastically written-up head-shrinking Indians who live in the Oriente section of Ecuador. Incidentally, he considered them peaceful and well behaved, an opinion borne out by numerous others who had lived among them. "Many years ago," the man continued, "I was hiding out in the High Sierras. They were after me and it would have been a bamboo wall and a rhapsody in lead. It was a political mess. I had to live and there was nothing but *machica*—roasted and ground barley flour, the same stuff the Indians used. They always lived on it. So I lived on *machica*. It's the plainest food there is, I guess, but it gives you all the strength you need. The Indians couldn't exist without it. They just mix it with a

93

little water, knead it into a ball and eat it. No cooking, no pots. It'll keep you strong as a horse, Bill. The Indians eat it all the time when carrying loads across the mountains. And you know how much they carry—anything you can put on their backs, a piano or half a household; and they don't walk, they run with it, trot uphill over stony roads in the thin air of the high altitudes."

"That shall be my food, *machica*," I said.

"And something else you should have. *Raspadura*."

"What's *raspadura*?"

"Raw sugar—sugar with all the molasses in it. They sell it in round packages wrapped up in leaves. You can get it right across the street in the market." He pointed across the street at the teeming market stalls of Quevedo. "That will give you all the energy you need. I guess you know that sugar gives you energy."

In Peru, *raspadura* was called *chancaca*. I took about seventy pounds of it. . . .

I had known the value of the whole grains, raw sugar and molasses for many years, having been interested in nutrition since my youth. I had tried whole grains and raw sugar during long periods while working many hours at the hardest kind of labour, under conditions similar to those I could expect on my voyage.

Long ago, in my days on the Galveston docks, we loaded hundreds of ships each season with grain for Europe, and every week-end when going back to our farm about twenty-six miles away I used to take a bag of whole wheat along. My mother ground it in a little grist mill fastened to the kitchen wall and baked it into bread. Those were my strong-man days and I wanted the rest of my family, my mother and sister and two little brothers, to be strong and healthy too. It paid off. Raw sugar I brought home too, the regular commercial raw sugar shipped to the refineries, but by no means as nourishing as the South American *raspadura* or *chancaca* I had now. I unloaded ship after ship from Cuba during the season. My family lived entirely on unadulterated, unrefined food in those days. Whole rice we bought from the nearby Texas rice farmers.

When I wrote my wife from Ecuador that I would use barley flour as my main food item she felt that I had made a good decision. She answered me she had just read that Tibetans and other tribes of the Himalayas used this same roasted and ground barley flour and prepared it the same simple way for eating—just kneading it into a ball, like the Indians of the Andes. I believe that a diet of nothing but whole grain ground into flour was the secret of survival in Europe and Asia throughout the ages, during thousands of famines that swept over the lands in the wake of wars or bad harvests. From ancestors of European peasant stock that lived through these catastrophes I had inherited my reverence for such food.

The raft was steering pretty well right now and perhaps I could get a little more sleep, ten or fifteen minutes or so. The wind was steady, blowing southeast out of the darkness.

I lay down on the bamboo deck, a flashlight in my hand, my face within an inch of the compass, almost touching it. My ears had become trained to alert me if the raft ran too close to the wind. They could tell by the change in the sound of the seas. I had to know before the sail started flapping. Not only my ears, but all my senses warned me when something went wrong. It was a lot of work to bring the raft around again once she ran off. And there was always the danger of damaging the sail or rigging when the wind struck me from ahead.

My eyes were like lead but I would take a chance. It is strange, sleeping when you first tell yourself to keep wide awake—meaning your subconscious. I took another look at the darkness around me broken only by patches of grey

95

where the seas broke. The wind enfolded the raft like a blanket. "Make your own way, *Seven Little Sisters*!"

The raft sailed without running lights through the night. I had not seen a ship nor a light since I left Callao. So I was not afraid of being run down. I felt better to be alone in the darkness, to know that the last possible link with the world was broken. I wanted no one, only the elements, to know where I was. This was a voyage of the spirit—was becoming so more and more. I suspected that my radio was not transmitting, which added to my feeling of isolation; I intended to test it further before locking it up and forgetting it. That would be hard on Teddy, of course, not knowing anything about me. She had become a little giant, though, living with me all these years. She would hold out against the world: "Yes, Bill will come back. . . ." Hadn't I told her so?

Was I sleeping? I heard the pounding of the seas a few inches beneath me, striking the bamboos on which my head rested. I dozed off, feeling each sea beating against me; I became one with the crash and the roar. I must have slept for the sounds receded. Only the big seas registered.

The author and his wife take leave of each other.

*Courtesy of Ultimo Hora, Lima, Peru*

(*Below*): The author at the wheel at the beginning of the 6,500-mile voyage. The cylinder in the foreground is the radio transmitter.

*Courtesy of La Prensa, Lima, Peru*

A view from the stern, 1,000 miles at sea.

Into the sunset, 2,000 miles at sea.

## ★ IO ★

## DAWN SONG

THE sun was near rising and the sea was alight. The whole sky was covered with pastel-coloured clouds. Creation was singing the dawn song and the universe stood hushed.

The *Seven Little Sisters* made her way through the foam, gliding over the jubilant seas, bathing their sleek bodies. My white sails were racing the clouds into the virgin day.

A thousand songs were floating on the light and enfolding me. I was carried away. My lungs filled with new life and my arms went up in worship. Come with me, all you dwellers of the cities—you toilers of the mills and shops and dreary offices, come with me on this lonely voyage, into this wonderland of stars and seas, of clouds and light and loneliness. Come with me and hear the song of creation. . . .

Every morning I stood on winged feet, I who had tottered almost sleepless through the long night, struggling with the sails and hanging on only by will. Each dawn I soared in the beauty of the new day and my strength was without measure.

It looked like I would be able to take sights today, the sky was almost clear. I seemed to have at last sailed out of the grey cloud blanket of the coast. For two weeks I went without a sight, just setting a course by dead reckoning. The only thing that worried me were the Galapagos. I could not feel good till I had cleared them, for the Current, I knew, swings way to the north during the winter. Yesterday, on July 2, my dead reckoning position was Lat. 7° 30′ South and Long. 83° 25′ West, 450 miles out of Callao and quite a way yet from the Galapagos, at least 500 miles.

I worked on my stove and straightened up the gear lying in the canoe. Also I had to change a block aloft that didn't lead just right. I had to forget the beauty around me; it was there whenever I looked up, all day long. Every day brought new problems for I was far from knowing the raft, far from having things shipshape for every emergency. Unfortunately everything I did had to be done on the fly, with one eye on the compass and the sails. Sometimes I even carried the compass to where I was working, to keep me from jumping aft and checking all the time. The simplest tasks had to be dropped many times when I had to make dashes to the wheel when she ran off, and often a job requiring only a few undisturbed minutes took hours. I had to develop the patience of a mountain.

Yesterday I worked a good part of the morning on my two stoves, using box after box of matches, but could not get them started. Perhaps the kerosene was not good or the fault was with the stoves. I had had trouble ever since I left. If I couldn't get them going it meant a diet of raw fish, once I caught them; so far I had not caught any.

Of course Meekie, my little cat, wouldn't mind raw fish. She was shaping up well, affectionate at times, and a good sailor. I had seen her crouching on the bottom logs and the seas hitting her and she not giving an inch, just crouching and watching the tiny fish swimming beneath her in the cracks. Occasionally I bawled her out for going too close to the edge of the raft. When she was gone a long while I would start looking for her and generally found her crawling over the main logs beneath the deck, making her way slowly—seeing, feeling, quivering with strange excitement from head to tail, discovering a new world of intoxicating smells, of tiny crabs and barnacles and other sea creatures, of fantastic little plants growing on the logs in the luminous blue of a glass-clear sea. Meekie was six to eight months old. I generally kept her tied up on account of Eekie; she had been after him ever since she came on board. . . .

About two weeks before sailing from Callao one of the Lima newspapers had printed that I was looking for a parrot and a cat to accompany me on my voyage. The response was most generous. Pets from all over Peru were offered to me. The trouble, however, was that I had no place to keep animals while we were living in a hotel. One day the company that supplied me with my water sent a parrot to the raft and I had to accept it. I put it on board a cruiser lying near the raft to be taken care of till I sailed. All I needed now was a cat.

A parrot can be put in a cage but it was more difficult with a cat. I had to arrange to get one on the last day, as I could not expect people to hold a cat for me and bring it to the raft just before sailing. Besides, the sailing date was uncertain.

I had my eye on a few tough-looking cats that hung around the Navy base, thinking I would pick up one of them the last day and shanghai it for the trip, in good old sailing-ship style. With this in mind I had started to feed one or two, hoping I would get friendly with them and be allowed to get close enough for the snatch. Peruvian cats are by no means as tame as ours. But as with the deer season in the States, when all the deer vanish the day before the shooting starts, so all the cats at the base were tipped off by some untraceable instinct to keep out of sight as the day of my departure came near.

I spoke of my dilemma to a group of officers and a sub-

99

marine commander suggested I come with him. We went to the club-rooms and he gave an order to a sailor. The man came back carrying a black cat, not quite grown. It hung over his arm like a black rag that had just been through a wringer. I had never seen an animal so unresponsive to my efforts to make a good impression. "Get away from me, get away," she seemed to say in every line of her. Cats are clairvoyant, they say. This one obviously knew the whole story of what lay ahead of her and didn't like it.

"How do you like her, Mr. Willis?" the officer asked.

"I like her. She's sort of unresponsive right now but I hope she'll get over it."

"She'll be all right—take her. I'll send a man to the raft with her tomorrow, just before you sail."

The next day Meekie was shanghaied for the voyage to Samoa on the *Seven Little Sisters*. She had a little shipmate, of course, Eekie. But the two would never get along. They were born enemies.

I sometimes thought Eekie was raised in a girl's school—he would laugh and sing, babble and giggle, break out in little shrieks and melodious chuckles, like a whole classroom all by himself. He was a little master when he felt like it. He entertained himself and asked for no company. He was small, alert, and pretty in a green coat with a patch of red above his tail and a few blue feathers on the wings. I fed him corn on the cob and after that was gone there would be shelled corn and rice, enough grub to last him a year. . . .

We were sailing through fairly heavy seas but the raft took them easily. The sun was near going down. Meekie was asleep and Eekie was babbling away with his back to the wind; his cage was standing on the motor box against the forward end of the cabin. I had no batteries for my receiver and instead used a generator driven by a small motor. It was time for my broadcast.

The Peruvian Government had given me the call letters 7HTAS, an abbreviation for *Siete Hermanitas*, which is Spanish for *Seven Little Sisters*. My Marconi Salvita III transmitter was operated by turning a crank and was set for two frequencies, medium wave of 500 and short wave of 8,364 kc., both international ship disaster and SOS frequencies. The Peruvian Navy had requested that I send my position at 11 a.m. and 6 p.m. EST when the navy station in Callao would stand by to pick it up. They would relay it to the U.S. Navy in Washington to be sent on to my wife. The Peruvian Navy had also promised to listen fifteen minutes every four hours throughout the twenty-four for any message I might send.

It took a little practice to turn the crank of the transmitter with one hand and tap out a clear message with the other. I always gave it fifty full turns with both hands first to get it warmed up. The transmitter received also— but only on the 500 frequency, and ever since leaving Callao I had been requesting an answer consisting of the two letters—OK—to signify that my messages were being received. So far no answer or any signal had come through. I was almost certain therefore that either my set was not working properly or that my aerial was not long enough. The manual that came with the set indicated that the latter was the case.

My chronometer also was not running and had been consigned to its pretty double box. It was brand new and I wondered what had happened to it. The Peruvian Navy had tested it for me for ten days and found it a perfect instrument. I was using an ordinary pocket watch for my navigation instead and hoped nothing would go wrong with it. I had nothing else. It was bedded down on a piece of soft cloth and lying safely in a box, like the crown jewel of the Pacific, for if my receiver or generator should go on strike too (I took them along solely to get the time) I would have nothing to navigate with.

For an hour last night I had tried to get WWV which broadcasts Eastern Standard Time around the clock by code and voice from Washington, D.C., but had no luck because I had to jump on deck every few seconds to take care of the steering. I would try again today. I had been told that early dawn was the best time. The Amateur Radio Club of Lima had been very helpful in giving me instructions. If I could not get time signals for setting my watch, which was far from running correctly, I would have to find my way by latitude only, getting it from noon sights, when the sun was at the zenith, and which required no watch. That's how they navigated in the early days of the sailing ships before they had dependable timepieces, by dead reckoning and latitude.

Everything was turning towards the primitive with me; I just didn't have the right touch for machinery. A surprising lot of things had gone wrong since I left Callao and in each case I discovered it was due to my own fault. But I knew my nature—starting off on one leg and off balance but finishing strong.

We kept running steadily over the seas and down, day and night, rolling and pitching, buried under foam and seas and shaken by the wind, watching the thousand faces of the day—the clouds, the winds and the light as they drifted past above us in endless changing patterns, turning the sea to grey or blue, to dull or dazzling masses. The wind was strong and fairly steady, and always cool. The *Seven Little Sisters* took the seas as if born to them but laboured incessantly and with unpredictable movements. She could very well say to me: "We'll stay on top but hang on if you want to make it. No walking on the deck unless both hands have something solid to hang on to." Sometimes it took quite a while to get a cup of coffee to my lips, the edge kept trying to hit my nose, my ears, and to give my eyes a wash first. I was using instant coffee—usually made with cold water.

How the seas sneaked up sometimes! There is no truce with the sea. On the last mile the last wave may roll over you—and go on. Some waves stole up like shadows, making a quick, panting noise just before breaking on top of you with wide-open white jaws. But my Ecuadorian balsas knew how to block them or ride them, as if they had studied them from afar, from the cloistered seclusion of their dark forest where they had grown apparently rooted for all time, yet had peeped over the high heads of their companions towards the far Pacific and perhaps dreamed of a day when they could bathe their slim bodies in it and carry a white and gallant sail.

Drive them, you big squaresail, you mighty windplough and you, hard-standing mizzen bringing up the rear, drive the *Seven Little Sisters*! Let their bellies drag deep and their hair stream white in the flow. Every mile counts. Let every stitch pull to beat the hurricanes. Drive them through the long day and drive them into the night; let the stars come out and hide behind the clouds, let the winds howl and the moon come silvery sharp, and wax and go, and darkness come again. Across the Pacific!

What a raft we have to live on! Eekie and Meekie feel as I do. *Seven Little Sisters*, why did I call you that? First I named the centre log Teddy, after my wife, and it was Teddy and her six little sisters; then it became *Seven Little Sisters*, and so it stayed. Did you know that you have a namesake in the heavens above you, in the very highest that mortal eyes have scaled? There they stand, a shrine blazing amid shrines, the Pleiades, commonly called the Seven Sisters and known to all sailors. The Greeks named them after the seven daughters of Atlas. They have waited long for man, deep below, on this earth made beautiful by their rays, to create something and call it in their likeness. *Seven Little Sisters,* you are under the protection of your celestial sisters.

A thousand rafts have sailed before you but you can hold your own with the best. I have seen you pull away from seas that thought they had you. We are sailing into the hurricanes, into their vast breeding strongholds and we know just what they are. Even if they hit you, you will come through, though most likely without rigging, deck, and house, but you and perhaps Meekie will make it. Maybe I'll make it, too, lashed to you, still breathing.

I had tried to take out insurance on my life with Lloyd's of London but they were not interested. Everyone thought that I was crossing the Styx. A large American news service had taken pictures of the leave-taking. Why? To have a record of me in case I shouldn't come back, they told my wife. "Take your pictures," Teddy had told them, "but he'll come back." Their faces turned blank at that. "They don't know you, Bill," my wife had said to me later.

And I say they did not know my *Seven Little Sisters.* I had faith then, and now I knew those balsas, standing day and night at the wheel, feeling them beneath me, moving like seals, like beings alive and made for the water.

## ★ II ★

## LONG TOM JOINS THE RAFT

JULY 10. Lat. 3° 26′ South, Long. 88° West, by dead
reckoning, moderate wind and sea, sky heavily overcast.
I took a look at my chart and found that I was approximately 150 miles southeast of Santa Maria, the most
southern of the Galapagos Islands. I was steering north-
west by west and thought that would let me clear.

A school of dolphins swam with the raft but I could
not interest them with lures or spoons, I would have to
wait till I got some flying fish on deck for bait. Dolphins
are gorgeous-looking fish from three to almost five feet
long, moving in and out like shapes of blue light, with
tail fins of a golden colour. Sometimes they move faster
than the eye can see. They usually kept beneath the raft,
darting out if something aroused their interest. Sometimes they trailed behind the stern, big fellows close to
the rudder, smaller ones farther off. They were a study
in grace of shape and movement, one moment blazing
blue, the next blending with the deeper blue of the sea
and becoming invisible. Again and again I was astonished
at their phenomenal speed.

Sharks, too, had been around lately, and one in particular had been with me for some time now. I called him
Long Tom. He was about nine feet long, a beautiful
specimen, slim and brown, with all his fins tipped with
white, the model of a stratosphere plane. He swam close
to the right aftercorner of the raft, beside the wheel and
almost near enough to touch; he was there day and night.

His presence made me a little uneasy at first but by now I was used to him. If I were to fall overboard he probably would have his teeth in me before I was fully in the water.

One night I dropped a flying fish over the side to see if he were there. He was. The back fin and then the tail fin came arching up out of the darkness; he had seized the fish and disappeared.

I was living a strange, dream-like existence—like being on a bit of land floating in watery space, or like sailing on a plank with no shelter, no solid deck beneath. Living directly on the sea where one had to take what she gave, for better or for worse, I stood alone with Nature. Perhaps this is man's natural condition, one begetting a constant feeling of exhilaration and strength.

I was getting along fine on my diet of *cañibua* and barley flour and molasses sugar. My stomach had shrunk at the beginning and then had become used to the diet. I always ate the cereals slowly, mixed with just enough cold water for a thick paste. The morning was perhaps the best time, for then the stomach was strongest. One or two tablespoonfuls were enough for a meal. In three or four hours I would eat again, sometimes throughout the twenty-four hours, depending on the amount of labour I did. Ordinarily I ate my sugar in the afternoon but when exhausted I ate sugar at any time—also before tackling a hard job, I ate as much as half a pound at a time. It caused thirst but not excessively so.

I expected my Stone Age 'disaster diet' of cereals and sugar to affect my mental state, causing my mind to contemplate Nature and the Sublime. It did and also brought about a merciless study of myself. It also brought peace.

Things were shaping up better every day and I was satisfied with the speed of the raft. Every day was a study in raft sailing. And the nervous tension caused by many months of preparation was being relieved. What a glorious feeling to be alone in the universe! What humbleness it begets, what resignation! What strength of the spirit! What hope to purge oneself of a thousand stains!

I knew that I was sailing into the hurricane season but felt calm about it, more so every day. It depended on the wind whether I could make land before bad weather struck. If I should lose my rigging in a storm I'd have to drift and take whatever came my way; it could become a drift lasting years. I was mentally prepared for it and the prospect was not frightening. I was having a lot of stormy weather and sometimes I carried only the jib and reefed mizzen. But the raft was holding up; there hadn't been an inch of slack in any one of the numerous lashings. The rigging too stood solid and the raft sailed like a real ship.

My long contact with the sea had bred confidence and I had learned to keep calm in all her moods. A man believes he knows the sea in her friendliness and in her aroused strength, knows how far she can go! How far she can go! He knows very well that she can at a moment's notice tear up all man-made agreements and fling the fragments before the approaching storm, before the volcanoes of wind belching from her dark centres. Between dawn and dusk she can change the face of the earth and its history. Little man on a raft, she holds you in the hollow of her hand—it's not up to your cunning.

I was falling deeper and deeper into my detached state— into this strange severance of mind from the world I had left. It had been noticeable almost from the first day at sea. I could not and cannot yet quite understand it. Such a state had never seized me before, at least not with such abruptness and so completely. It was a little disturbing at times and I dug into my mind to stir up what memories I could to rebuild the bridge and recapture the world I had left. But the bridge was down. My mind, like my body, was adrift in space with no shore in sight.

Perhaps this was at least partly the reaction to the intense nervous strain during the many months of preparation. Nerves can take so much and then must give. Perhaps I had just hung together by sheer force of will, just long enough to get going—and now everything within me was letting go. Happy oblivion—it was healing, leaving me free for a new life. There were problems enough every day but they could be solved, if they depended entirely on me. I had no hidden antagonists here, no endless little worries nibbling at me. There was only Nature, who strengthened even as she struck; she destroyed only ignorance and weakness and lack of faith. . . .

I was sailing through fairly heavy weather. The wilder the sea the more impressive it is, the more sombre and threatening. Dark, rolling high and breaking—what beauty there is in the majestic ranges moving across the waste!

Sailing through the night. . . . It sounded like we were in the breakers, lying on a rocky shore and breaking up. The seas kept on smashing into the logs. Every stitch was pulling, I felt, at the wheel. She was fairly ploughing through the darkness. Plenty of wind! Something might give way aloft but I was letting her go. I wanted to see what she could do. I thought that she was built to take it, below and aloft too. I hoisted the yard with the halyard and brought it down with three downhauls. All split-second work, I would call it, getting it up or down in a wind, or else I would not have a sail. Twelve tons of raft needed plenty of sail to drive it. Sometimes I thought I was driving a big square-rigger through the seas.

In spite of the spirit of bravado that had seized me I watched closely to see just what the rigging could stand.

I had taken along only one set of sails, which I knew was a mistake and could bring about my downfall, condemning me to a drift that might never end. I was standing by every moment now to lower the yard, quivering as much as the *Seven Little Sisters* buried beneath me in foam and straining under the pressure of sails and seas. One could hang on too long, carried away by pride. . . .

I remember the time in 1909 when I was a youngster on a square rigger and we were driving into the howling darkness of the Horn. Suddenly we saw two four-masted barques come out of the haze like white phantoms, racing neck and neck before the gale with every sail set. Racing in that gale! Each had three men lashed to the wheel and another man standing by to keep on the course, for with a point or so to either side the masts would have come down. Seas were breaking house-high behind them, almost boarding the poop—death seas, as any seaman knew.

We on our ship gazed at the two barques, hanging on to our rigging, grey-faced, cursing their skippers, feeling for the sailors. Titanic sight! Titanic captains! And the gale took up the challenge and howled, and the seas rose to mountains and then broke as they passed the ships. Eighteen knots they were making, we thought. There . . . ! High aloft on the steel mast a sail split, fluttered once, and was gone, ripped out of the bolt-ropes. One yard stood bare. Sail after sail went, as if shot down from the sky. But the titans kept on—neck and neck while we lay under reefed topsails. Soon they were out of sight. They were never heard of again. They had sailed into the seas with every stitch and stick standing and every man at his post. Swallowed up—no homeward passage for them. Let the women wait! One of the ships we identified as belonging to Leist Brothers out of Hamburg. The other ship we thought was British.

Another time we were coming up the west coast of South America after rounding the Horn, sailing before a gale with all sails set. But it was no death gale this time, with a falling glass and rising seas. We were glad to have cleared the Horn and glad to have a chance to get out of it on the blow and to the north. The skipper was watching closely. He was no titan, just a man who knew his ship and was willing to lose a sail or two to get offshore and north. We were overtaking a big square-rigger with white-painted masts and yards—a beauty of a ship. She had all sails furled except the topsails. She was afraid to sail and we spat as we passed, our poop awash and both watches on standby. The other ship couldn't take the shame of it and before we knew it she had all sails set and was passing us as if we were anchored. She could sail. But we knew her skipper hadn't the guts to let her go on her own. . . .

I continued to wonder at my mental state. It was not only that the past had become dim but things happening now made little impression, even when they were of a serious nature. I was apathetic at times and at other times would fly into rages. To be alive and sailing and steeped in Nature and beauty seemed to be all I required. My diet, lack of sleep, and endless labour no doubt affected me strongly. Most noticeable was my almost complete turn towards the spiritual. It reminded me of times when I had lived alone in the woods or by the sea, writing poetry. But now more than ever before I was aware of being really apart from my body and from ordinary thinking.

In spite of mishaps, I was not worried. I always seemed to find a way out and thought I would continue to do so. Fear had disappeared. I visualized other emergencies and what I would do. Probably the greatest danger was from falling overboard or slipping on deck and breaking a bone. Long before the raft was finished I had decided to have one or two lines trailing from the stern at all times so that I could get back on board if I should be washed over the side, but so far had not done so. I knew this was inexcusable but still I did nothing. The idea of a good piece of rope getting slimy and worn in the sea stopped me.

The ever-present danger of slipping on deck and breaking a leg or arm was real and with me always, especially at night when I had to make wild leaps over boxes, the canoe, water cans and centreboards and uneven parts of the deck, to work the sails, and always while the raft was acting like a mean horse trying to throw its rider. I saw myself breaking an arm or leg and didn't consider it serious, or that it would put me in a hopeless position. I would still sail on or drift on and ultimately reach a shore. Of course, I knew that in time the ropes of my lashings would disintegrate and the logs soak up so much water that they would sink. Then I would have to go on in my canoe.

All these things could happen while I was lost in time, time which had come to mean nothing. Days or months, what were they? They had become mere names signifying units in the world that I had left. I was in a void where time could not enter.

But I had splints ready for a broken bone. A broken arm would be much more serious than a broken leg. I could always drag myself over the deck but I needed my hands to work the raft. An old Ecuadorian in Quevedo had given me a salve. "If you break a bone on the sea when you are alone," he had said, "rub this salve across the break and it will heal quickly." I had taken it to please him.

I had been warned of sickness, such as appendicitis, but since I had never been really sick in my life I didn't worry. But my rupture bothered me considerably and always needed manipulation before beginning any work requiring exertion. I was sorry not to have taken along a belt or truss.

Smash through, little raft—drive us through! If this wind holds all night we will be sure of clearing the Galapagos. At three o'clock tomorrow I will know, when I work out my sights. Then we will really be in space, with the earth's last outpost dropping behind.

Through the darkness and through the foam! To our right the Big Dipper, what's visible of it, standing on its head, pointing to the North Star beneath the horizon. Home country up there! You will never see it, *Seven Little Sisters*—Polaris will never guide you through the night, for this is about as far north as we will go, about three degrees south of the equator. Don't know what I will find in this latitude farther west. It's wind that I want and if I don't get it I'll swing back south. I'll hunt wind like the old square-riggers did. I want all that the south-east trades have—I want those sails full.

Let's get past the Galapagos. Strange-shaped, scattered rocks lying in the grey haze of the Humboldt Current, like forgotten outcasts who had died in their chains 700 miles off the coast of Ecuador, and straddling the equator, these islands are the hangout of the world's last beachcombers—men who want to be free and who shackle themselves to loneliness. The twisted caves and strange, locked beaches still hide Inca loot from the mountains of gold on which they were slain, loot of a thousand mines and emerald diggings, of thousands of Indians who dug with backs bent, to bring up the gold for the Incas. A lot made its way into the caves of the Galapagos and disappeared.

Just let's get past, little raft, without touching them, without even catching sight of them. . . .

"You are taking plenty of water along, I hope," one of the Galapagos men had said to me one night in Guayaquil. "About a hundred and twenty gallons," I replied. "Take plenty," he had warned. "You can't take too much." And he went on to tell me of his own experience: "I was out fishing one day when my motor went bad. It was getting dark. Fishing had been good and I kept on pulling them up. I was far from my island. I started to drift and drift fast. I knew I was finished. I drifted all night and just before dawn I thought I saw a rock looming up; I wasn't sure but seemed to remember I knew a rock around here from some years ago. That rock was my only chance. I jumped overboard with some matches and fishing hooks. Sharks or not, I had to swim for it. I made it. For three months I stayed there before they found me, living on fish. I had no water, not one drop in three months. I squeezed water out of the fish; good thing there were plenty. But for three months drinking fish water——!

"The islands get you," he went on. "I wouldn't live any other place in the world. On one of them there is a scorpion under every stone—and there are nothing but stones; and I was on one that had a centipede under every rock and there were nothing but rocks. I was afraid to put my hands in my pockets, afraid I would come up with a centipede; and they are no babies.

"But on most of them there is no drinking water, that's the worst of it. The wild goats and cattle walk into the sea and drink salt water. There's plenty of meat; all you have to do is get out and shoot a cow or goat—that is, on the big islands.

"There's a fellow around here in Guayaquil who tried to get rich on the Galapagos, shooting wild cattle and bringing the meat over here to Guayaquil. He thought he had a big idea. He got permission from Quito to shoot enough for a shipload once a year. So he got himself a ship

113

that could freeze meat, and started out with a crew of hunters. The islands are all rocks piled up like dropped out of the sky and shoved up from hell below, and the cattle are wild, like tigers. When they finally cornered an old cow and shot her they had no shoes left from climbing over the rocks. And the nearest shore was ten miles away and their ship was standing on its head in the swells. They didn't take out enough meat for a meal. He lost his shirt on the deal and is still crying. You got to take it easy on the islands, they are made for taking it easy. I fish less than a month out of the year and make all the money I need," he concluded. . . .

The night will soon be over. Then on your knees with your spirit—then the soaring and uplifted hands and the beating of the breast. . . . See your make-up, man—the will of your Maker within you, and you will hear the singing.

114

## ★ 12 ★

### OVERBOARD!

It was about ten o'clock on the morning of July 12 that I put a flying fish on the hook and threw the line out. I was now twenty days out of Callao and had sailed about a thousand miles. My position was, roughly speaking, south of the Galapagos. I was fishing from the side of the raft, forward, near the right leg of the mast. Most of the dolphins hung out beneath the raft and I had been catching a few from this spot.

The raft was sailing rather fast, however. Its speed pulled the line alongside and the hook caught in the logs, so I had to lie down flat on the deck and bend way over the side to get it out. This was quite an effort; dangerous, too, on account of sharks. So after a few luckless tries I took my line and went to the stern, on the bare logs. I made the end of the line fast to the crosslog and tried a few casts. No dolphins were visible. I let out all the line I had, about two hundred feet.

In less than a minute the line snapped tight with a pull that threatened to break it. It remained tight, quivering a little and moving with the raft. A big one, I thought, and started to pull in. Was it a dolphin? I hoped so, but it did not feel like one. A dolphin would have leaped and zigzagged and smashed the water into foam in frenzy at being hooked. This fish was pulling steadily and strong, and going down. Now and then it came along easily— then sounded again. It felt like a shark. I kept pulling as fast as I could in order not to give it a chance to get under the raft, among the logs, where I had already lost a dolphin. When I had my catch within eight feet of the stern it came to the surface. It *was* a shark—a powerful, squat fellow about six feet long.

I got him about half-way up across the end of the logs, his tail in the water. The hook was in the corner of his mouth, which caused him to turn on his back. He was thrashing fiercely but I did not give him an inch of slack. Then he quieted down, no doubt taking stock of the situation. I kept the strain on the line, holding it in my right hand while with my left I reached for the gaff behind me and hooked him solid through the lower jaw, on the opposite side from the hook. Then I slacked up a little on the line and bent over the crosslog to take the hook out of his jaw. I had no use for the shark but wanted my hook back. With a shark this is always dangerous, as he will snap; any carelessness could mean the loss of fingers or the entire hand. I had done it many times before and was sure I could get away with it now.

I stood in a bad spot, for the logs were overgrown with seaweed and slimy from long immersion, and the raft rolled as usual, so that my feet and legs were slashed by the seas. I held firm with my knees braced hard against the log, bending over farther and farther, my right hand reaching out to twist the hook from the tooth-studded jaw. The wide mouth stood open a foot wide, and the dull, pig eyes were watching me balefully. While I twisted and pushed at the hook I kept a steady strain on the gaff in order not to give the shark any slack. The hook was loosening. It was a double hook, $2\frac{1}{2}$ inches long, the kind used by commercial tuna fishers.

The shark did not budge, and with a last push I got the hook out. At the same moment the shark started to thrash so fiercely that the gaff jerked out of my hand. I was thrown off balance and went headfirst over the log into the sea. My left hand shot to grasp anything at all. Blindly I thrust it into the shark's mouth and the hand was gashed. All at once I was in the foam and swirl of the wake. The shark, of course, was gone.

When I straightened up and was able to see where I was, the raft was already sailing away from me. In one strange, all-seeing moment I took in its beauty as it rose on the blue sea, white sails spread out in the wind—my golden raft, mingling with the clouds and receding with them, sailing away. . . .

This was the end. I struck out desperately—but then checked myself, feeling that wild effort was useless. But what could I do? Then I realized that the fishing line was still around my right arm, not the line, actually, but the wire leader at the end of which the hook was fastened. The other end was tied to the crosslog on the raft. I gripped the wire and then the line, which tightened as I was being dragged through the sea. I still had a chance! If the line didn't break I might—*might* make it back to the raft. She was sailing away like a yacht, and, like a thing with a will of its own, pulled me along.

Hand over hand, I pulled myself along the line towards the raft. If it would only hold! It was an old, worn line given me by the captain of a tuna clipper in Callao. It was badly frayed, no longer able to take the shock of a hooked tuna.

Two hundred feet away! . . . Did I have the strength to pull myself farther? The raft was moving fast, the sea was moderately high, the wind was getting strong. My clothes were leaden; my woollen socks and sneakers were dragging me down.

My left hand was gashed, and streaming with blood, dyeing the water around me and leaving a broad, red trail. Where was Long Tom, I wondered. I thought of the other big fellows I had seen yesterday, any of which could take off a leg with one snap of the jaws.

I took a double turn around my right hand, to rest a second. No jerk—a steady, even pull. Feel her out as you go—see the way you drag as the raft takes the pulls. No jerking . . . easy, like a fish coming along. And kick your legs with all you've got to take some of the strain.

One hand after the other. Easy does it—feel her out. Another double turn around the right hand to rest a moment. All right again. Foot by foot. . . . Don't look towards the raft. My left hand was spouting blood. I thought of sharks but the line was the thing. Would it hold? I knew that if a shark hit me anywhere he would pull back at once, with all the power of his tremendous breast-fin leverage, and twist his chunk out of me and so break the line. I kept in mind that I must kick with all my strength the moment he came close—hit him on the nose, a vulnerable spot. I had fought sharks and knew them to be cowardly but strong, cunning and persistent. A big one like Long Tom would, of course, make short work of me, taking a leg clean off.

One hand after the other. . . . Rest again. My left hand was getting numb. *Keep on kicking, Bill, don't drag like that!* The raft stood high before me; it had just crested a sea. Before plunging down it paused a second and the line eased. Make the most of that, Bill!—every time that happens. Don't lose your head—that's no way to do. Easy on that line! . . .

I grabbed a badly worn section of line that was frayed half-through, probably bitten by a tuna. Aboard the raft I had new lines, bought in New York . . . useless to think of that now! I began to feel as if I weighed a ton, but I couldn't let go the line to take off my two sweaters, flannel shirt and pants. My left hand was beginning to give out. . . .

I was resting now, close enough to my goal to hear

118

the seas hitting the raft and the roaring among the logs. I pulled myself past another bad spot in the line. Yet it had held the shark. The line was now above water, slanting up to the crosslog where it was fast. A few feet more. . . . Don't get reckless now. Inch by inch—easy. . . . There was the rudder. Easy now, easy!

I gripped the top of the iron rudder, then the chain that controlled it and, inch by inch, pulled myself up on to the end of the logs where I had landed the shark. I had made it. I lay face down on the slimy, seaweed-covered logs in the wash of the seas. My head was spinning. I had made it! As the raft lurched I started to slide backwards into the sea. I wedged my fingers into the chain and hung on. At last I crawled over the crosslog and got all the way on board.

I was bleeding badly. My left hand was spurting blood. Wave after wave of stupor passed through my brain. I was not safe yet, not with this hand. I had to take care of it at once; the deck was getting red with my blood.

I cut a piece from the fishing line and took a few turns around my forearm. Then I reached into the cabin for the marlinspike hanging on a hook, where I kept it ready for use at all times, and made a tourniquet. It helped but did not altogether stop the bleeding, so I raised my hand above my head and waited awhile. That stopped the flow. I then took a sewing needle from my kit; it had a white thread in it and I sewed up the gash as best I could. A vein had been cut, and possibly the artery running from the base of the thumb to the forefinger. The large artery on the inside of the wrist had been grazed but not severed. I had a hard time getting the edges together and when I had finished the blood was still oozing from between the stitches.

I put vaseline on the wound and bandaged it carefully. I realized that the main thing was now to prevent infection. After I had finished I discovered a tube of penicillin salve in my medicine chest. But I didn't want to take the bandages off again; it would have to wait till the next dressing. I lay down flat on my back and worked a few minutes pushing in my rupture.

After mixing myself some coffee and eating some sugar I began to feel better. I was safe on my raft, standing on my course across the Pacific, every sail was pulling. . . .

I remembered how, in New York, I had promised Teddy to keep a rope or two trailing from the raft at all times. If I had, it would have been an easy matter to pull myself in on a line, especially with knots every foot or so. But I'd just never got around to doing it. I couldn't help thinking how hard it would have been on Teddy to wait through the years, never knowing what had happened to me. . . .

Free of my soggy clothing, and in good spirits again, I filled my lungs with air and roared a song. Then I went forward. I felt as if I had been away from the raft a long time. Eekie, cracking a kernel of corn, just gave me a look and kept on eating. Meekie lay under the winch, sound asleep. I went aft again and, though the thick bandage greatly handicapped me, I pulled up a few buckets of water from the sea and cleaned the blood from the deck and cabin. It was near noon but on account of my bruised hands I decided not to take a noon sight. I also wanted to avoid the strain on my eyes, ducking in and out of the cabin twenty times or more to put down the readings.

The afternoon wore on. Daylight faded and again there was stillness and peace and a hush above the restless, tumbling seas—the hour of contemplation.

I felt humbled at this hour, after my chastisement by the elements. Again I had been shown my insignificance, plain in all my weakness against the background of Nature and of eternity, since the two are one. . . .

Night fell and the big seas rushed past. "Tell me," I asked them, as I often did, "where are you going so fast?" And they seemed to answer: "You almost did not make it back to the raft today. Maybe we helped you a little while you clung to that line. It was closer to breaking than you thought. We gave you a little push now and then. . . . We've got to hurry on now."

I had had help, I knew that. But my hands had not given out. They'd come to my aid before, in many a bad spot. In 1938 I had been really up against it. I had fought a mad convict leper while standing up to my knees in the mud of a Maroni River, one foot caught under a treacherous mangrove root. The big convict had his fingers in my eyes, trying to tear them out. Though blinded, I managed to force his hands back, hanging on to his wrists. I hung on for long minutes, struggling with him. At last a little light came to my left eye, just a glimmer, and I let go his wrist and snatched the corner of his snarling mouth—I gave it a twist and a rip. The whole leprous cheek came away. I managed to get away in my canoe. Yes, I knew my hands were strong.

Today it had been close despite my strong hands. And it was my own fault, as usual. I should have cut the line when I saw that I had hooked a shark, or at least when I had him on the logs and was in a bad position for getting the hook out of its jaw. How often had Teddy begged me to cut the line and forget about the hook, after pulling up a shark off Florida or in the Bahamas?

Dreams kept drifting through my mind, dreams of the past, the golden past, of men with whom I had lived and toiled. They came back to me in the unforgettable nights when the day's work was done and the *Seven Little Sisters* made her way through the Pacific, through wind and seas.

And was not this a night of nights for dreaming and giving thanks?

Walk past, you men of all the earth that I toiled with. Walk past, America, as I once walked over your wide levels wearing your garments of labour; show me your frontiers again that saw me submerged in the vast, soothing rhythm of toil—growing, maturing slowly to full power. The million years of flesh and blood that made me had to be obeyed in a life of labour. That came first, and then came the gazing at the stars—for man is both blood and spark.

The moon broke through the clouds, miraculously clearing half the heavens. The clouds were standing, halted in silent worship, like floating alabaster shapes. Beneath this wonderland of light lay the dark rolling sea.

# A BIRDS' AND DOLPHINS' PARADISE

My transmitter was not working, that is the conclusion
I reached after many days of testing it. Not once had I
had an answer. Since both indicator lights glowed brightly
as they were supposed to, the fault was most likely with
the aerial, as I had suspected. So I was really alone. By
this time Teddy no doubt had steeled herself to the silence
that had swallowed me.

I figured that yesterday, July 14, I cleared the
Galapagos. I put my dead reckoning position at 92° 37'
West. There had been no sun for the last few days so I
didn't know my exact position. I was about twelve
hundred miles out from Callao.

The day started sultry and the wind seemed tired,
barely blowing. The sky was full of slow-moving, low
clouds. Now and then the mainsail flapped as if panting
for air, begging the wind to keep it full. The raft moved
slowly and at times seemed to have stopped. Finally a
rain cloud came out of the north-east and wetted the
deck. It continued sultry for a while afterward and then
began to freshen up, and the wind came steady and strong
again and we were jogging along at our regular speed.
Every mile counted and light winds or especially calms
were hard to take. It felt good to see the sails stand full
again and the foam drift past. How I remembered days
on the big sailing ships when we were becalmed for
weeks, lying beneath the equator, rolling from beam

to beam and afraid the masts would come down any moment.

I was not out a month yet but it seemed I had been at sea for a year. I had changed course to the south, for though the charts say the south-east trades reach well above the equator during the winter (I was south of the equator where it was winter) I was not taking any chance of getting caught in the doldrums or any equatorial pocket of calms. I had had one or two bad days at my farthest northern point and that was enough; I worked day and night to get out of it. There was perhaps less current on my intended course but the current was not important any more, the most I was getting out of it was from ten to fifteen or twenty miles a day.

I worked out an azimuth today to check my compass with the bearing of the sun and found it about right. The variation between the true and magnetic north in this part of the world is about eleven degrees east. Taking a sextant sight was a job on account of the incessant movement of the raft and its low position on the sea. It was almost impossible to get a level horizon. I had two compasses, one about three inches in size that I bought before leaving New York and my regular five-inch compass, the same one that brought Teddy and me through the Caribbean hurricane and some other tough spots.

I had no barometer. A number of Navy men and friends in Callao had asked me to take one along but I could not see any use for it. What could I do out here if I saw the glass falling? There certainly was no escape from bad weather. If it came I had to take it. It meant getting the big sail down before it blew away. I had rigged up some extra gear to manage it quickly.

Meanwhile I sailed into a paradise of fish and birds. For two days I had been in it and I wondered how long it would keep up. Thousands of black frigate birds filled the air, wheeling, banking and plunging down to the surface of the sea to snatch up the flying fish forced out of the water by dolphins.

Dawn was just breaking when the first bird appeared. They are birds with long, narrow wings—marvellous fliers, aerial acrobats. The flying fish came out of the sea on gossamer wings, hardly visible from above with their dark-blue backs, changing their course continuously as their big eyes watched the pursuing dolphins a few feet beneath them. As soon as one escaped into the air, perhaps only an inch or two ahead of the jaws of the dolphin, the birds came swooping down on it. Its tender meat was a prize morsel of the sea. Like a dart the hunted fish flitted over the waves, skipped over the crests, while the birds went into an aerial circus to snatch it up with their long beaks, and the sea beneath was churned up by the torpedo-like rushes of the dolphins. The ferocity and speed of the dolphin was awe-inspiring—like shrapnel tearing the water. They are almost knife-thin, but from back to belly their wide bodies are the ultimate expression of speed Nature can bestow on a fish. The forehead rises high and perpendicular like a cliff, acting as a wedge and a frontal rudder, and gives the dolphin the aspect of wearing a high helmet. To enhance this warrior head a fin begins at the very tip of the nose and runs like a high-arching mane over the whole body to the tail—a helmeted Indian with head feathers streaming behind him to the very heels. Their bodies generally stayed beneath the surface but occasionally one caught a glimpse of the high head or fin ripping through the sea.

At times the battle was right around the raft and flying fish were driven on to the deck; sometimes it moved farther away as nearby swarms were annihilated or scattered. But fresh swarms of gossamer darts continued to rise from the sea—there seemed to be an endless supply in this region.

In spite of the continuous gorging of the birds, the hunt went on all day long; their bodies somehow could absorb fish after fish. From other voyages I knew that the same birds could fly endless miles without food, soaring day after day on tireless wings over a storm-battered and fish-empty sea.

Occasionally a bird picked up a fish a bit too large and flew around while half of it protruded from its beak, till after a minute or so it had room and let the fish slide down its gullet head first. Even in their most intricate manoeuvres to keep their balance the birds moved gracefully, and the finale—the pick-up of the flying fish—was done smoothly and seemingly without effort, like a lady picking up a cigarette in dainty fingers, making it appear as if the flying fish sailed willingly into their beaks. Below, in white-streaked rushes following the flights of the weary fish, the dolphins also swallowed them whole.

Only when it became too dark to see did the birds let up. Then, on slow wings, with their bellies full and heavy, they flew back to their cliffs on the Galapagos some 200 to 300 miles away. The dolphins could be heard throughout the night striking the water in their leaps.

For a few days I found a lot of flying fish on the raft and I feasted on them. The flesh is tender and not as firm as that of larger fish. They are six to eight inches long, and ten or twelve made a good meal. I found them on the cabin roof, in the canoe, and in all parts of the raft. Now and then they even struck my body and my head. Many got away again through the numerous cracks of my bamboo deck but there was enough for Meekie and me. They were a welcome addition to our diet. Meekie almost went wild with her first fish. I generally turned her loose nights so she could do her own hunting. The moment I heard the staccato drumming of a flying fish on deck or the thud as its head struck the hut or something equally solid I rushed over to get it before it had a chance to bounce and wriggle to the nearest crack and drop back into the sea. Often Meekie and I got there at the same time. When she beat me to it she grasped the fish and made off for the main logs where I couldn't follow her.

My single-burner stove had gone out of commission and also one burner on my double stove. This left me with just one burner that also did not work well. If it quit on me I would have to eat my fish raw. I had twenty-five cans of vegetable shortening which would go to waste if my last burner quit on me.

Meekie had been waiting for fish more eagerly than I. She had never taken to the canned food I brought along for her. She wanted her vitamins as they came out of the sea, as I discovered one day after pulling up a centre-board and one of the bow planks that had been in the water since I left Callao. These had some barnacles and moss growing on them and Meekie went to work pulling off the barnacles and eating them and grazing on the moss like a calf. She did this day after day even after the moss had dried in the equatorial sun. Now that she had fresh fish she didn't look at the planks any more. If we should run out of fish at any time I could always dig up a meal for her out of the barnacles and moss growing on the logs.

Meekie was in high mettle now with flying fish around for the taking. She slept most of the day, knew the best places where she could get the early morning sun or the coolest and shadiest spots in the afternoon, and did not come around me till about sunset. She stayed with me till the first flying fish broke water nearby, then her eyes went to the sea. She was fascinated by the dolphins darting in and out among the shadowy waves. Time after time I had pulled her back from the edge of the raft, thinking she might fall off. I was beginning to suspect, however, that she had better balance than I. When the flying fish started hitting the deck she went down to the main logs with one, right where the seas rush and roar and wash, and did not come up again till she had eaten her fill. Then she would lie down on the motor box beside Eekie's cage, as close to it as she could get, and go to sleep. When I flashed my light on her during the night she would look at me out of her big yellow eyes as if to say: "I haven't done nothing." But Eekie knew that she was after him and always got into the farthest spot on his perch, sleeping fitfully and with one of his red eyes open.

So far I had not had a minute to myself when I could sit down and even think of relaxing. When I was not steering or busy with some other work I tried to get a little sleep. Ten minutes or so at a time enabled me to keep going for hours. Sometimes I lay down dead tired and exhausted and literally passed out. At such times someone seems to be watching the raft for me, for again and again it happened that I awoke from deepest, stupor-like sleep to find the raft just on the point of running off. . . .

I had a few Spanish books and pamphlets standing on the shelf between my Nautical Almanac and Bowditch but never opened them. They were a reminder of a friend in Peru. A few days after coming to Callao, a heavy-set, shapeless sort of a man with grey eyes and red, fleshy face boarded my raft, embraced me most violently, almost crushing me, kissed me on the cheek and rattled away in staccato Spanish. He took me over completely, swept me off my feet. I finally made out that he was a writer and humorist and was overflowing with kindness towards the

Meekie on the cabin top, which is beginning to get bare.

Eekie closely inspects the wheel.

Evening under
full sail
far at sea.

Westward ho—
2,500 miles out.

world which at this moment included me, on whom he poured out his tremendous vitality. There was no doubt about his sincerity. I stood there helpless, not permitted to say a word.

"Alone," he said, "you want to go alone! I have no fear either, my friend, I am afraid of nothing, I assure you, but not alone—I want company." Then came a laugh that could be heard all over the submarine base. "You are going to God's country, *Señor* Willis," he went on; "to His last stronghold on earth, to Polynesia. Do you realize that?" He embraced me, crushed me, and hung on. I felt his belly shake with his tremendous laughter. "The women of Polynesia are waiting for you, do you realize it? They will never let you go again. You will become the king of Polynesia. I will send you some of my books so that you don't go crazy on your lonely voyage. My books will make you laugh—you must laugh or you will go crazy, all alone. I laugh and still they say I am crazy." The raft, and the dock too, shook with his big laughter. "You must read my books. Dante and Cervantes, they are the masters—I am only a butcher." He flung his heavy arms around me and held me like a rag. The pistol-toting Peruvian guard on the dock above us looked down at me, wondering whether I needed help.

After my friend had managed to climb back up on the dock amid cursing and complaining and elephantine grunts, I heard his laughter go booming along the base till it faded away. It took me a while to recover from the meeting and the raft looked sort of empty without him. Later, he brought me his books with the order to read them and so laugh my way across the Pacific. I took them aboard but never opened one. I did not have the nerve to throw them overboard. I respected him—his big, human heart. . . .

I never lay down in the hut, regardless of the weather.

The hut was for cooking, for frying fish and for making coffee, since it was much too windy on deck. My navigation was also done in the hut. I would sit right beside the door to get the most light. I worked out my latitude sight at noon and about three hours later my position lines for a longitude fix. I usually worked out two or three lines. It was impossible to take star sights due to the movement of the raft but I was satisfied with the sun. I knew my position at all time within a few miles and even better. The noon sight was hardest to take due to the raft's movements. I had to take from twenty to twenty-five sights to get at an average. This put an almost blinding strain on the eyes but was unavoidable.

I envied the navigators on big ships who work out the time on the Local Apparent Noon beforehand, at the proper time pick up their sextant and go out on the wing of the bridge and shoot. Then back to the chartroom and in a minute or two they have their latitude. Sometimes I wondered which was harder about my noon sights —the actual taking of the sight on the tossing deck or keeping my balance. Any slip on deck, especially with seas coming over, could mean a broken sextant. A few times I had taken a fall on my elbow and once I thought I had broken the instrument. It frightened me a little and I printed a warning to myself on a piece of paper and pasted it in the box where I could see it:

BUST YOUR BONE BUT SAVE THE SEXTANT.

I had a spare sextant but it was not very dependable. For my navigation I used what seamen call the 214 Method, employing the *Tables of Computed Altitude*, published by the U.S. Navy Hydrographic Office (Publication 214). It is fast and dependable and used widely on American ships.

To provide for emergencies I had two compasses, two sextants, one chronometer, one watch, two copies of the *American Nautical Almanac,* and other books needed for navigation. I also had two sets of charts but they were of such small scale that it was not practical to mark my daily position. I merely made brief daily entries in my log book. For working out my position I used plotting sheets, such as are used by all navigators on long sea voyages. On July 15, the last big day of the flying fish and frigate birds, my log book entry read: Dead reckoning Lat. 3° 13′ South, Long. 93° 30′ West, about two hundred miles south-west of the Galapagos.

# ★ 14 ★

## A BIT OF HEAVY WEATHER

The night of July 16 was wild. Hour after hour I stood at the wheel as one sea after another broke and roared and wallowed underneath the raft. I was engulfed in spray and never-ceasing tumult. And far off above the smash and shatter I could hear the steady howl-moan lying on the waste. Behind me, at my very heels and breathing on me, were the white-maned wolves of the sea.

This was not sailing according to the rules; this was a fighting through, a catch-as-catch-can affair. At times when I was busy with the mainsail it was as if I was fighting for my life against three or four tough men. I covered miles on deck in brief minutes, climbing and jumping from one end of the raft to the other (while Eekie squawked or screamed and Meekie ducked beneath the winch, carried away by the wildness and fierce tossing, the howling wind and boarding seas).

A boat can be rigged so that one man can do almost everything from aft, no matter what the emergency. With a raft it is different: I had to be all over for every manoeuvre. Consequently, I worked almost daily on the rigging, improving or adding new gear to enable me to handle the raft in a squall or gale, for this was winter and the season for bad weather. Normally a ship would require a man to steer at all times, especially during squalls and strong winds; to do all the work on the raft single-handed required perfect timing and utmost speed.

From every emergency, and there were many, I had learned something and so far had managed to get by.

I sailed over the dark and ominous-looking sea, the water almost black under the canopy of the approaching squall. It was coming fast.

Hear the moan? Down with the sail! Time it, Bill! All the gear ready for running? Get a little closer with her. Everything lashed solid? Slack that starboard brace—get it just right, so the yard doesn't go crazy and tear the sail as she comes swinging down.

Feel the wind—she came up fast. Back to the wheel! Lash her like that. Out of the way with the compass or you'll smash into it. Forward and across the canoe to the port brace—haul in, but not too much—remember the last time—leave enough slack. Don't go over the side, right out of the canoe—boy, that was close! Watch yourself, you fool! Rig up something here or you'll never finish this trip.

How is she heading now? Back to the wheel—quick. Over the top of the house—quick—watch that aerial. Look out, man, you'll break your neck. Hear that wind coming up! Hurry up or you'll have the rigging down on top of you. What a sight! Boy—this is living! Look at that black sea! Hurry up! Everything clear? Quick—let go the lifts and the halyard. There she comes. . . . Get hold of that starboard downhaul before she swings around the forestay. Move—get it down straight—down with her—down! Watch that yard, Bill—get that downhaul. She's going crazy up there—you won't have a sail! Down with it! Something's stuck up there. . . .

Boy, you're in a fix now! Get that yard down or get up that ladder. Pull, pull—bust it, but get it down! Get up that ladder—it's stuck solid. Get up quick or you won't have a sail or mast—you'll soon be drifting on your logs. . . .

I went up the ladder and it started swinging from side to side at a terrific rate. I went through the hardest time of my voyage fighting to hang on and not be thrown on deck or into the sea. At last I managed to get to the top and clear the line that had caught in a block. I went down again with my mouth wide open, panting and shaking from exertion. Now, down with the yard. I lashed it to the legs of the mast and lashed the sail. Let her blow —we could take it now. The squall was almost on top of me. The deck looked like a wreck with all its loose gear.

Here she comes! Back to the wheel and see how she does. Forward again and out on the bowsprit and clear the jib. There's that jib downhaul getting fouled again. Sure going to fix it good next time. Should have been done. . . . Halyard all clear? Up with it—hand over hand and fast to the winch handle for the time being. Haul in the sheet, to starboard—that's how she takes it. Quick now to the wheel before she runs off—*quick!* The mizzen's reefed already. Off with the lashing and up with it, hand over hand and two blocks and belay. Now grab your wheel and let her go!

What a sight, what a sea! . . . I just made it. . . .

The long night passed and day came and the hours moved on over the stormy sea. I was steering and with my hands always at the wheel, studying the winds and clouds and seas, their shapes and their drift—studying them with all the thinking power that was in me. Even the feel of the air told me something about the weather. The winds were my Gospel; the clouds and the sea were the smile or wrath of my Fate.

I saw the sun setting on the high-running sea, painting the western slopes red. Each comber and long rolling swell, each wavelet was lighted up. The eastern slopes were dark, almost black. All the seas, the whole mass, were running—white-crested, painted and dark beneath the crimson and purple clouds toward the setting sun. . . .

I got everything ready for the night. Eekie's cage, lashed to the house so that no sea could take it, had been getting a lot of spray, so I wrapped an old raincoat around it. Meekie was asleep under the hand winch beneath a piece of canvas that was her shelter during bad weather or the day's heat. She got a few good soakings, but she was used to it now and did not mind. I ate some barley flour for my supper and topped it off with instant coffee made with cold water. Then I filled my lantern with kerosene and cleaned the chimney. It would go into its box and light up the compass during the night. I wiped the salt water from the face of the compass and then again went forward. Everything looked O.K.

I sat down on a box that stood on a plank that bridged the low after-end of the raft beside the wheel. There was no deck here, just the bare logs. The sun was now down to the horizon. It was evening, the quiet hour of meditation. The raft was rolling and wallowing along more quietly. Even the tumultuous sea itself was feeling the hush of the approaching night. I thought of the far-off earth.

I sensed immense truths around me in space, revealing themselves in beauty and yet shrouded in eternal mystery. Slowly the stars came out, one by one, as if they had been waiting for silence to fall before taking up their procession through space. There was my soft-blazing planet, Venus, whose light I steered by, breaking through a little to the right of my mast. It would be the brightest light in the sky before long. When it had sunk into the sea it would be far into the night.

I thought again of the fight on the ladder while I was taking down the sail. What a mess that was, and at such a time, with hell breaking loose behind me! I had a bad ladder. It was strong but long, since I had such a high mast, and there was no way to break its swing. It started at the winch and went up to the top of the mast. It was a trick ladder and more than once already I had been almost thrown from it in the rolling and tossing of the raft.

This time it had been especially bad. Halfway up, at the worst spot, it had lashed me around fiercely, twisting me from side to side with almost inconceivable violence. I was like a battle flag in a gale. I felt as if the winds had sworn to rip me off, to fling me into the sea or to the deck. Hang on, Bill! There lay the *Seven Little Sisters* beneath me, labouring through the seas; I was their banner, their symbol of defiance to the wind and elements.

Fingers couldn't do it any longer; I hung on with elbows, knees and thighs, making myself into a cable of muscles wrapped around the rungs and ropes of the ladder in the dizzy, side-to-side whirling. The weather had eased up a bit and I had managed to get up, clear the block, and then come down. But it had been a fight, taking all I had. And my rupture had had quite a time of it.

I kept thinking about it during the night, while I watched over the raft. It was like being on the yardarm of the windjammers, when I used to fight with the chained sheet that had fouled in a block during a gale, beating big sparks out of the steel yard and grazing my skull time and again in its wild, wind-maddened frenzy, and I fighting with both hands to get a hold, with nothing to hang on with but the soles of my feet while swaying in the footrope.

But last night I had made it. It was perhaps the toughest thing I had had to go through, so far, on the raft. I had made it and forced my will over the wind and sea and the crazy ladder— as in the olden days. It had been a real test. Next time I would do it again and maybe do it easier. Now I was coming to real grips with the bad weather and holding my own. But my rupture felt as if another stitch or two had come loose.

ner and hidden in the oilskin days in Hell Corta Acita
feet Next, thinking I would do it again until another was in
order. Now, I was coming to feel that was with the best
weather and holding my site, but my expense felt can hes
another stitch of wood.

## ★ 15 ★

### SOS

I WAS working out my sights the following afternoon, July 17, when I felt a pain in the pit of the stomach, in the spot generally referred to as the solar plexus. It continued, an ever-increasing pressure. I finished my sights and wondered whether I should set the mainsail again but decided against it. The sea was still high and the wind strong and the sky seemed to have a lot of wind yet. It might blow up more during the night.

The pain continued and I took some bicarbonate, thinking that perhaps my stomach was upset. There was no relief. I became a little worried and about half an hour later took some more bicarbonate. It brought no respite; instead, the pain was becoming acute. I didn't know what to do. There was a continuous, contracting pain, increasing steadily. It was strange and an entirely new experience for me.

My solar plexus gradually tightened to the hardness of stone. The whole front area of my body seemed to be drawn slowly but relentlessly into an ever-hardening knot. Was it my stomach? But how could that be, I wondered; I had never before had any stomach trouble. The bicarbonate had not helped. Besides, there were no symptoms as of ptomaine poisoning or indigestion, which one ordinarily associates with stomach disorders. Was the pain an aftermath of my straining on the ladder, with the centre of my body acting as a pivot around which upper and lower parts were twisted back and forth so violently? Or was it an after effect of the long, nervous strain of my preparations for my voyage? Was it the rupture? If the pain would only let up for a moment! Then, I thought, it could start again and even become worse. But there was no let up until after nearly five hours, when the pain gradually subsided and disappeared. It was then night.

All the stars were out. The Southern Cross, tipped forward, stood blazing on my left, like a beacon hewn out of space. A little behind it and above rose the big southern constellations amid myriads of lesser lights that looked like cities and highways on the slopes of eternities. Ahead, my golden planet hung low, and at my right three stars of the Big Dipper, standing almost on its head, showed their heels to the sky.

The wind increased during the night and I was glad I had not raised the mainsail. The raft steered well on this course with the jib and reefed mizzen and I managed to get some sleep.

The next afternoon, July 18, at almost exactly the same time, the pain in my solar plexus returned. It was the same continuous, contracting pain that kept getting worse as time passed. I took some more bicarbonate, but without relief. I repeated the dose and again it failed. Then I tried brandy which a friend of mine in Lima had given me for an emergency, as he put it. I thought it might relax the muscles around the solar plexus. It did not. I tried it several times to no effect. Soon I could no longer stand but lay on deck, assuming different positions in the hope of finding relief. Finally I began rolling about in ever-increasing agony. Hours passed and it had long since become night. The wind howled and moaned and the combers rose beside me as I lay wet and helpless— rose high and looked down at me in their buoyant, unbreakable strength, their white, feathery crests gleam-

139

ing in the darkness. They sank down and went on while others rose behind, one after the other, in endless procession. Other seas crashed into the logs. I could hear the wind rushing beneath me through the empty spaces between deck and logs, coming in with the seas through the open sides.

I kept hoping the pain would become so severe that I would become unconscious and that during such time the muscles would relax and the pain disappear. But there was no sign of becoming unconscious; the pain increased, affecting no other part of my body but the region of the solar plexus. There was never any change, only a steady, awful tightening.

As the hours went by it seemed to become a question of survival—to live or not to live. What was this strange thing, this monstrous tightening that was squeezing out my life? I imagined a living, demoniac thing.

The pain became so severe that death seemed to be the easier way out. I had had several accidents resulting in broken bones and mangled flesh but the pain on those occasions could be called pinpricks compared with this torment. At times I felt as if I had been shot through the stomach, but the sensation that to me was sharpest was of a mysterious tightening that would continue till all life was blotted out. I was convinced that it was relentlessly and inexorably moving towards that end. Aspirin occurred to me and I took large quantities, twice, hoping to bring on oblivion. I got out all the medicine kits given me by well-wishers in Lima, wholesale drug houses, and others; I even had a kit from the *Santa Cecilia*; I had loads of stuff. Flashlight in hand I went through the collection of bottles, salves and pills, looking for only one thing, morphine. But I found no drug that would put me to sleep.

As the raft, buried by seas and spray, smashed through

the night, I thought of sending an S O S. Perhaps a message on the 500-kilocycle frequency would reach a ship, if one happened to be within a few hundred miles of me. But I was out of all shipping lanes. I had told some sailing-ship men in Callao that I would most likely sail between the tenth and twelfth parallels at this stage of my voyage, following the general course taken by the *Kon-Tiki* expedition some seven years earlier. After clearing the Galapagos, however, I had decided to run no farther south than the fifth parallel. At this moment I was at the third, following the strong winds that I needed to beat the hurricane season. In these latitudes I was all alone. Who would pick up a message in these lanes? And would I even send an S O S? It meant, in case it was picked up, the end of my voyage. I groaned in rage and pain.

One does not mind losing in a fair fight—I had lost many in my time—but I saw no fairness here. I felt I had broken no law of Nature for which I had to pay. I thought and thought, lying there, twisting in agony.

Death was beside me now, on every sea rising out of the night and striking the raft. I felt death in the wind that buffeted the cabin and rustled the leaves on the roof —saw it in the hard, swift sweep of spray across the deck. I was not afraid. Only one thing was uppermost in my mind: the end of my voyage. Defeat. . . . Beside this fact life or death meant nothing. And then a tiny voice began to whisper that I was myself to blame for what was happening to my body: Take the pain or go over the side. Cut it out with a knife. Loosen the knot; it has drawn most of your life into its grip. My eyes kept going to the thin-bladed, fish-gutting knife stuck above the door of the cabin. You have a knot there, tight as steel and still tightening—you must cut it. . . .

Strange how the idea fascinated me. But how could I

cut into my body? It would possibly bring relief from the pain but then I would have a hole in my body. For hours my thoughts dwelt on soldiers on the battlefield, shot through the stomach, lying in some gully or in deep grass, incapable of moving, waiting in agony to be picked up. Fight it out, Bill—this is nothing—fight it out, man!

Death and life had become small matters. The big thing in my consciousness was my voyage. I had to hold my post. The raft had to make the voyage. I had become the voyage. Hours went by. The dark seas that rolled over and past the *Seven Little Sisters* could have seen and heard strange things aboard.

Not a moment's let-up. Could a man go mad like this? Could he do terrible things when driven too far? The solar plexus, the hollow below the breastbone where the ribs come together, was the pit of life. Was something eating a hole into it? Was some swift-moving corrosion or cancer devouring it?

The heavens moved above me, pulling the stars along like celestial jewels caught in the vast net of time. The dark, thundering seas went their way with the winds and my little raft made its own way, climbing sea after sea, smashing through all obstacles. West by south was the course, but how long could the *Seven Little Sisters* go on without me? Brave little raft, must I desert you now? Years of dreaming and now this . . . ! Some inscrutable power had laid its hand heavily on me: *Here and no farther! No farther! Your will—your accursed will, O man, shall be broken!* I heard it as I lay grovelling on the bamboo deck.

I saw things clearly: This solar plexus was the centre of life, right in the middle of the body, and around this centre the body was built. And here I had been stricken.

I took my aspirins, poured the tablets out in a heap

and pounded them to a paste with water and drank it
down. . . . No relief!

Dawn was breaking.

What evil thing had I done? I scanned my past. My
frantic mind tried to pick up any thread that might lead
to this agony. I must have done something terrible to
deserve this death sentence on the very threshold of
achievement. Such punishment could only be an act of
retribution.

How big I had considered myself to be—but in truth
I was small and pitifully weak. I saw this thing, my body,
disintegrating like a substance that had never really been,
like ashes in the wind. Whom had I wronged on the face
of the earth? This must be retribution. It was not due
to physical causes. . . . Or was it my rupture? Give me
answer, you heavens!—why was I stricken? . . . How cold,
how stern you look—how detached from me. And I
thought I was one with you during every moment of
living—as I still feel one with you and the world. And
in the world of men I committed some wrong. The strong
shall become the weakest, shall be punished according
to their strength.

Hidden guilt—perhaps guilty thoughts! For in my
philosophy thoughts are deeds and more powerful than
deeds. What a wreck of a man lying here for all creation
to see, stripped to his real self, and pleading like a beggar:
Make it short!

Spiritual forces act through the physical body, strike
physical parts. It was no mere stomach ailment; my spirit
was the cause. I was so close to Nature, I felt so utterly
one with her that perhaps in my ignorance of her powers
and made careless by her lifelong goodness towards me
I had unwittingly broken one of her sacred laws. I had
never recognized any evil power in the universe, only in
man, but here something demoniac was at work to strike

143

me down on the voyage to the shrine of Nature herself.

The hours went by and time marched across the Pacific, swinging the sun in a tremendous arc across space. My little raft sailed on under jib and reefed mizzen, bearing me with it. "Tough guy, you've got to take it now; we've got you pinned. Get out of it, you fool! You can't hang on any longer. Send that S O S. Soon we'll be through with you and leave you lying on the raft. Some day, somewhere, they'll find some part of you, dried out and sunscorched and with birds sitting on you. You wanted this. Hardships—adrift on a raft—to show what a man can take. . . . Take it now—take it! We'll show you, we powers of the universe will show you that there is a greater force than man's misdirected will."

The wind had become strong again and the seas came up higher but the raft handled itself well. At times it went off and then a sea smashed into it and staggered it and it rolled back on its course. My hands must have been inspired when I built it; perhaps an ancient Indian rising from the dust of the past had guided them; I knew I had had help from some source.

Again I took some aspirin, still hoping I could stupefy myself but again it gave me no relief. I dragged myself to Eekie's cage and filled it full of corn, enough to last for weeks; I also put in water. I took several flying fish that had fallen on the deck during the night and which I had kept in a bucket and placed them where Meekie could get at them. Then I crawled aft.

I wrote out a note describing what had happened and gave my last position and the date—July 19. It was nearly sundown. I wrote a farewell note to my wife. I tacked both notes to the door of the cabin.

An hour or so later I began to realize how foolish it was not to try to send an S O S. I had been so blinded by my own fanatical purpose that nothing else had mattered.

But what about Teddy? Didn't she have a right to be considered? I began to see the enormity of my selfishness. Yes, I would send an S O S; at least I would try it. Perhaps my message would be picked up.

I was almost helpless and it took a long time to rig up my transmitter. But at last, after an hour or so, I was cranking away. I was sending over the 500 frequency. This international ship disaster frequency has two silent periods in each hour of the twenty-four, from fifteen to eighteen minutes and again from forty-five to forty-eight minutes after each hour, when all ships on the sea are requested to stand by and listen for possible distress calls. I was far too ill to time my message; I just ground away, barely managing to stay coherent:

7HTAS Lat. 3° 36′ South. Long 90° 31′ West. S O S . . . S O S . . . S O S. . . .

While turning the crank with my left hand and striking the key with my right I felt as if I was signing my own death sentence. It was my life's darkest hour. I was deserting my post, the post I had sworn to defend. I was giving up.

I crawled into the cabin and took more aspirins. I poured out the tablets; it was just a white substance that had proved to have no effect on my body. I made an enormous amount of paste and swallowed it down. Nothing could hurt me in my condition; my pain was caused by something that could not be healed by medicine, I was convinced of that. But still hoped the aspirin would send me into oblivion.

It was night again. For over twenty-four hours I had been tortured. I lay in the spray and seas and darkness. I had not bothered to light the lantern for the compass— my course was run. . . .

145

I stared into the night, trying to find myself. Suddenly I realized that I had been dozing. The pain had lessened. Really, the pain had lessened! I searched my body, testing, probing. No doubt about it! In a broken voice I croaked my joy into the night. I was as weak as a rag but the strength of my joy was boundless. I had come through.

I wrote down a message and crawled to the transmitter:

7HTAS All well . . . All well . . . Need no help . . . Need no help . . . Need no help. . . .

For hours, whenever I felt strong enough, I sent out my message, cancelling the S O S.

I had made it. Had the stars ever looked brighter to mortal man? My feelers went out again to grasp the firmament, the waves beside me, the rushing wind. I was alive again. One last message: 7HTAS . . . All well. . . . But I also knew that I had been thoroughly beaten.

## NO STRENGTH TO STAND

TWENTY-FOUR hours after my strange attack I crawled into the cabin, took the mirror from a nail and looked at myself. I did not recognize what I saw; it was just the dregs of a man looking at me from sunken eyes. I had truly taken a beating.

But the sail had to go up; I had to get up the mainsail. The wind had slackened and the sail should be set. I couldn't go on like this, I had to sail!

I had been thinking hour after hour how to get the sail up. I was so weak I could barely move a finger. What a grotesque face!—the sort of face that inspired primitive mask makers. Was this what I was really like when the polish was off? I couldn't blame Meekie for keeping away. Eekie didn't care, his mind was on woods and high trees.

That sail should have been up last night. The wind was still quite strong and the seas high but it was ideal sailing weather. I couldn't lie like a sick dog and just let the raft drift.

I lay thinking and thinking about raising the sail, watching the seas rise with foaming crests around me and rush on westward, where I had to go. And above me white clouds sailed like raft flotillas across the blue. The sun felt warm on my body, on my worn-out limbs. It was bliss, lying there and not moving. But I had to get up. How that wind would drive me!

I felt I could get up—but how could I raise that big

sail? How those trade-wind clouds sailed across the sky, showing me the way, high in the sun and the light. And the seas rushed past like flowing glass. Some gave the raft a push and dived gurgling among the logs. I had to get that mainsail up and get going. Before I knew it hurricanes would tear the ocean apart.

Everything was clear for hoisting away. Downhauls were clear and so was the halyard. The topping lifts gave the most trouble. I really needed a few extra pairs of arms just to keep the gear from getting fouled. Sheets and tacks were fast to the mast legs, down to the canvas. I couldn't give her any extra slack going up. If only that yard doesn't start swinging! I checked to see that the port brace was all clear on the canoe. I pushed in my rupture. O.K. now.

Up she went, hand over hand. Faster—faster. Long pull now—long pull. Get her up. Heavy does it! Once again! Two blocks with her! Up with that yard! Put your weight on it! Another inch! Good enough and make fast. Pull in the lift a little more on the starboard side. Make fast.

Slack that weather sheet and brace. Now aft to the wheel. Pull in that lee brace. Now up with the mizzen, quick—she's all ready. Up and make fast. You can straighten up the deck afterwards; see how she takes it first. We're sailing!

I raced around the cabin and over the top of the canoe to the weather brace. Then I leaped forward to the sheet and hauled in a little, slacked up on the other side. And each time I had to jump back to the wheel and check the course. But finally she was trimmed just right. I could ease up a little. I'd clear up the deck later. I should have put another centre-board down forward. I'd see first how the wind held. She was making a pretty good course. A little to the south made no difference; I had thousands of miles of open space in which to get north. It felt good to be sailing again. The sail was standing like a white, curved wall.

When I got hungry I crawled to the cabin and took a spoonful of barley flour and mixed it with water to a thick paste. I made my coffee the same way; cold water mixed with instant coffee. I ate my sugar too, lots of it. I always had a jar near the wheel. I kept everything I needed within reach. It was important in my present weakness not to take extra steps. I studied for hours how to eliminate all unnecessary movements. Because it was too much of an effort to start my stove I ate flying fish raw. Some day when I was strong enough I would fry fish again.

The wind kept up for a few days with hardly any variation. During the last twenty-four hours I had made eighty-two miles. The Galapagos lay about 500 miles behind me, bearing about north-northwest. I was knocking off the miles, sailing deeper and deeper into space. I was getting stronger every day. I had never felt happier. I had come through a great ordeal, had been brought to the very edge of the end and been lifted up again. Nothing could really happen to me now to keep me down. How could anything be worse? I could fall overboard but that was all. Once again life had shown me the smallness and helplessness of man. That absolute faith in Nature which had been my life-long dream and aim had weakened in the last hours of agony. But the fault was with me. . .

I had been sick before, I recalled. On the water too, lying in a canoe, on the dark water of the Maroni, the river that divided French and Dutch Guiana.

I remembered it well now. I had been burning with fever and sweating heavily and the blankets on which I lay were as soaked as if they had been dipped in the river.

149

I had chills. Jules, my partner, piled everything he had on top of me to keep me warm. I kept shivering. Jules was a French convict who had served his time in the prison stockade and now was a *libéré* but had to stay for the rest of his life in French Guiana, or Devil's Island as it was also called. He was as much a man as any I had ever met. For months my life depended on him and he never failed me.

Jules had to tie me down to the thwarts of the canoe when I became violent. My raving sounded strange in the heavy, heat-drenched silence of the jungle. Not a leaf stirred. Now and then a flock of gorgeous-coloured parrots flew shrieking from the trees. I thrashed around so much that the canoe almost turned over. In my fever I was living through all the horrors of the previous days—of being shut up in the death house and trying to get out, hammering against stone walls with bare hands, then trying to smash through with my head.

When I became normal again, I asked: "Where are we going, Jules?"

"To somebody who can heal you, *monsieur*."

"I can't move, Jules."

"You will be all right again, *monsieur*."

"Where are we going?"

"Upstream, *monsieur*."

"You are paddling fast, Jules." I had never seen him sweating so nor his face so strained.

"The tide will turn soon and it will be easier."

"Have we passed St. Laurent?"

"We are long past it."

Where was he bound? I was too weak to think or ask or care. I asked for water and Jules dipped a rusty can into the river. I gulped and promptly vomited up the water. I kept on drinking and vomiting, which was the way of yellow fever. As time went on I drank and vomited gallons of water. Jules never refused me. Much of the time I was out of my head.

Jules had paddled all night, stopping once to eat a little food while we were tied up under an overhanging branch of the rain-swollen river. In the morning we came to a little Bush Negro village far up in a creek.

Jules left me in the canoe and after a while came back with the headman, whom he knew.

"This man is very sick with fever, chief," Jules had said in Bush Negro dialect.

"I see he is very sick," the chief answered.

"I came to you, chief, to save his life."

"I will try; he is a very sick man."

Two Bush Negroes came down to the canoe, picked me up, and carried me to an empty hut. The sides of the hut did not come down to the ground. Inside the hut, on a mat spread over a thick layer of leaves, they laid me down. An old Bush Negro woman took up her place beside me, squatting on the bare earth. She gave me water whenever I asked for it. In the meantime some of the Bush Negroes had gone into the jungle with bows and arrows. When they came back the headman started his cure.

The tribesmen took a rainbow-hued, blue Amazon parrot, split its living body in half, and placed the split surfaces—the whole raw, hot mass of blood and flesh and organs, still quivering—on the naked soles of my feet. They packed the flesh tight with pawpaw leaves and tied it securely with bush-rope. When they took it off after three hours the healthy pink meat of the parrot had become a blackish, poisonous-looking green. Another parrot was split and put on my feet. After many three-hour changes, lasting for days, the raw meat, when taken off, had a less ugly colour. During this time, when I asked for food I was given a broth of monkey meat. At night,

151

when the mosquitoes came out, smudge fires of certain leaves that contained a drug put me to sleep.

Finally they tested my blood, squeezing it out of a leech that they had put on my arm, into a gourd filled with water. The blood mixed with the water and spread out thinly on top. I had pulled through. When blood goes down in pussy threads the fever is still in a man.

The Bush Negroes had saved me, for I had already had the black vomit which nearly always precedes death. . . .

Now, lying on my raft, I could again see Jules's face clearly, rising out of the past. To me, in my weakened condition, he was a link between those far-off days and my ordeal on the vast ocean reaches of the present.

## ★ 17 ★

### LONG AGO

Was I born to the sea? Deep down within me, I doubted it. Neither my father, a German, nor my mother, Czechoslovakian, had ever seen salt water when I first set out to sea in 1908, at the age of fifteen. Nor had any of my ancestors. No, I was not born to the sea. But I was one with the sea. When I was four years old, a tot standing on the waterfront in my birthplace of Hamburg, Germany, I gazed at the horizon lost in the haze and smoke of the teeming harbour. "There," a voice within me said, "that's America over there!" I remembered climbing into a rowing-boat and managing to untie it. The tide took the boat while I struggled with oars that were much too big for my tiny hands, and down the river I went.

Tugboats and ferries moving past almost upset my helpless craft. People began to notice—sailors, longshore-men, harbourmen. Finally a police launch came up. "Where you going, little fellow?" "I want to go to America." "Is that so?" We went to the police station and hours later my frantic mother rushed up the steps. "My son is lost. . . ." "Better keep him tied up for a while. He was half-way over to America when we grabbed him," the police told her.

Years passed without my seeing the sea. But the harbour was in my blood as a thing of beauty and romance and I constantly dreamed of the lost horizons beyond the farthest seas.

When I was twelve we had to choose a poem to declaim in front of the class. I wanted a poem that would truly describe the sea's fury, which I had never seen. I wrote my own. When I was fifteen I left for the open sea on a square-rigger. No, I was not born to the sea, I was just a dreamer of the sea. . . .

My mind was filled with such memories in the days following my illness. My solar plexus was still sore. I steered and watched the sail, my mind mostly blank, immersed in Nature as in a void. I was too weak to think long.

It was now over a week since the attack and I was still extremely weak. My escape had been close; my face told the story. My temples were sunken; the cheekbones stuck out like knobs. My neck was a bundle of cords with the texture of an old alligator hide. The flesh and skin on my body were hanging down in folds; and I had always been lean, down to the last ounce.

But who cared about the looks?—the weakness was worse. I thought for hours before getting up on my feet to do something. I schemed and schemed, trying to find excuses.

And yet my spirits soared. They soared because I was living in the heart and breadth of Nature, soared because I had been allowed to go on. What did it matter if I was weak? I was 650 miles from the Galapagos, 1,650 miles out of Callao.

The solitude continued to affect me. It had a sort of fascination that grew and grew. I began to feel more and more at home in it, and had no desire for a change. I am content with the sea and the sky. It is easy to see how men who have lived in solitude seek it always and even resent the intrusion of human beings. But there are moments of suffering, too; a vague uneasiness which comes when one realizes that he lives on the edge of an abyss. Man must talk to someone and hear the sound of human voices

I was now steering towards the fifth parallel, which would let me pass about a hundred miles north of the Marquesas. They were still 3,000 miles away, however, and I was not yet making a final decision on my ultimate course.

I was getting no real sleep, just a little more surrender to the moon and the clouds drifting over the sea and over me, just a little more of a blackout of my own little self, with the elements taking charge. And so again and again and night and day, I felt that I was becoming part of Nature.

A great peace had come again and entered into me. I felt like going on forever and believed that if I were permitted to do this an understanding of all things would come. My thinking became vague and mystical, a submersion in Nature, a mingling with it, which gave me strength of mind and spirit. I had experienced this sensation before and always longed for it. I had been spared to go on with my pilgrimage. I could go on to prove that I had lived right, that I had not squandered my energies.

For no apparent reason I saw myself once again firing coal on a Liverpool tramp, the S.S. *Lynrowan*. The little Cockney at the next boiler was coughing blood but shovelling coal with the last energy of his stripped, lean body. "Aye, kid, blimey, she's a tough one, and that rotten coal." Biting into the sweat rag around his neck, such as all of us wore, he wiped the bloody froth from his lips, shouting, "Gee, she must be a hundred and forty down here, blimey!"

How memories came, like waves that sank and rose again, purged by the dark, iron pressure of the depths. Some came up with white crests standing high, like witnesses above the waste, and then went back into the silence. In all my years at sea or on land I had never before been through anything like this sickness. I could find no explanation as I lay on the bamboo deck.

How much could a man take in the way of suffering before he cracked? . . .

Four of my logs were lying on the banks of Quevedo ready to be rolled into the river and floated down to Guayaquil when an old-timer joined me one night at the little restaurant. He was a European who had done a lot of prospecting for ancient mines. He had a little hacienda near Quevedo now and was growing bananas and cocoa.

"Bill," he said, "do you mean to say you will trust your life to seven logs? I know a little of the sea myself, a little and yet enough to know what it is like out there. I've been around a bit. I know the Pacific; you will make your trip among sharks, hundreds of them. You might fall off the raft, might get washed off by seas."

I nodded.

"I just thought of something," he said, staring at me. "What will you do if you fall off—I mean about the sharks—when they start tearing chunks out of you?"

"What can I do?" I asked.

"Listen to me. I mined a lot among the Amazon Indians. I am honorary member of a few tribes. They gave me some of their *curare*, the poison they put on their arrows and spears when they go hunting. I'll give you some, and if you fall overboard you can prick yourself and be out of it. Works like a shot. Then let the sharks fight over you. Don't you think that makes sense? I always have some *curare* when I go out."

My mind wandered on. . . . The day after the old-timer offered me the poison I went to watch the rest of my logs being loaded for the trip to Quevedo. One of the workers had sat down on the end of a log and almost at once leaped into the air with a shriek. The other men started laughing while the workman ripped off his trousers. He had sat down on one of the big black ants one finds around the roots of jungle trees. They are commonly called *conga*, after the dance. A man is bound to perform a dance getting out his pants after being bitten. Another popular and fitting name is *quita calzon*, meaning, take your drawers off. . . .

A dolphin jumped nearby and struck the water with its tail and it sounded like a pistol shot. He was not chasing a flying fish but just feeling good. Dolphins seemed to go crazy sometimes in the moonlight. All day long they jumped around me. Sometimes they went through the air in long graceful arcs, repeating their jumps three or four times. Sometimes they leaped straight up, aiming for the sun and striking the water a terrific blow when they came down. When they were to leeward of me I could not always hear the loud slapping of belly or tail but could see their chisel-sharp silver-and-blue bodies glistening in the sun, often miles away.

Bonitos jump too, but their chubby bodies end in an amateurish head-over-heels flop without real control. There is a little more grace to their movements when they hunt. Their prey also are flying fish, sardines, and anything they can swallow. Bonitos, too, move like darts in the water, turning continually and diving when they are pursued.

I didn't bother with dolphins right now; they were too strong for me to handle in my weakened condition. A few days ago I had put a flying fish on the hook and thrown the line over. A dolphin had struck faster than eye or thought could move, but I had no strength to pull it in. Even if I could have brought it on deck it would have been too much for me. He would have wrecked the deck and got away. Dolphins are like tigers when they come fresh out of the sea and have been only a few seconds on the hook.

Meekie did not care whether I landed them or not; she was getting all the flying fish she wanted. She did her own catching; they hit all over the deck. A lot sailed right into the canoe and I even found them on the cabin roof. Attracted by the light of the compass lantern, they occasionally struck me on the head or face. I was now eating them raw after letting them soak in canned lemon juice for a few hours.

There were still many dolphins around but the big hunt when the sky was alive with birds was over. I could still see birds fishing, but in small groups and at a distance. Yesterday I saw a few divers; they had a different shape from that of the sabre-winged frigate birds. They were big also but heavier-set and with a long, thick neck. They hurtle down on their prey from a considerable height, attacking so as not to cast a shadow and disappearing in the sea in a burst of spray. They usually came up with a fish. They went mainly after sardines, no doubt a steadier target than the elusive flying fish.

The raft edged off the course a little and I realized that I should get up and pull in an inch or so on the weather sheet. But what could I do even after I managed to get up? I couldn't get any slack out of that rope; it was standing like an iron bar. I could put a tackle on it, of course, but all that work. . . . Impossible. It would wear me out. I'd let 'er run; in a day or so I'd feel stronger. I just couldn't move. I was happy and didn't worry. I had come through the great sickness. I thought that nothing could happen to me now. I could stick it out for a year now if I had to.

I could no longer lift my big 'midships centreboard and so cut the strop and let it slide down into the sea. It was $2\frac{1}{2}$ inches thick, 2 feet wide, and 18 feet long, made out of solid, heavy mangrove. It went down like lead. Perhaps it would make a raft for marine creatures—snails, starfish, barnacles, and occasionally an octopus. I now had no use for the hand winch I had taken along solely for the centreboard. Perhaps I should put the ladder on it and so take the slack out of the ropes. That ladder was a problem. Sometimes it was all right and I could go up and down it all day long without any trouble. But let the masts swing just so and the raft roll just so and I was in for it. Maybe I could work out something . . . but not just now.

My thoughts turned to the canoe now and the hard time I had had getting it. I had advertised for one in the Guayaquil newspapers and had gone to half a dozen villages along the coast but could not get one. Finally a Czech with whom I had become acquainted had to go to Manglaralto, a fishing village north of Guayaquil, and he promised to get me a *bongo* (canoe) even if he had to take one by force. A few weeks later a *bongo* arrived from Manglaralto on a truck. The sea almost got both the truck and it when the driver made a detour over a stretch of open beach due to a landslide, and the tide came in while the motor was being repaired.

My Czech friend told me about his difficulties. "I went into the jungle to a village where the Indians were making *bongos*. I heard that one was almost finished. 'I'll buy it,' I said, 'but get busy and finish it.' It took the Indian ten minutes to decide that he would finish it sometime but it was impossible to pin him down to a specific date. Dates mean nothing in the jungle. With an Indian everything has to be just right for his work—the moon, his axe, the weather, his wife, his mother-in-law maybe,

159

and many other things; but mainly, he has to feel like working."

My friend kept after him, however, and the *bongo* was finished. Now the village had to have a feast to celebrate the event. When every man, woman, child and pig was gloriously drunk all the men grouped themselves around the *bongo*, and amid chanting, shouting and prodigious gruntings grasped the gunwale, lifted the *bongo* high overhead and smashed it down on the rocks. If the canoe did not break it was a good *bongo*. This one cracked. That meant the moon had not been just right at some time during the building or something else had been wrong.

It was not a serious matter; a crack could be fixed simply enough. But repairing it was a lengthy process. The moon and everything else had to be just right again; and above all, the Indian had to recover from the feast and feel like working. The *bongo* might very well not be finished till the following year.

My friend went back to the coast and induced a fisherman to sell him his seagoing canoe. This wasn't easy to do, for tuna and other fish had just started to run. The high price offered swung the deal and I got my *bongo*.

In Callao I rigged it for the open sea, putting in two masts, one 8 feet high, forward, the other 9 feet, aft, with booms and sails. I also had a jib. Then we decked bow and stern with heavy canvas to keep out seas and spray in case I should be forced to use it. If I had had time I would have put a keel on the bottom; instead I took enough bamboos along for an outrigger. . . .

My raft was proving itself remarkably seaworthy but one never knew what might happen; some sort of disaster might strike to demolish it and force me to take to the canoe. I definitely foresaw use of the canoe in case I reached the islands and found no way through the reefs

Eekie ponders flying fish and rare mackerel shark which arrived on deck during the night.

After 6,500 miles, Samoa at last.

that generally surrounded them. In such an event I would take in my sails, drop my seventy-five-pound anchor on all the cable I had in order to slow up the drift of my raft, and then find a way over the reefs in my canoe. Many of the Polynesian reefs have breaks in them big enough for a ship's boat to get through. Villages were generally located near these openings into the lagoons and I might be able to return later with natives to bring the raft to safe anchorage.

Meekie was playing forward in the moonlight with a flying fish, tossing it up and catching it, stalking and pouncing on it, whirling and leaping high with consummate, feline grace. Her beautiful, slim body, all black, was supple, and she moved extremely fast. I was told that Peruvian cats are not as tame as ours. Meekie was great company and I learned much from her. They say that cats do not belong on the sea since they fear water. Not so with Meekie. If she had her eyes on a fish she would not dodge a sea no matter how big. She generally got a good soaking a few times a day but did not seem to mind. Her favourite hang-out when not tied up was beneath the deck on the main logs where she was continuously in the wash of the seas.

The moon broke through the clouds, clearing an ever-widening court around it. Time and space had become magic. A fairyland lay on the water. Seas and winds and clouds had put on magic garments. The endless Pacific became a moving, shadowy mass of silver.

## LOSS OF WATER

THE day broke rather calm on August 6. It was cloudy and the wind sluggish, the sea rolling grey and listless. An hour later it brightened up and the dark, slow cloud masses disappeared and sky and sea were sparkling blue in the sun. A fresh wind began to lift the sea.

I had all my drinking water in sealed five-gallon tin cans lying lengthwise in the cracks beneath the logs, underneath the bamboo deck. Whenever I was out of water I raised a section of the deck and took out a can or two. The day before, I had taken up two cans, stood them beside the cabin on a piece of plank and opened up one by unscrewing the top and then breaking the tin seal. This morning when I needed water for my coffee I picked up the can to fill my pot. The can was empty. A leak? All the water had run out. I grasped the next one standing beside it, not yet opened. Empty, too! Both cans empty—not a drop left. Ten gallons of precious water gone. . . .

Fear gripped me. How about the other cans beneath the deck? I lifted up the bamboo section and exposed the cans that had been lying there since the voyage began. I lifted can after can and tossed them on deck. Empty . . . empty . . . empty. . . . One was less than half-full. One was half-full of salt water. Three were apparently intact. The rest was gone, leaked out. Practically my whole supply of drinking water—gone. Without water, in the middle of the ocean. . . .

Then I saw water trickling out of one of the three

full cans. The seams barely held together, and now, after the cans had been disturbed, were beginning to open. The water came out in little jets that sparkled in the sun.

I grasped everything I could put my hands on to save my water—pots, pans, basins, jars and bottles. A kind soul in Lima had sent a case of rum on board. It lay in the stern end of the canoe. I picked it up, tore it open and poured the rum into the sea to fill the bottles with water. My largest container was the drum that contained my *cañihua*.

When I finished, the bamboo deck was wet and looked like a junk shop turned upside down. To one side lay my five-gallon water cans, solid-looking but empty, all empty, light as feathers and still sealed tight. What a joke on me! A few weeks ago, perhaps only days ago, they had been full of the finest water brought down from a Peruvian mountain spring.

Rags, funnels, bottles and pots lay around the deck in messy disorder. And the raft was ploughing along as determinedly as ever, doing its work. Only I had blundered again.

I cut open one of the water cans. It was bright as a mirror inside, but a rusty red thread ran along each seam. The salt water had eaten into the seams like acid.

I sat down and looked abstractedly at the light of the sky and clouds and beyond into space. Then I considered myself again and all the mistakes I had made.

The moment I had touched the first can and found it empty I knew it was all my fault, knew the whole story. I knew they had to rust for they had been lying in pounding seas. I had to expect it. I had been utterly wrong in using such light cans in the first place and then stowing them beneath the deck, directly in the water.

I had been warned beforehand by my own common

163

sense. And still I had done it. I had merely painted the cans with a thin paint mixture used on ships for the inside of water tanks, thinking this would keep them from rusting. Careless, careless, Willis. I had originally decided to coat the cans heavily with asphalt but then had taken the easier and faster way out, by painting them with a thin composition not meant for the purpose. A thick coat of asphalt would have saved the cans.

Besides the twenty new tin cans filled with spring water I had taken along five other cans of water, for emergency only. These cans were old, had originally contained paint, and had been burned out with torches. But when I opened one some weeks before, the water was so bad I could not use it even for washing my hands. I strained it through a cloth but it still could not be used. I was also afraid there might be traces of lead in the water despite the burning. I did not feel like taking a chance with lead poisoning out here, especially after my solar plexus attack. I remembered hearing that, during the war, the whole crew of a torpedoed ship that had taken to a lifeboat had died of lead poisoning after drinking water from a tank in which were chips of paint containing lead. These old cans were useless except as ballast, to shift from side to side according to wind and seas. But during the night of my attack, when I lay helpless, heavy seas had washed away all but one.

Another misfortune had overtaken me—one after another. This looked like a catastrophe. I was sailing close to the equator and had two or three months to go. I was about sixteen hundred miles from the Marquesas. It would have been so easy to take proper care of the cans. And such fine water, the very best, from a high mountain spring. . . .

I had wanted to take along a fifty-gallon wooden keg, a charred oak keg that would keep the water cool and pure, and lash it in the stern behind the house, just to have for an emergency. It would have come in handy now. But I hadn't taken it—too much trouble going to a few ship chandlers in Callao and have one sent to the raft. I had been in too much of a hurry to get started, being two months late.

This had to happen to me, I who knew the sea and the laws of the sea, who knew that it is a crime to sail with all one's drinking water in frail cans, cans intended only for limited use ashore. I should have had strong, heavy tanks or kegs. That was the custom of the sea. At sea you only last as long as your water. I had known that since I was a youngster. Perhaps a ship would come by? No, I was out of all shipping lanes. I had to find another way out.

At noon I worked out my latitude and in the afternoon my full position: Lat. 5° 31′ South; Long. 114° 10′ West. I was forty-five days out from Callao.

It was night again and the stars looked so calmly down. There was a light, steady breeze and the *Seven Little Sisters* made her way so quietly and easily over the swell, as undisturbed as if nothing had happened on board.

I had to find a way out. It seemed I felt much calmer already; I was getting my bearings. I had had so many disappointments that I was hardened by this time. I still had my raft, all in one piece and as solid as ever. "I'll get through, I'll make it!" I kept saying, speaking aloud, as one gets the habit of doing when alone.

I had some water left, about nine gallons. I figured it out during the day: thirty-six quarts, about two and a half of my cups to the quart. Ninety cups of water altogether. In Callao I had estimated a 200-days' trip with a 400-quart supply of water. Now, after forty-five days out, I was left with ninety cups. And anything could happen to slow me up; I could lose my sails or the rigging could come down or some other disaster might overtake me. I had only ninety cups of water. Maybe I should head for the Marquesas.

I could squeeze some water from the fish I caught, though now and then they disappeared for days. I could not count on rain at this time of the year, in this latitude. I would have to be in the doldrums for that, north of the equator and well out of the south-east trades. I wouldn't consider that. No doldrums for me, no going off my course and perhaps getting caught in the Equatorial Counter Current which ran eastward and began about five degrees north of the equator.

I had lost all my emergency rations also. They had been stowed on the logs in another section beneath the deck, also exposed to the corrosion by the salt water. I had to throw everything overboard. It was Teddy who had insisted that I take emergency rations along in case my flour should become mildewed and spoiled by the sea air. She said they might also be useful as presents to the natives in case I landed on some lonely atoll.

One cup of water a day, for three months. Could I manage on that? Could I survive on that, working twenty-four hours a day, much of the time under broiling sun?

I would sip my daily cup slowly, drop by drop, and get every bit of good out of it. But I would need more. Suddenly, an answer came. Salt water—I would drink salt water!

That was it—I would drink some salt water to help preserve my fresh-water rations. I knew I could drink it; I always had been able to as a youngster—I didn't know why. Perhaps because I used very little salt; I had no craving for it. I was not a meat-eater—maybe that had something to do with it. I would drink a cup or two of salt water a day and so stretch out my supply of fresh water. I had done it before on ships, had often drunk a cup of water merely to keep my insides in shape. Old-timers knew that a cup of water now and then was like medicine.

I had first learned about drinking sea water when I was a youngster of fifteen. I was standing on the deck of the four-masted bark *Henriette,* looking down at our cook who was stretched out flat on his back, naked. Two sailors were holding him down, and the mate, a two-hundred pounder, was standing barefooted on the cook's belly, stepping around and around, kneading it with his feet to loosen up the cook's insides. The cook had been constipated for weeks and was near death. "The fool," an old sailor remarked, "should have known enough to drink a cup of sea water now and then to keep his bowels open. On a square-rigger, with no fresh food for six months—he should know what to do for himself."

That's when I had first learned to drink sea water. I had always wanted to keep in top shape and felt that the old sailor was right. I tried it at once. The first drink went down easily and I felt not the slightest ill effects from it. As recently as four years ago, on a tanker on the Port La Cruz run, I had drunk a cup of salt water a day, for the ship was gassy from the crude oil, which upset me, and I thought sea water would help me. I had also drunk it while sailing with Teddy from the West Indies, and later while cruising off Florida and the Bahamas. Teddy used to watch my face, screwing up her own while I emptied a big cup. My face remained placid. I could never induce her to try it though she agreed with me that it might do a person good.

I also figured that if goats and wild cattle on the Galapagos Islands could drink salt water, I should be able to get along on it for three months or so. One cup a day I knew I could take without even thinking about it. I had done it before. Certainly I could do so now.

I reached for my tin cup beside the cabin and after

making sure that no shark was near I dipped it into the sea and brought it up filled to the brim. I raised it to my lips and drank it, emptied it to the last drop. I had no qualms, didn't even shudder. It stayed with me, too.

Again I thought of the goats and wild cattle that survived, generation after generation, on the Galapagos and on other islands scattered over the earth. Cattle on the Galapagos needed plenty of water, living on those hot rocks all day. I also knew that on some of the Polynesian islands and in other parts of the world the natives drink only brackish water—it was all they had. Brackish water sometimes contains a considerable amount of salt.

But there was no excuse for my carelessness. It was the same with my stoves and kerosene supply. I had not taken proper care and now I could expect to be without fire at any time, which meant I would have to eat my fish raw. I knew I could manage that, too, but it would have been a lot more pleasant to sit down to a plate loaded with golden-brown fried dolphin steak than to eat it raw, washed down with salt water. I could only tell myself that I had wanted shipwreck conditions and now I had them. Losing my rigging and having to drift would be the last stage in a survival test. I was not afraid of that either, for I felt within me that the sky above would come across with the right answer for that, too.

Nature had made me a part of her. Sometimes I felt as though my thinking had almost stopped. I was body and mind carrying on the business of life and working the raft, but my spirit was apart—off somewhere, looking down at my body and watching it at its labour and its thinking. Yet my spirit was the real me, the true self of me. It was passionless and part of Nature. It showed me my faults and weaknesses with impartial clearness, holding me up to myself. It showed me all my past thinking,

168

too, and I could see that I had been to the depth of evil thoughts. And then, while I was aghast at myself, Nature, like a flow of limitless and never-failing salvation, enfolded me and gave me new hope.

I lay beside the wheel on a plank, hard against the compass and blissful in my weariness. The raft sailed on alone. I was aware of the seas. A bank of clouds was making up in the south-east and should arrive soon. But it had not come yet. Doze a little. Everything would be all right.

Into my subconscious came the impression that somebody was busy on deck, handling the raft. I often had this impression. At times it seemed to be Teddy, or someone from the distant past—my mother or sister. As I began to regain my senses, this impression became more definite and I felt relieved of all responsibility. Then I awoke fully and saw that I was surrounded by black clouds. Seas were rising dark above the raft and for a moment I felt that I had been unfairly deserted by my shadowy partners. Only then did I realize that I was alone in space, severed from the earth.

I was in solitary, in my vast cell of heaven and sea, lighted by the sun and at night by the thousand candles of the stars; I was a prisoner of the universe. Perhaps all people had died and I was left alone. No, I would not want to live on that way—not for a thousand years of life. No Nirvana for me—give me instead a thousand lives of tears, trudging beside my fellow men.

There was so much work that I was often near exhaustion. The balancing, the ceaseless shaking I was subjected to, also threatened to wear me down. Time continued to pass and to leave no impression. Had I been out weeks, or months? The calendar told me exactly but figures meant nothing. Each dawn I would wind my clocks and watches and scratch out the previous day on the

OCP/931—F*                    169

calendar. I did this merely for my navigation. My mind was almost a blank about what had happened to me recently. I recalled my sickness only vaguely. I was living in a vacuum. I did not look at my chart. It would have been too much effort to take it out, and, since I did my navigation on plotting sheets, was not necessary. I had to save every ounce of energy for the real work, handling the raft.

I was making sixty, seventy, eighty or ninety miles a day, and even more; I was fighting for every bit of distance and would rather have dropped down exhausted, unable to get up again, than lower my sails and let the raft drift while I slept. I was out here to sail! I no longer worried about beating the hurricane season. I would take whatever was ahead. I thought that I could get through even though I might pile up on some reef or be dismasted. But while I had the raft intact and could stand on my feet, I would sail.

Once I got close to the Marquesas I would start watching my chart. Now I did all my position work on plotting sheets. They are nautical sheets representing the earth's surface, scaled to corresponding latitudes but having no numbered meridians, and so can be used over and over again. Since passing the Galapagos I was not concerned about what lay ahead on my course, knowing that I had thousands of miles of open space. I knew my meridians and latitudes by heart, of course, and knew I was heading about one hundred and fifty miles north of the Marquesas. And so I avoided taking out my chart, shunned the task of spreading it out and then leaving it to jump to the wheel. I intended to keep well clear of the Marquesas. They are high, mountainous islands of volcanic origin, with deep cliffs rising from the sea, with no sheltering bays—death to a raft coming up with the wind. I would keep well to the north and not take a chance of being becalmed and eventually drifting ashore.

I intended to keep away from all islands till I was ready to land. I was sailing like a yacht; I was knocking off the longitudes, running my westing down.

Every day brought some crisis, with new decisions to make about the sails and steering, new winds and a new sea, and a new arrangement of centreboards. I could take nothing for granted. What worked one day could wreck me the next. It was a struggle for survival every day and moment with wind and sea, for food and water. Bringing the big mainsail up or down in a wind while keeping the raft on its course forced me to move fast and take hold solidly.

The sea changed while I sat dreaming, roaming the universe since the beginning of time. The moon was nearly down. My golden planet hung low, its light dimming. Deep valleys lay on the sea. There must have been a blow to the south to have brought up such a swell. The valleys looked almost motionless in the light, like an Alaskan landscape. I felt that I had seen them before somewhere, had walked through them some time.

It had grown grey behind me. Big day today—first day on my salt-water diet. I knew just what it meant; it enabled me to go on calmly, made me feel freer, at one with the vastness around me. I went forward to the left side of the mast, knelt down, and dipped my white enamel cup into the sea. I held the full cup high, facing the light: "Only strength and goodness is in you. You are giving me life. I am taking you into my body." I put the cup to my lips. The drinking of salt water was a sacrament.

# ★ 19 ★

## THE MAGIC OF SINGING

WHENEVER the sun lay hot on the sea there was a spot forward, beside the left leg of the mast, where it was deliciously cool from the wind that spilled down from the big sail. This was Meekie's favourite hang-out at such times. I was sitting there on the edge of the deck, letting my bare feet hang down in the bluest and cleanest of waters.

A few large dolphins, bosses of the troop that hung out beneath the raft, swam about ten feet away, golden tail fins shining now and then as they caught the light. I bent forward to massage my feet, for they were subjected to constant strain. As I was bending over, hanging on with one hand to a line, I saw a long, dark shape a few feet directly beneath me. The shark must have been hiding in the darkness beneath the raft when he saw my white, glistening feet in the water. Maybe he had no evil intentions, though I am inclined to doubt it. Anyway, I moved fast, for I couldn't see myself hanging on with both hands to the mast and yelling while a six-foot shark helped himself to a piece of my leg.

It was a beautiful day with a strong, fresh wind and a moderate sea. White clouds streamed by overhead, pushed by the trade wind. Man must have clouds to look at; they are the bridge between the earth and the absolute. It would be too overpowering always to see the eternal heavens lying directly above.

In spite of hardships and exhaustion I had picked up

weight after my illness and considered myself in good condition. I just felt like going on and on. I was at peace with myself and the world—a state of mind so hard to attain in the city. My only regret was that my wife was not by my side, she who had done so much to make my voyage possible. She should have been beside me, sharing the strength that flowed from the sun and the sea, sharing with me the peace that reigned in this solitude. I could not help feeling selfish, having all this to myself. I thought, all people ought to share it with me. More and more I looked upon my voyage as an experiment for all mankind.

Eekie, too, was in fine spirits, it seemed. At times he did not open his beak except to sound off his dawn squawks and evening screeches. At other times he let out a series of squawks that sounded like a family of hoarse ducks in hilarious spirits. I sometimes thought he must have lived in a disreputable household where the woman was very quarrelsome and threw all she knew in Spanish at her husband, along with the crockery, when he came home drunk, while a flock of children around her joined in a chorus of weeping and laughter and song. He was a show in himself, little Eekie, and demanded neither attention nor applause. On two occasions while I was aft he let loose a particular bit of his repertoire with such mastery that I refused to believe it could have come from the throat of a bird and went forward to see. His performance had been almost incredible.

Now and then I fastened a line around his foot and let him out of his cage. He usually celebrated his freedom by climbing up a rope. There he would sit, as far as he could go, flapping the stumps of his wings, gazing over the sea, no doubt dreaming of green forests and the snow-capped Sierras far away. If I didn't watch him he would bite through his line and roam around the raft on his own.

I was afraid Meekie would get him some day. I was sure he would put up a good fight with beak and claws but Meekie could move as if shot out of a catapult.

There were times following my sickness when I felt quite forlorn. Something was lacking. I was not as consistently happy as I wanted to be. Each morning I lived through ecstasies of the dawn and with undiminished reverence and humility saw the beauties of the universe moving above me throughout the day. But there was a void.

And then one day I started singing and I realized that my soul had been hungering for this. What a joy to discover singing again. I knew I had mastered the last big obstacle in my voyage. Now let the sky smash down on me but I would meet it singing. I recalled that I had always sung while living in solitude in different parts of the world. But singing had never affected me so profoundly as now. A wild mood would sweep over me as I toiled all alone, wrestling with the ropes, or swinging aloft to clear running gear, or working with the flapping sail and barely able to manage it. I would then burst out singing, roaring some old sea chanty learned long ago and long forgotten, now coming out in the wildness of the moment. I would shout defiance to the winds and elements, my untamed partners playing with me in their strength as I stood with legs straddled on the tossing deck. Singing made all my work easy. Many a wild night heard me, as many a dark sea rose beside me and ran past.

Singing was a miracle that worked for me at all times. Would it do the same for others adrift at sea? I didn't know. It certainly was not the musical quality of my voice that soothed me and brought my spirits into harmony, for I can sing no better than Eekie.

People do fear the solitude. To most men in the States, in Ecuador, and in Peru, the fact that I wanted to sail alone had appeared incomprehensible and foolish. Voluntarily to submit to solitude for many months, to be flung about on the sea, have no one to speak to, no one to see—the very idea overwhelmed them. Many believed that madness would be the inevitable outcome. Men at the Navy base in Callao, good, sturdy seamen, asked me the same question throughout my six weeks' stay: *"Solo, Señor?"* They could not understand how anybody could undergo such torture of mind and body.

From my first conception of the raft, this was one of the rewards I looked forward to—being alone. I knew that I needed this cleansing, this lifting up. I needed to go back to the bourne whence I had come, to stand before the reckoning and receive new strength before going on. I knew that I had gone far astray, as men will. Have not man's spiritual leaders throughout the ages accepted solitude at some time in their lives?

Yes, man has become afraid of loneliness. In Alaska, years ago, men were taken out of the wilderness every spring, men for whom the solitude had been too much. And they were iron men, physically, able to stand incredible hardships, men from all parts of the world who had come to dig the frozen ground in search of gold, veterans of the gold fields of Australia, New Guinea, California, and South Africa. I had lived with them and knew their strength. . . .

I recalled one late afternoon in the Alaska range. I had arrived at the log cabin of a prospector near the Healey River and thought I would stop for the night and rest up before going on the next day. The prospector, a grizzled, bearded man, came to the door and stared at me. I realized that he was far gone. About ten huskies were crowding around me, sniffing and snarling.

"I don't know if my dogs will stand for it; they ain't

taking to you," he growled. "I don't understand why people come around here pestering me. You go ahead and make that trading post." He jerked his hand towards the valley. "Ain't no more than fifteen miles. I ain't got nothing to eat here for anybody." He slammed the door in my face. I picked up my pack and hit the trail, feeling that a 30-30 was aimed at my back. I had heard his "Damn you all!" as the door slammed.

"He is due to go out next spring," I was told at the trading post. "You're lucky he didn't take a shot at you. If you had kicked one of his dogs he sure would have. Yeah, they'll get him in the spring. And he ain't the only one."

I had seen others like him in California, Nevada and New Mexico, lonely prospectors, mostly old men who went into the hills with their burros.

In French Guiana I had met convicts who had been in solitary confinement. The sentences were for one, two, and even four years. Few came out sane. In the cells on the Island of St. Joseph, the place of confinement, they could at least hear the step of the guard making his rounds on the catwalk, could hear his voice and even see him, or hear the howling of men in the other cells, listen to the code-tapping on the walls. Even though they suffered, they felt they had not been altogether abandoned. Those in absolute solitary cracked more quickly.

The full terrors of solitude come to a man when he is lost in the endlessness of water space. Following the last war, many seamen drifted alone in lifeboats and on rafts after their shipmates had died of wounds or starvation. I had been on ships with such men and knew their stories.

There was one, an able seaman, who had been torpedoed five times and had once been adrift in the Atlantic alone for forty-five days. He had tasted thirst and starvation and solitude to the dregs. But he wanted to ship out again, insisted on a ship on the Murmansk run, something everybody else tried to keep away from. Why did he want that particular run? "You see," he said, dead serious, "I got knocked off five times, I want to make it six even. Get the idea?" They sent him to a seamen's rest home in the country to recuperate. Yes, solitude can cleanse or break a man. . . .

And now the night was over. I sat beside the wheel and ate my breakfast, the raw liver of a twenty-five-pound dolphin that I had just caught and about half a pound of the meat. I had soaked the liver and the meat in lemon juice. It tasted fresh and clean, like raw scallops.

The water was full of sharks this morning, all around the raft, but I saw no dolphins. A flying fish had flopped on deck, however, and I put it on the hook and threw out my line. It was taken in a flash by a dolphin that rushed through the water like a white streak, with a dozen or so sharks after him. He came aboard quite easily, in fact almost flying. But once there he smashed around, trying to get back into the sea.

Meekie sat with her head turned away till the dolphin had been killed and cleaned and the deck washed. Then she came for her fillet.

I heard the howl of the wind and, looking behind the mizzen, saw a squall coming, still about half a mile away —a long, dark band of cloud. More wind, more speed, an extra five or ten miles—I wanted those squalls to beat the hurricanes.

Crossed the 116th meridian yesterday. . . . My logbook entry read: August 8. Noon 14 hrs.; 51′ 20° Eastern Standard Time; sun's altitude 68° 10.5′; Lat. 5° 29′ South; Long. 116° 14′ West. Day's run 62 miles. Light winds.

The famous pathway of the square-riggers for a hundred years—those heading north from the Horn to

Seattle, Vancouver, Portland and San Francisco, all famous sailing-ship ports in the old days—was between the 110th and 120th meridians.

I was not on a proud square-rigger now, foaming through the Humboldt Current on the south-east trades with royals and studding sails set, but I had been, once, as a boy, and I saw my ship again now, like a giant ghost traced against the clouds.

Where have they gone, those mighty square-rigger fleets, sailing north from the Horn, outward bound from Europe and the Atlantic Coast? They are no more, sunk beneath the tide of time with their iron men, blasted out of the sea by shellfire and storms, or smashed on a lee shore. They are no more. The remaining few left in America are tame, carrying guano for the Peruvian government. Up and down the coast they ply, their iron sinews slack, mere hulks though still carrying sails . . . the last rotting remnants of a giant race.

Sharks had been around the raft more often than usual. Long Tom was still there, now fully accepted as a daily companion. He kept alongside the raft, moving like a shadow, always in the same spot and keeping his eye on me. Maybe he thought something was going to happen on the raft. Other sharks came and went, circling the raft, swimming away and returning, but these eventually went their own way. Long Tom stayed. I could have got rid of him by putting a bait of dolphin on a large hook attached to a chain and swivel, catching him, and let him drag alongside till he drowned or was devoured by other sharks, who would have torn him apart the moment they realized he was helpless. But I had decided against catching sharks; they messed up the raft. And besides, I wanted no killer atmosphere around the *Seven Little Sisters*. It was bad enough catching dolphins. I felt bad every time I pulled one out of the sea, destroying such

178

beauty and perfection for a meal. But it was root-hog-or-die out here, with me and Meekie both on the bread line.

Sharks, incidentally, have none of the headlong ferocity of the barracuda, but you can't trust them. They are unpredictable. I saw one leave the head of a dolphin, to swallow an old sock soaked in kerosene that I had used for cleaning my lantern.

My hands and fingers looked as if I had worked on the docks for months on end. My fingernails were broken off. Both my hands were sore from constant gripping. My legs, from continuous balancing and bracing to keep from being thrown, were as hard as those of the Indian porters who trotted over the Andes with big loads on their backs, nourished by the same *cañihua* and barley flour that sustained me. I ate it as often as six times a day.

A black squall came up a little after sunset while a streak of orange was still in the sky. I thought it would be another bad night, like so many previous nights, but the sky cleared and the moon came out. There seemed to be no rain in the sky at this time of the year, for thus far I had not had a drop. I certainly wanted rain.

Meekie sat beside the winch in the moonlight and looked wistfully at me. She had been sitting there an hour, patiently waiting for me to come forward, untie her, and take her aft with me. It was the highlight of her day. She had learned to follow the leash like a dog. She continued to sit there, pleading silently. If I had gone forward and said to her, "You can't come aft tonight; it's squally and I'll be busy; I might run over you, rushing about the deck," she would have been satisfied and crawled under the winch and kept out of the way.

Eekie, who was sometimes quiet for days, just letting out a few squawks in the morning and evening, today treated me to a new repertoire; he was always digging

179

up something new out of his past. This one seemed to be a scene from a bar-room. I knew quite a bit about him by now. He hadn't been around a church much, if at all, nor in refined company, ever.

They say parrots can live to a hundred years or more. To judge by Eekie's deliveries, he had been around pretty near that long. Only the other day he had startled me with the pitiful wail of a baby getting its first spanking. I had rushed over to see what was happening, thinking that perhaps Meekie had him by the throat. No—he was sitting in his cage paying no attention to anything, seemingly, just lost in his memories and babbling. Then, as soon as I was gone, he opened up with his old-hag act, one of his masterpieces. In this act the lady was in her cups, holding on to her bottle as if someone was trying to take the flask away, and cackling so volubly that her head and teeth rattled, winding up with a screech that shook the masthead. Sometimes Eekie sat silent as a green Indian, just eating and watching everything with his red, quick eyes.

The Peruvians had liked the names, Eekie and Meekie. When I told the sailors at the navy base that I would take a parrot and a cat along, they asked me what I would call them. "Ike and Mike," I said, having previously decided on that. They had a little trouble pronouncing the names in Spanish and I wrote them down on a piece of paper. "Ah," they exclaimed, staring at the letters, "Eekie and Meekie!" "That's it," I said; "Eekie and Meekie." And Eekie and Meekie they became.

There is a bit of my past connected with the names, Ike and Mike, which was why I chose them. It went back to 1920. We had sold our little ranch in Texas and moved to San Francisco. I went to work in a shipyard as a riveter and one day a tiny piece of steel from a hot rivet struck my eye. I thought it was dust and paid no attention to it.

A few days later I had to stop working. They pulled the bit of steel out with a magnet; it had embedded itself in the cornea and started an abscess. The eye was in bad shape and for a period of six months I went to the doctor every day.

For the first time in my life since leaving school I had nothing to do. I sat down and started to draw. Drawing was my first love. I had begun at the age of five. One eye was bandaged, but I could use the other, and I worked out a number of comic strips, finally settling on one that I called "Ike and Mike."

After the eye had healed, leaving a scar and impairment of vision, I went back to Texas and the Galveston docks. When times were slack I kept working on Ike and Mike, thinking that some day I would market my strip. The day did come, in 1923. Some of the syndicates were interested. In Cleveland I became friendly with one of America's topmost cartoonists. "Stick it out," he said, "and you'll get in. I am behind you a hundred per cent." Then I became frightened at the thought of spending my life in a big, dark city, shut off from light and Nature. I wrestled with myself for a week, walking the streets for hours at a time. Eventually I went back to San Francisco, to roam the valley of California, half outcast, but happy.

That is the story behind Ike and Mike—or rather Eekie and Meekie, as the Peruvian sailors preferred it. . . .

Each night aboard the *Seven Little Sisters* appeared more beautiful, more inspiring than any other I had ever lived through. I gazed at the sea and the clouds that passed in an ever-changing panorama around me. The big constellations came up and marched across the sky like tall gods on horseback.

## THE FISH AROUND US

THERE must have been a storm in the south-east or perhaps one was coming up. The deep, long valleys of the sea were on the move. High in the sky the clouds were running wild with mares'-tails—long-streaking and twisted as if scourged by fierce winds. Below were trade-wind clouds and far-off squalls. It looked like North Atlantic weather. There was a lot of wind somewhere but I could take more before shortening sail. I wanted to get west while winter lasted. Perhaps I would have to shorten sail before the day was over. I was cutting down the miles to Samoa, though I still had about 3,500 to go. It was August 22—exactly two months since I had left Callao.

I should have fished this morning but decided to let it go till tomorrow. I could still eat dolphin I had caught, though Meekie might turn her nose up at it—she didn't seem to want fish more than half an hour out of the sea. I would catch another tomorrow. Fishing took a lot out of me. If I hooked a big fellow, it was like wrestling with a hunk of dynamite.

I had quite a few sharks around the raft again this morning. They seemed to come in droves when there was an impending change in the weather. Seven of them swam beside me, all the same size, about five feet long. They swam in V formation, spaced to the inch and seemingly not moving a fin or a muscle.

The previous evening I had seen several whales. They seemed to travel in pairs. All were small fellows, from thirty to forty feet long, probably sperm whales. They were barrel-bodied, like hippos, and brown in colour. They always came close, though never touching the raft, and I could look right down their blow-holes. They were the most peaceful creatures in the sea, playing around the raft for hours and coming to the surface with serious snorts. They liked to swim in the foaming wake of the raft, just beside the rudder, where they usually dived. It was always in the evening that they came, and by the time I could get my camera out it was too dark. Generally they came from the south-east and continued north-west on leaving.

A few weeks before, I had seen a large whale from the masthead, coming straight in my wake, high out of the water. It was one of those days when the ladder was on the warpath and I had my hands full hanging on. By the time I was down and had my camera out of its air-tight, tape-wrapped case he was gone. This one was a lone traveller. I saw his fin once more, standing like an aeroplane rudder in the sea, about half a mile to the north-west.

"Yes, Meekie, don't look at me like that. Here's your dolphin. See, just cut fresh from the back—real tender loin, if you ask me. Never saw better fish than this. Want me to show you how to eat it? Yes, I'm eating it now, just like you. A baby could eat it. Here—look! Okay, turn your little black snout up—don't eat till tomorrow. It's good enough for me. Remember, there may not be any dolphins around tomorrow. . . ."

"Well, what are *you* doing this morning, Eekie? What have you done with your water again? Everything messed up as usual. Here—an ear of corn! Your corn on the cob is just about finished—getting mouldy, too. It'll be shelled corn after this, and then rice. Teddy bought enough to last a year. She was sure worried about you.

I know you like fish. Some people wouldn't believe that, but I found out. You sneaked over to my plate one day and really dug into my dolphin. And what you didn't eat you messed up. Okay with me, I can feed you all the fish you want; but after my stove quits for good you have to eat it raw just like Meekie and I. . . .

"Meekie, you can sit on the box and sun yourself beside Eekie. Okay, little girl, I know you like to be petted. Yes, yes, I know you are the blackest and gentlest little cat that ever sailed on a raft. Can you imagine, some fellows in Peru said you would bring me bad luck because you are black? They had a nerve, didn't they? I have a lot more trouble with myself than with you or Eekie. Do you think you'll ever get Eekie, you little black panther, you disguised little black wolf? You two little characters are really perfect. Yes, Meekie, don't you worry, some day we'll be back on land, and boy!—ain't that old earth going to smell good to you! And all the grass, and birds, and everything? I can just see you stalking through the grass, shivering and quivering down to the tip of your tail. You know what I'm talking about, don't you? Sure! Yes, Meekie, I know I shanghaied you. You can tell that to the judge in Samoa. But you're getting along. You eat fish and sleep all day, and if there are no fish you just sleep. What a life! Outside that you have nothing to do except listen to my singing and not let a flying fish hit you on the nose. Just you lay off Eekie and you won't get into trouble."

Now, I began to include Long Tom in the family. He lived a little to one side of the raft, of course, but he certainly had made himself a member of our gang. I think I would have felt a little sad if one day I looked into the sea and did not see his long, brown torpedo shape trailing along like part of the *Seven Little Sisters*. Nights, he usually swam four to six feet beneath the surface, and during the day he came up within a foot or two. It was a mystery to me what he ate, and when. He did not get enough from me to keep his weight normal. He could probably go a month without food. He slept while swimming. Two or three pilot fish, about six inches long, were always swimming just in front of his terrible jaws, often touching them and looking like part of the shark itself. He never paid the slightest attention to them.

Sometimes I lay flat on my stomach and looked at him over the edge. Presently he would come up a little closer and I could see his dull eyes watching me.

"Do you know anything about the future, Long Tom?" I asked him. "Do you feel something is going to happen on the raft and that you will get a feast? Come on, fellow, tell me. You have another guess coming if you really think so, Long Tom, old boy. You aren't getting anything from this little raft except a dolphin head now and then —certainly no part of me! If you didn't get me while I was hanging on to that line like a half-drowned cat, you never will! Why don't you take a little swim for yourself, say, a few hundred miles or so, or even a thousand? Haven't you got a home somewhere?"

Whenever I caught a dolphin I got rid of the head by dropping it through the middle of the raft, between the cracks of the logs, to keep it from Long Tom. But he was aware of it at once and went after it. If other sharks were around, they all dived after it. When they came up again and cruised around as before, I could almost see their shark's grin that told of having tasted blood.

A dolphin leaped near the raft in a high, wide arc. He looked a golden green. Most dolphins were a vivid blue on the back with a silvery belly. They all had a lot of gold among their colours, which is why, in South America, they are called dorados, the golden ones.

Perhaps I should have fished this morning; a few more jumped farther off. Others nearby began to leap straight up, trying for height. I wondered whether this meant a change in the weather.

The sky continued to look wind-beaten, high up. Some of the white streaks went clear across the whole sky. Farther down, the clouds were massing thick. Something was trying to make up in the north-east. The wind was south-east. There were more whitecaps now. I poked the mizzen with my finger; I could just about tell by the pressure on the canvas how hard it was blowing. The wind was coming up a little, all right.

There was a lot of moss on the logs now, especially on the outside ones. I guess I had been out long enough for that. The iron rudder was coated solid. It had barnacles, too. Barnacles like to attach themselves to iron. The bow logs were covered with a green, leafy, thick weed which made the whole bow look like a lush, green mat. Along the sides the logs were trailing a thin, hair-like growth about a foot long.

I went forward with my cup, dipped it into the sea, and drank. It went down easy. I had been doing this every day, as a matter of course. I always knelt at the same place, between the left leg of the mast and the bow of the canoe, dipping the cup into the foot-wide crack between the two outer logs.

I never drank less than two full cups a day and suffered not the slightest ill effects. I drank it only when really thirsty and just enough to quench my thirst. Fresh water I used sparingly—for coffee or for flour paste, and now and then I took a sip.

Sea water did not cause undue thirst in me. I kept in the shade as much as possible, under a little awning stretched from the cabin to the side of the raft—I also avoided all unnecessary physical exertions, though there were occasions nearly every day when I had to work almost to the point of exhaustion. I hoped to get rain some day from one of the many squalls that swept down on me.

What a shock it had been when I first saw that my water had disappeared and then to see what little I had left spurting out of the cans. How I had rushed about looking for containers! And now I had become used to it and fully accepted it. I had always used very little salt. Time after time I had seen men sit down near me in a restaurant and put more salt on a single dish than I could possibly use in months.

Perhaps a sort of spiritual approach is necessary for drinking it; I could only speak for myself. This is perhaps the best approach to meet all survival conditions. Men will be shipwrecked again as they have been since the beginning of time, they will look out of a boat or raft upon the trackless sea with water tanks and cans empty and see the sun coming up like a torch held against their brains. Sun and fear are the swift killers of men lost at sea. The sun can kill a man in a day, while fear, more slowly devours him from within.

A little patch of awning over the head to keep the sun off may save lives. And so perhaps will the realization that one can drink salt water in small quantities, enough to keep going.

## ★ 21 ★

## ALARM CLOCK AND SEXTANT

IT was dawn. I went into the cabin and wound my clocks and watches. Then I scratched the previous day, August 29, from the calendar stuck above the door. This was my routine. I was almost seventy days out from Callao, approaching the Marquesas. I had sailed about 3,500 miles.

I cleared the deck of all rope for I planned to do some fishing. My topping gear always lay on deck at night, clear for running, in order to get the yard down quickly if necessary. This was the last thing I saw to in the evening, for without light and especially on a stormy night, everything might get hopelessly fouled and I might even lose my yard and sail.

She steered pretty well and I lashed the wheel. The sea had gone down during the last hour and, with the coming of dawn, the wind slackened. I had heard a dolphin jump while it was still dark, so there were some around, most likely.

No flying fish had come on deck during the night. I checked every crack and box, and especially the inside of the canoe. Instead, I found two squid, about seven inches long. They had been coming aboard regularly for weeks. I tossed them overboard. Squid couldn't be used as bait; neither dolphins nor sharks took them.

I cut a strip from the belly of my last dolphin, that still hung, almost dried out, from the side of the canoe. It

188

would have to do for bait. I always kept the belly for this purpose. Sometimes, when the meat had dried out, I soaked it in water overnight to soften it, for dolphins are wary.

I cut the strip in the shape of a fish and put it on the hook. Meekie was awake now and watching my preparations with interest, though from a safe distance. Before this, she had tangled with a thrashing dolphin and almost was thrown over the side. From his cage, Eekie, too, looked on.

I coiled up my line and made the end fast. I used just thirty feet of line. With more line out than this the sharks would get the dolphin before I could pull it in. A longer line would also give the dolphin a better chance for a run, which would mean a harder fight for me, and besides, would give him a chance to get well underneath the logs where he could not be dislodged.

Everything seemed clear on deck. Light came flooding over the sea from the east. There was Long Tom, at his customary spot. He had seen me getting ready, tying my fishing line to the leg of the mast, and knew what I was up to.

When fishing from the side of the raft I could clearly see every fish, especially the brown-and-white-tipped sharks and every move they made. I could see them throughout the day, regardless of the position of the sun, and in almost any weather. If there were too many sharks around and they went for the bait, I could nearly always snatch it away in time.

Half a dozen sharks, five to seven feet long, swam close by, which meant they would probably try to get the bait, not being too big yet to be lazy, or consider the bait too small. They probably didn't know how well I could see them.

When I had a fresh flying fish on the hook I could

fish any time of the day, but with an old piece of dolphin belly I had to do it before it got too light and the dolphins could see what it was. As a rule they were ravenous at this time and struck at the bait even if they were in doubt about it.

The deck was full of cracks and openings for the centre-boards and I covered them up as best I could. If I had had a regular deck, like on a boat, I could just pull up a dolphin and let him be till it was all over. On my deck, however, he would get away at once. I left nothing to chance, for if I hooked a dolphin, especially a big one, I had a fight ahead of me, often more than I could handle. First, I made sure my rupture wouldn't bother me for a little while, something I always had to take care of. I put on a pair of heavy gloves used only for fishing, to keep the wire leader from cutting my hand. Everything ready, I jumped back for a look at the compass. She was heading all right; I didn't think she would run off for a few minutes.

I threw my line out at a right angle to the raft. The bait struck the water with a splash, like a flying fish flopping back after a flight. This was the sound that excited the dolphins. . . . No bite. I pulled the line in, quick, to make the wobbling bait appear alive and to alert the fish for the next throw. Then out again. A strike, the very second the bait touched the water!

Rather a light pull, then a frantic zigzagging to get away from the hook. A bonito. I hauled in as quickly as possible before Long Tom could get started. I didn't see him just then. The bonito was trying to get under the raft, knowing there was no escape towards the open sea. He succeeded, and the line suddenly felt as if a ton weight hung from it. I pulled with all my strength. Now it came easy again and with a quick pull I jerked the bonito out of the sea and swung him, flapping fiercely, to the deck. It was a big silver-and-blue one, bleeding profusely. Long Tom had bitten off its tail. Bonitos seem to have a lot of blood. I took it off the hook, disappointed in my catch, for bonitos are by no means as good to eat as dolphins, either cooked or raw. I lay down flat on deck, bending over the edge of the raft. There was Long Tom, just far enough back in the shadows where I couldn't see him from the deck. He knew from experience that I would shift to the other side if I spotted him.

I went back to my bonito, deciding I'd had enough fishing for the day. But when I cut the belly open I found a flying fish, swallowed perhaps an hour before. This was perfect bait so I would try again. I put it on the hook, washed the deck down so I wouldn't slip and go over the side, and threw the line out again. A strike came like an exploding bullet and I pulled in, sure that I had a dolphin. I hoped that he wasn't too big. He zigzagged away from the raft but I didn't let him get started with his tremendous speed and dash. Like the bonito, he turned and made for the underside of the raft to escape among the logs. I pulled in as fast as I could. Suddenly he changed course, heading away again. I guessed he'd caught a glimpse of Long Tom and knew what it meant— he had dodged sharks since he was born.

Four or five dolphins swam around him, wondering what had happened. All belonged to a group that had been swimming quietly until the victim began to thrash madly, trying to get rid of the hook.

I pulled him out of the water. He followed the line in a high leap, mad with fear and fury. He was a big enough fellow for a dolphin, about five feet long and weighing about thirty-five pounds. This was always a supreme sight—a dolphin coming like a blazing green-and-gold jewel out of his element into the light—*our* light—the light of death for him. It always made me sad to catch one and for that reason I postponed my fishing as long as possible.

I had him on deck and held him high up by the line hoping he was hooked so solid that he could not possibly get loose. He was thrashing around fiercely and I could hardly hold him. Suddenly he was free and on deck—he had torn the hook out of his jaw. In a flash he was past the winch and at the edge of the raft. I was hungry for meat, I was almost starving. I grasped his tail with both hands and jerked him back. He flung me off—it was like trying to hold an engine. I threw myself on top of him, locking my arms and legs around him, holding him, pressing him to the deck with my chest, my belly, my face. Again and again he got clear and almost slipped into the sea. It was a life and death struggle, man and his prey. I heard the sail flapping; the raft had gone into the wind. I listened—I didn't care—let the sail rip. I had to get that fish.

At last it was over. . . . I had been lucky. I had not beaten him fairly—I had grasped an iron bolt. I was covered with slime from head to foot.

I got the raft back into the wind and then sat down aft. The golden one of the sunlit ocean was already turning colour. Soon he would be drab and grey. I made myself some coffee. I would take it easy for a while. I was all in. There was no hurry about anything.

Eekie had given a few squawks when I pulled the dolphin on deck; he was looking at it now. He knew very well what had happened, just as did Meekie, who was trying to make up her mind whether it was safe to get a little closer to the fish. She knew that she was due for a good meal. Beyond, I could see the other dolphins swimming stiff and still, like mourners.

After the dolphin was cleaned and Meekie and I had all the meat we wanted, I hung it up by the tail between

The author looks for an opening between the islands of Olosega
and Ofu, American Samoa.

The *Manuatele* coming up behind the raft.

the canoe and the side of the raft, with a piece of canvas around it to keep off the sun. It was the best place for keeping a fish, cool and shady, with a lot of draught coming up from between the logs. I got to work, then, washing the deck and scrubbing it down with a brush. I pulled up bucket after bucket of water. On such occasions I sometimes even had to scrub the side of the cabin. I always put my compass out of the danger zone before starting to fish, for a dolphin on the loose can get all over the raft and smash up everything in its effort to get back into the sea.

Meekie, content with her meal, lay down beneath the winch for the rest of the day. She rarely drank water, probably got what she needed out of the fish. The sharks got the head and insides of my catch and what was left of the one that had furnished the bait. Long Tom was back in his regular place. He knew the procedure and wouldn't have rested till everything was properly done. My raft really had a fine escort.

A piece of flesh had been bitten out of my dolphin's back. It looked like a rather fresh wound. Quite often I pulled up a dolphin or bonito with such fresh wounds. Frequently I saw fish beside the raft that had been attacked. A fierce struggle went on all the time beneath the surface. Sharks sometimes tried to gang up on dolphins but these moved like lightning when sharks surrounded them. Within a second, other dolphins would join in battle with the sharks. Then the water would be churned up by thrashing bodies. I often saw blood. When there were more sharks than dolphins the latter stayed close together or travelled in pairs or little groups. At such times, also, they sought shelter under the raft, keeping in the shadows. No doubt they could hug the logs closer and move among them better than the much bulkier sharks. Occasionally all fish except Long Tom disappeared for a few days. Then a troop of dolphins would show up again.

I sailed through territory where flying fish were quite large, as much as ten inches long. These specimens were beautiful, and usually rose from the sea in pairs, flying high and for a considerable distance. I saw them sail swiftly, a hundred yards or more, at a height of ten to fifteen feet. They sometimes flew clean over the raft. But there were not many of the big variety. Dolphins would have a hard time catching them on account of their long-range flying.

The sun was climbing now and sea and sky looked like a fairyland just created. All weariness fell away as I gazed, but I knew it would return soon enough.

The sunrise reminded me of the alarm clock which Teddy had bought me in Callao.

"What's that for?" I had asked.

"Why, you set it to wake up at a certain time. You allow yourself so much sleep and don't have to worry about sleeping too long. When we came from the West Indies on our boat I stayed awake and called you, but you'll have nobody on the raft to wake you up."

I never used it, not the alarm part of it. I kept my local time with it, setting it an hour ahead every fifteen meridians and so marking a new time zone. Once, the alarm went off accidentally. The clock had previously fallen from its nail and something had been moved, and about an hour later it went off. It started Eekie squawking wildly, and had Meekie frantic, trying to hide somewhere. I had quite a time getting my little fellows calm again.

"Don't you worry," I had said, "we ain't going back to civilization yet." I generally spoke plain, ungrammatical English to them since they seemed to understand it best. "Don't you worry. No alarm clocks, no telephones, and no tooting of crazy automobile horns to scare your little wits out of you. You ain't done nothing to deserve that. Yeah, that alarm clock had a nerve, letting out a noise like that out here for no reason and pollutin' the whole atmosphere. If she does that again she goes over the side."

I stretched out a little, just keeping a lazy eye on the compass. Later I would have to work on my centreboards. There was always something to do on them. One—smashed by a sea a few days before, had broken clean off with a bang like a cannon shot and was gone. I had lost others. I had already taken up my catwalk on the bowsprit and pried up all the planks in the stern and bow, and made centreboards out of them.

The centreboards did the work of a keel, keeping me from drifting sideways if the wind was from the beam, that is, from the side of the raft. When the wind was straight from the stern they were of little importance. Since I generally had the wind from the port or starboard quarter they were indispensable. I found it impossible to work out a fixed rule for their use, much depending on the wind and the seas which rarely were constant. I spent hours each day studying how many centreboards I needed, how many to have before the mainmast and how many in the stern, behind the mizzen, and also 'midships, and how deep to lower each into the sea. Once I had them right—a thing that was hard to achieve—I could handle my raft almost like a ship.

After a short nap I then took out my sextant, to clean it. I'd got some spray on it yesterday and didn't think I got it all off. Salt water would ruin it. It was a fine instrument and deserved the best of care. I checked it every day before taking a sight and always found it perfect. The mirrors were large, which made it perfect for work on a low-riding, tossing deck. Teddy had brought it down with her on the plane from New York, holding it on her knees the entire trip so that nothing could happen to it.

"Here it is," she had said after passing through the customs at the Guayaquil airport. "Take it. It didn't get bumped once. If the plane had smashed I think they would have found me still hanging on to it, trying to protect it."

I had got it in 1947, making a special trip in midwinter across the Atlantic on the Liberty ship S.S. *Peachtree State* to Bremerhaven. Teddy and I had decided to take a vacation through the Caribbean the following year. We intended to buy a native sailing boat and sail it back to the States. I needed a good sextant and binoculars for such a voyage and Europe was the place to get them without paying a lot of money. It had been a hard trip, with northern Europe swept by storms that almost tore the British Isles from their moorings. On the way back to New York we had almost broken in two, passing the Azores. . . .

Now I was so sleepy I could hardly keep my eyes open any longer. I put the sextant away and just sat there, seeing and not seeing, wishing I could lie down and sleep.

## ★ 22 ★

## WITHOUT SLEEP

I SAT beside the wheel and every once in a while dipped
a handkerchief into a basin with salt water and daubed
my eyes and temples. My eyes had been bad for a few
days. They had given me trouble on and off but this time
it was pretty bad. Sometimes I couldn't see the reading
on my compass, though the light from the lantern was
right on it.

From the moment the sun came up, it shone down on
me till it set almost dead ahead. There was no escape.
My bamboo deck and the cabin caught the rays and
threw them back at my eyes, while the sea danced around
me like a thousand mirrors. I had rigged up a piece of
canvas beside the wheel and ducked under it whenever
there was a chance.

If it should get worse I would have to tie up my sails
and let the raft drift till my eyes were all right again.
But I hoped it would not come to that; I didn't want to
lose time.

The noon sights especially were hard on me, with the
sun high above and glaring down on my cabin roof till
it was a white, glaring mass. The sun had been seventy-
five degrees high the day before yesterday. I didn't get
a noon sight today—just couldn't get anything near good
enough to work with, as the seas were running high and
the raft was dancing crazily. And then a cloud came
across the sun and that was the end. I could have worked
out a latitude by means of the ex-meridian formula but

197

I let it go, to save my eyes as much as possible. One day didn't matter.

I took three afternoon sights, however, for a position line, and worked them all out as usual. My logbook entry for today was: August 31. Noon 21—10—50, Greenwich Civil Time; sun's alt. 75° 53′; Lat. 5° 18′ South; Long. 137° 48′ West. Day's run 62½ miles.

I had been having good wind and made as much as ninety-one miles a day. That was really blasting through, for a raft. It meant that I had actually sailed over a hundred miles during the past twenty-four hours. The raft had swung considerably from side to side while I was not at the wheel. If the wind kept up we would soon pass the Marquesas, now about 180 miles to the south-west. I intended to keep on my present course till I was about fifty miles beyond, and then start shooting south to Samoa.

The night wind felt cool on my eyes. They felt a lot better already. The water had helped. I wished the sun wouldn't come up for a few days. The starlight was soothing.

The raft was getting a real test again with the seas smashing into it like landslides, looking for a weak spot amid the lashings. Hammer away, Pacific—hammer away, you won't find a weak spot! I had long ceased to think of the *Seven Little Sisters* as a raft, something that could come apart. To me the *Seven Little Sisters* was a ship, a solid entity.

But I was worried about the sail when driving through like this. The mainsail was my only weak spot, I believed. I could see it standing in the darkness like a slab of hewn white marble. Well, if it went, it went. Then we would just drift under jib and mizzen and I would sit down and do some sewing. That was about the only thing I had missed so far—having the mainsail in ribbons. I

198

sometimes felt like saying: "What next, partner? You are sure giving me the works, but at heart you're soft on me. I know I'll make it, if only on the bare logs."

It was one of those holy nights that draw your innermost being out of you, to let it wander. What, after all, is the essence of life but the struggle to commune and mingle with Nature, with other created things? That, I reflected, is man's approach to eternity.

How I slid back every day from my dream of perfection! It was a long, long struggle, this emancipation from pettiness and weakness. I sank back each day, fell as low as ever—nervous, petty, angry; but there was always the sea and the sky to remind of true values.

Water was coming into the canoe. She was taking it over on that side It came right over the house. My old U.S. Navy storm suit was soaking wet. I tried to get Meekie to take it easy in the cabin for once but she preferred to stay outside, right in the smash of the seas.

I heard birds crying around the raft. Three of them had followed me all the way across from the Galapagos. As a rule birds travel in pairs but there were three here. I heard them nearly every night crying around the raft, flying about fifty feet high but never touching it. When the moon was out I sometimes caught a glimpse of them. But I always saw them in the dawn and at sunset, about a mile away and generally to leeward. They flew along on aimless, flapping wings but when they fished they were masters, skimming over the sea or rolling among the combers, seemingly lost in the depths of the furrows but always appearing again, rugged veterans blending with the vast certainties of sea and sky.

I had drunk no fresh water today besides what I mixed with my coffee. For an average drink of coffee I used about a quarter of a cup of water or even less. But I had drunk about two and a half large cups of salt water—

almost a quart; one cup in the morning and the rest throughout the day and night.

My stove had now failed completely. No more fried fish. I only ate it raw, when it was absolutely fresh, within an hour or so after it was caught. I became as particular as Meekie.

It was a time to sing, for my eyes felt fine again. What deep alchemy is involved in singing? What is the secret of harmonious sound: Were we created by a song? Was sound the first and would it be the last manifestation of the universe? . . . I was singing a great deal; that's what kept me going. I could be staggering with weariness but I felt strong as a giant and indestructible when I sang, which I did at all times, and especially when the weight of loneliness was on me and the beauty around me became almost unbearable and made me sad. I took my singing seriously, like a prayer wrung from the depths. I usually started with 'My Old Kentucky Home'. The moment I noticed a slackening of my concentration, or rather, devotion, I sang the line over and over again, until I was in full vibrating tune.

I wondered about the strange power of sound. But had not men always spoken about the angels singing and about the music of the spheres? And did not even the lowliest of creatures sing and chirp and make noises on their tiny road through their tiny day, getting into tune with the vast song of life? Yes, men always had to sing—a song of joy, or of battle, or of death. . . .

I had to slack up the weather brace a little, about ten inches. The seas were hitting a different way. Perhaps I should have raised that left centreboard forward a foot or two, or even more. I would wait and see.

A quick dash forward around the house and over the canoe to the brace, just as fast as I could go, and then forward and up with the centreboard with a bit of hard lifting, and I was back at the wheel. There was too much wind and I could not take any chances with the steering. She was really wallowing through, leaving a mass of white foam behind the stern. My hands were slowly giving out from all the pulling—twenty-four hours a day of it. They were all swollen and the knuckles spreading. But they always came through in a pinch. Hands never really give out. I think—not on a worker anyway.

She was lying better now with that centreboard up. Not many more hours like this and I would be up to the Marquesas. But I would keep to my course, well to the north, about a hundred miles in the clear. I wanted no part of them. Good thing everything was solid aloft. My gear really had come through!

How the wind howled, far off, running with the seas! And in the rigging was the whine of the ropes. The rudder also never gave me any trouble. Would have been pretty serious if something happened on a night like this; she would go broadside to. And that would be tough in the darkness. But that's where I had taken most pains —building that rudder.

I wondered what the swarms of tiny fish were doing now among the logs, wondered how they managed to hang on with the seas tearing along underneath. Long Tom was there, I knew—I didn't have to stick my hand over the side to find out. And the dolphins were there too, gliding along in their sleep. I would try to catch one in the morning. A piece of raw dolphin liver was always welcome.

Roll along, little raft, take them and leave them, rise and fall on your way! This was like sailing a small boat. That's where a man learned to sail—in a small boat, for then he was right in the sea, had the sea right against his heart. Waves come up around him like tombstones, ready to stay on top of him if he makes a mistake.

The night wore on. If the weather let up a little I would try to get some sleep; I couldn't take a chance now. I mixed myself a little coffee; that helped to keep my eyes open. I sure was glad Teddy hadn't come along. This was really no trip for a woman. It had been tough in spots, and who knew what lay ahead? I didn't trust the weather. We could get in trouble yet. I had thought too much about getting dismasted and having to take to the canoe. On the whole, however, I was as optimistic as the wide sky. I would have to look at the chart tomorrow and see what lay west of the Marquesas.

I finally dozed off and lay like dead for a full twenty minutes, my head on the compass. Suddenly I awoke for it sounded as if we were among rocks and this was the end. The whole raft was drenched. I had pushed the compass around in my sleep and dazedly wondered where we were going. Just before waking, I had again dreamed that someone was at the wheel, taking care of the raft.

One of these days or nights I would smash up, going to sleep like that. Every night it was the same struggle to keep awake. I had known it, of course, before I started the voyage. But I had been through the same thing many times before in my life, going for long periods without rest. . . .

Once, on a tanker, I had gone four days and nights without sleep, cleaning tanks while at sea, rolling without steerage way in heavy weather, fifty miles off Sandy Hook, getting the muck and gas out of the tanks to have her ready for the dry dock. Four days and nights in the gassy tanks, shovelling out the slush and rust from ten months of carrying crude oil. Nose and lungs right in the gas, right in the bilges, inhaling the fumes while digging with shovel and scoop. I was damaging my lungs, perhaps beyond repair, but a man is trained to stick to his job.

Half my shipmates were hauled out of the tanks on a rope, overcome by gas. They lay green-faced on deck but went down again after a few breaths of fresh air.

But it was on the Galveston docks, around 1917 and 1918, that I really went without sleep. Month after month we loaded ships for Europe. Time after time we went into empty holds and didn't come up again till the ship was loaded down to the mark and the pilot came on board. We came up just to eat, working stripped, carrying 280-pound sacks of flour and cotton-seed meal on our backs, running with it barefooted, dropping sack beside sack—rising layer after layer till we were under the deck beams. (As a youngster I had seen Chilean stevedores carrying 320-pound sacks of saltpetre the same way. They all died young.) It used to take us four to five days to load a ship. After a day's rest and sleep we started on another one—one ship after the other; the submarines kept us busy. A man can take a lot if he is physically fit. I used to dream of sailing a schooner singlehanded across the Atlantic or, what really intrigued me, of rowing a boat across, pull for pull, through days and nights. That, I thought, was a man's job! . . .

A sea had come over and almost washed me off the raft. I had dozed off again, while dreaming of carrying sacks. We had almost run into the wind that time. And there had been the shadowy figure of my mother near the wheel again, just as the sea hit. Nobody around here, Bill—just don't let that lead get set in you when she is pounding along like that; you should know better.

I went forward to see how Eekie had got through that one. As long as the cage was not washed overboard he would be all right. He had been soaked before, but knowing it would be a bad night I had covered him with the old raincoat. Meekie, I saw, was wedged in between two coils of rope and sound asleep. She could sleep through a hurricane.

I made myself a sip of coffee and ate some raw sugar. I ate quite a lot of it tonight. I liked to chew on dried fish, too. I had dried some dolphin meat in the sun; it was something to chew on when the weather was bad and there was no time to fix up my flour paste. An old Florida fisherman had shown me how to do it with mackerel. But it had to be taken in at night while drying, especially when the moon was out, this old fisherman had said. . . .

## ✱ 23 ✱

## STORM

I DID not like the sunrise on September 1. It had a coppery tint that generally meant wind and bad weather. I was north of the Marquesas, just starting to swing south, steering south-west by west. I had had a lot of squalls and short periods of calm lately but on the whole had continued to make good time. It was getting on to spring, south of the equator, and I had to expect unsettled weather.

I had been on a straight westerly course for about two thousand miles, following the fifth parallel across the Pacific, and now had turned south, feeling out the weather.

My logbook entry for September 1 read: "Noon 21/16/5 GCT, sun's altitude 76° 8.5′; Lat. 5° 25′ South; Long. 138° 56′ West."

The Marquesas lay in a general north-west and south-east direction between the parallels of 7° 50′ South and 10° 35′ South, and the meridians of 138° 25′ West and 140° 50′ West. I was 150 miles to the north of them.

The day passed uneventfully. The wind was about the same as on the previous day, blowing out of the south-east eighteen to twenty miles an hour. I had made sixty-nine miles on the previous day's run. There was a moderate sea. I saw numerous birds fishing to the north; towards evening they flew back to the south, heading home to the Marquesas. I had not seen any flying fish for some time, and there were fewer dolphins. But Long Tom was still with me.

He had been with me now for 2,500 miles. A big hammerhead shark had also been around the raft a few days before, nosing around the rudder. He was larger than Long Tom. He stayed with me during the afternoon, and that night I saw his tremendous body and weird-looking head bathed in phosphorescence. But in the morning he was gone, probably heading for a Marquesas reef.

In the evening, I noticed the same coppery hue in the sky. It was clear and the ominous glow was quite noticeable. I felt certain that I had not seen that peculiar tint before. Recent sunsets had been drab and wintry, with pale orange light. Only now and then were there lurid red and other strong colours, when the sun set behind a heavy squall or a thick blanket of clouds.

Night came with the swiftness usual in the tropics. I felt a little sad. Perhaps the weather didn't feel right, or it was my nearness to the Marquesas. I kept wondering whether something was making up. A barometer could have told me.

I watched Eekie and Meekie in my feeling of loneliness, so unusual with me. They were both in their regular grooves and seemed untouched by anything. Eekie, in fact, had given one of his better performances earlier in the day—one of his one-to-three shows, as I called them, meaning one straight word and three bad ones, all in Spanish. Meekie, who heard it, sitting on the box beside him for a bit of extra sun, never twitched a whisker, which made me think that she did not come from a pious household either. Eekie had been using a lot of bad language lately. Maybe the voyage was getting him. "Trees," he seemed to say, "trees—I want trees. All I see around here is ropes swinging in the wind, and water—hills that go up and down. Who wants that?"

Meekie had become a crack sailor. She acted exactly as if she were born on the raft and intended to make it her home for the rest of her life. Poor little Meekie, I thought; she had forgotten altogether that there was such a thing as land, and looked at the sea as the only existing element in the world.

Eekie definitely longed for land; I knew by the way he watched the clouds and the seas, especially when he was not in his cage but sitting high upon a rope. He sometimes laughed like a crazy man in solitary. Then I would go over and talk to him till he calmed down, or I would put Meekie beside his cage so that he had someone near him. Meekie always acted indifferent, even bored, till my back was turned. Then she would stick one of her slim, black paws as deep into the cage as she could, not showing her claws, however. But Eekie knew what it was all about and always backed away with a few warning squawks and remarks that might be translated as: "Look here, you black-coated, slinking jughead, take your ugly paw out of here before I bite it off!"

I kept thinking of the Marquesas all day. I thought of the lonely peaks looking out upon the Pacific solitude a hundred and fifty miles to the south—peaks that had seen but few sails on their horizon since time began. They had attracted me strongly in my boyhood and I had read books of all the early discoverers about the paradisal valleys furrowing the islands and the strange and warlike people who lived there. Weeks ago, at the time I lost my drinking water, I almost decided to sail the *Seven Little Sisters* into one of the rockbound bays of the Marquesas and fill up my cans and containers. But it was not necessary; my water was holding out. Sea water had become a fully accepted part of my daily rations, along with barley and *cañihua* flour and molasses sugar.

A number of squalls came up during the early part of the night but without enough wind to worry me. I kept a sharp look-out, sitting at the wheel steering, and getting up now and then to take a look around. After midnight the squalls became stronger, looming up in long, black walls. Most of them struck me, and I was kept on my toes trying to guess how much wind they carried. Each one had its own song as it approached. Finally, a solid black wall was making up that looked really ominous. It was time to shorten sail.

The wind was moaning in the darkness. There wasn't much sea yet, but I knew it could come up soon enough. Now and then a sea broke near me with tons of foam. Better get that sail down.

My running gear was all ready, but I checked every line again and tried out the blocks. Fast work was ahead when I had to move over the deck at lightning speed, from one corner to the other. The *Seven Little Sisters* pitched and rolled. Another look at the course and I put the compass inside the cabin. With a last glance aloft, I hoped everything would run clear—sheets, braces, lifts and downhauls. "Don't foul up—any of you," I told them.

Slack away!

The yard came down a few feet and then the wind took it, sail and all—tried to tear it off and, balked, stood the yard on end and then tried to fling it with the sail around the forestay. I pulled like mad on the outside downhaul, knowing I would lose yard and sail both if they got around the forestay. I got the yard clear, but it kept flailing wildly at the sky. Then I heard a rip. "Quick, Bill, quick—the sail is tearing!"

*Rip—rip*—the whole sail—from top to bottom—and the wind came through the rent in a demonic blast of victory. My beautiful white sail was fluttering in shreds

208

The author sees people for the first time in 113 days. Note the
canoe loaded for landing.

Courtesy of Vercoe, Samoa

Three sturdy Samoans swim to the raft to fasten a tow line.

First step ashore—the author with the Governor of Samoa and Mrs. Lowe.

Courtesy of Vercoe, Samoa

The author stands beside his cabin in the harbour at Pago Pago.

The author demonstrates how he used the transmitter. Last message
sent is tacked to the cabin wall.

before my eyes. *Rip, rip*—more and more, in every direction. White banners were streaming from the yard, flapping and snapping fiercely. It was a sail no more, only a mass of angry white rags in the darkness.

I got the yard down and lashed it high to the mast to keep it clear of the seas. I lashed the torn canvas too, carefully, to get all the loose ends, the long streamers, the white strips that had been my sail. Then I went out on the jib-boom and almost got washed off as the raft dived into a sea. I had to clear the jib. When I was back on deck I hoisted it. The raft was working wildly and tried to go broadside to and I had to make quick leaps to the wheel. Then I reefed the mizzen and hoisted it.

By this time the wind was blowing a gale. The seas were coming up all the time. That coppery sunrise had told the truth. Well, my sail was gone, all in shreds. All I could do now was hold her down, ride it out, and hope for the best. It was a storm, all right, but how long would it blow? It was just starting now. It had been quite a while making up; that's why I felt so nervous. I could figure on two to three days, anyway. She was doing pretty good under jib and reefed mizzen, climbing and falling and not taking too much water.

No more squalls now; it was blowing steady. A few clouds were high in the sky, looking like black rags in the darkness. I ate some sugar and drank coffee, which were at hand near the wheel, behind my transmitter, so I could get at it while steering. Then I changed my clothes; I had been drenched on the jib-boom.

I stood by the wheel watching the compass, which I had taken out again. It was blowing up more all the time. The compass was lashed; also the box with the lantern. It was the only good lantern I had left and even it was not too dependable. Well, I could always pick a star, or the moon when it was there, or my golden planet Venus to steer by. I would keep on plugging away, knocking off the miles.

For a change, the lantern was burning clear tonight, and I could see the compass without trouble. We were pounding along—leaping, rather, smashing through the white foam. I looked at the cheap watch I always kept in the lantern box; it was my deck watch and set on local time. It was almost five o'clock. It would soon be daylight. As long as we took them like this I didn't care—let 'er blow for a week. I could tell by the foam drifting past that we were making good time.

Roll through it, my seven Ecuadorian beauties! Never dreamed of this, did you, in your dark, still forest! How times have changed for you—battling a storm north of the Marquesas, held together by ropes.

Yes, the sail is gone. Well, it'll be fixed again. It was tough getting that yard down. Maybe I'll get in a doze somehow. Don't kick so hard, wheel—are you trying to break loose? Wouldn't that be a mess, without a wheel in this storm! I wouldn't have that little old cabin long, with some of those big seas coming over, rolling broadside to.

Some day—yes, some day I'll tie down the sails, every stitch I have, lash them and lie down in the cabin, forget everything and go to sleep. Some day, when there is not much wind, I'll do it. Just to lie in the sea without sails and go into the cabin and sleep. . . . Yes, I'll do that yet!

The seas were still coming up, leaping higher. I'd never seen her roll like this; you would have thought she'd go clean over. The raft acted like a dipper held in a giant's hand, being dipped deep into the sea. Take it easy—what are you doing? Steady—steady! Straighten up! Must have dug down twenty feet into the sea with that side twist. What are you trying to be—a scoop? I don't want to lash myself down.

210

It had started from the south-east, but it seemed to be coming more north now. How she rode them! One might think it would take a regular ship to stay on top of such seas. How that wind howled underneath deck. The water was pressed up from below in jets. Another roll! She tried to scoop to the bottom with seas all around her.

Trying to eat up my little raft, are you, big fellows; trying to swallow her whole? There, she's on top again. Wash her down, wash her down—blow up her white skirts and wash her down—that's all you'll ever do to her.

The mast was taking it fine; the turning buckles were just right. I hadn't tended them the whole trip; they were exactly the way I had set them up on land in Henri Kohn's big balsa mill in Guayaquil. That's because the main logs were well lashed. But wouldn't everything have come tumbling down about my ears now if there had been a weak spot!

Here I sat like a worn-out ghost and yet the happiest man on this planet. When the weather got bad like this and I really had to pitch in, I found that I was not quite as strong as I used to be, but just about skin and bones. "Just right," I said; "get rid of all flesh, get rid of it— flesh of the years and bound to be half-dead, ashes. Start fresh, build up a new body—new blood, new flesh—that was part of your voyage."

She was doing fine like this, just going south a little more than I thought. But what was the difference? I would still be seventy-five miles clear of the Marquesas even if it should blow for a couple of days. That was the reason for keeping well to leeward. We still wouldn't pile up. . . .

Dawn already. I must have dozed while steering a straight course. The sky was clear and the seas running mountainously. We just dodged that one. It might have taken the cabin. There was foam for a hundred square yards, and we sat right in it. I had to put lashing on the cabin; everything I owned was in it. Many a ship would have been pooped by that one! I really thought it would roll over us.

My mind kept wandering.

I should have a line ready to put around me. Those lashings are getting a work-out now. I had better have enough sailing twine for sewing that sail. It would be just like me to run short. One of my rolls had been lost in Callao and Teddy had wanted to cable to New York for another but of course I had done nothing. I had some light fishing line from my Florida days which I could probably use in a pinch.

Beat that sea again! You are seven little champs, little girls—how you slipped away from that one! Who ever taught you that? You were born sailors. But I should put lashings on the house; can't expect too much. Some unscrupulous sea might pull a shift and bury us.

The sun was almost up. The whole eastern sky had the same colour of clear copper. Now I knew the storm would keep up for a while, at least for another day. That was solid wind out there. But it didn't look so bad in daylight. It looked as if the whole sea were going into battle. What a sea—mountains of crystal! Pretty near worth it, this weather, just to see this, about twice as high a sea as I had ever met with so far. The wind must have been batting around fifty or more. I was not showing enough canvas for the wind to get hold of and I was lying too low, also.

I pulled myself to my feet and stood beside the cabin, one hand behind me holding the wheel. The seas were blue and transparent. I could see big sharks swimming near the raft. Stormy weather alerted them and they were moving faster than usual. Their brown bodies stood out clearly as in a glass tank held up to the light. Seas rose and fell with them—I could see them half a mile away. Four or five big ones were right behind the raft. One was almost washed on board and had to scramble to get clear of the logs. A dolphin leaped as if hurled up by a spring.

As soon as I could leave the wheel for a while I would try to lash the cabin. And when it was all over I'd start sewing my sail; it would take three or four days, I figured. But everything had to wait till this storm blew itself out.

The logs were riding lower down in the water. I had suspected it for several weeks, and I could see now that they were about four inches lower than when I started from Callao. The logs were soaking up water. I had launched the raft on April 21 and it had been in the water ever since. It did not worry me, for the bow was still a little above the sea. If she sank lower, however, it would cut her speed and make steering harder, which was far more serious. In that case I would take up the deck and dump it; that would bring her up some. I would dump the winch, too. I'd drag the canoe farther aft where the raft had greater carrying power. The canoe was heavy but necessary; it was my lifeboat.

"It took a good man to handle you, San Miguel," I addressed the canoe by its original name. "Getting into the open sea across that Manglaralto surf with its three or four lines of breakers, high and like solid walls, was man's work. You don't like lying here on the raft, safe and protected and lashed down like a frightened old lady, smelling the sea of which you have been a glorious part, under sail and with oars in all sorts of weather. Now you are just getting your belly wet. Don't worry; when the time comes, I'll use you. I bet you are thinking back to the Humboldt Current and the calmer seas and the brown whales playing in the sun off Manglaralto."

If I had only one mast like the ancient rafts of Ecuador

and Peru, I would be in trouble now. With the sail in shreds I would wallow broadside to, till there was nothing left but the seven bare logs. And who knows what they would do under the endless pounding! Now I had my jib-boom and mizzen mast and could sail. The moment I had got the idea of building a raft, I had known that I needed a bowsprit, an aftermast, and a wheel.

I lashed down the house. The sea came up more; there was no let-up in the wind. More than once I was sure that the next big one would come over and sweep the raft clean. I wondered if the rigging would stand up when a big sea buried us. The raft howled below the deck like an organ being pounded by a madman. But always she fought clear, standing high and alone on the tip of a crest and surveying the wild sea before plunging down again.

## STITCH—STITCH—STITCH . . .

THE storm lasted for two days and then eased up. It was time to start sewing my sail. I began at daylight. The seas were still high and there was considerable wind but I decided to go to work.

I first disconnected all the running gear of the yard—the downhauls, topping lifts and the halyard, the sheets and braces, and brought the yard with the tattered sail from the fore part of the mast to the main deck and laid it down fore and aft. It took quite a while, due to the movements of the raft.

I next took my three blankets and stretched them above the deck for a shelter under which to do my sewing, to avoid becoming blind in the glaring sun. I sat on a low wooden box which I moved along as I followed the seams; needles, twine, knife and scissors, and a sailmaker's palm lay in a box beside me. I waxed the twine with brown soap, which worked faster than the commonly used beeswax.

I kept my smaller compass beside me to keep my eye on the course. My deck watch, also, was at hand. The raft was swinging quite a bit but was doing well enough. I knew I was lucky to be able to sit and sew and not have to jump to the wheel every few minutes. I worked as fast as I could and was making good time; I always liked to work with canvas.

For hours I sewed, head bent close, using thread after thread, cutting it off, threading the needle and running it through the piece of soap that was getting soft in the heat. Then, stitch—stitch—stitch, moving my box along under me, following the tattered seams. Now and then I stopped for coffee. Sky and sea were blue and the wind was fresh and strong. I sat there as undisturbed as in a snug sailmaker's loft ashore.

Shortly before noon I got up to take my sight. After I had worked it out I went back to the job. My food was flour paste, sugar and dried fish. Stitch—stitch—stitch, all day long, hour after hour. I was reminded of the compassionate lines of Thomas Hood's fine poem. "The Song of the Shirt".

At three o'clock in the afternoon I got up again to take sights for a position line. As usual, I took three and worked them out. I found it best to take three on account of the incessant movements of the raft. Afterwards, I wrote in my logbook:

September 5. Noon 21—28—55 GCT; sun's altitude 76° 33'; Lat. 6° 28' South; Long. 142° 40' West; day's run 42 miles.

This was making good speed considering I carried nothing but a mere strip of a mizzen and a jib. It showed the wind was still strong and the big sea pushing me. I figured two or three days more and I would have the mainsail up again.

I was still north of the Marquesas in regard to latitude but had long passed them to the west. Following the day's meridian on the chart, 600 miles to the south past the Marquesas and down to the next group of islands, I saw the Tuamotus and the island of Raroia. Here was where the *Kon-Tiki* raft expedition, which had also started from Callao, had ended after sailing 4,500 miles. I remembered that the *Kon-Tiki* voyage had lasted 102 days. I had been out exactly seventy-four days. This meant that I had covered approximately the same distance as the

*Kon-Tiki* in twenty-eight days less time. But I had been sailing through the winter with its stronger winds. The construction of my raft also accounted for my greater speed. Being alone, I had lost considerable mileage when I was not at the wheel. In regard to the current, I had less in the northern latitude where I sailed than farther south according to the charts. I figured I had an average drift of ten to fifteen and sometimes twenty miles a day.

I wanted to go on sewing, through part of the night, at least, but had no proper light. Only two flashlights were left now, and one of them was giving signs of wearing out. I also had only a limited number of batteries which I wanted to save for a real emergency. Teddy had brought a searchlight from New York, remembering how important it had been the time we navigated the Inland Waterway of the Atlantic Coast, when we picked up markers at night, though after a few weeks it had refused to work, the dampness of the sea getting the best of it.

I could have rigged up an electric light and run it on my little generator but I was afraid that something might go wrong with the generator if I used it more than absolutely necessary; for as a mechanic I was little better than Meekie. I needed the generator for my receiver to pick up the WWV time signals. I only turned it on every four days, running it about ten minutes each time, just long enough to get the ticks. So far neither motor nor receiver had failed.

I had put in a good day's work and thought that two more full days would perhaps see the sail up again. It looked as if I could leave the sail on the yard, too, which would save me a lot of work. One seam had ripped across from one side of the sail to the other, only about a foot away from the yard, but I thought I would be able to sew the tightly stretched material. With the rest of the seams I didn't expect any trouble.

217

It was night now. The sun had gone down in its usual pale orange colours. There had been some clouds but it looked like a good night. The stars were out big. I was leaving the blankets up and had to be careful moving over the deck in the darkness. The seas had gone down considerably and were not pushing the raft as they had been doing. I would be satisfied with thirty-five miles for the day's run.

Another night of dreaming had come; I saw a dream on every sea. The Southern Cross was as bright as I had ever seen it, a lowered lance head ready to strike the mark. My golden planet stood on my starboard quarter now, since I was steering a southerly course. The Seven Sisters (Pleiades) were beginning their climb into the sky, followed in eternal pursuit by Orion. Later, blazing Sirius would dominate the eastern sky.

Meekie was waiting for me. She was sitting on deck as close to me as her leash allowed, looking steadily at me. I had to get that old grey sweater ready for her—I hoped it was dry, otherwise I would have to get her something from the cabin.

Sometimes I let her stay near me all night. She was no trouble unless flying fish landed on deck—then there was no holding her. But I was always afraid I might trample her when I had to work the raft. She had not had much food for a week but did not mind in the least, showed not the slightest impatience. "If you don't feed me, I'll just sleep," she seemed to tell me. And that's what she did. When she awoke she would play a while with a loose end of rope, a bit of leaf brown from the cabin roof, or she would find a piece of balsa wood to toss around. Thus she kept in shape for any flying fish that might come sailing on deck; she would pounce on it like a black-furred bullet. She no longer was as squeamish as when there was plenty to eat. Now she didn't wait till the deck

218

was all cleaned up after I had caught a dolphin but dug right in the moment one was off the hook and quiet.

Another storm like the last one and my little tousle-headed cabin would be baldheaded; most of the leaves had been blown off.

"Okay, Meekie, stretch yourself—that's the way, and now come along aft. You've been waiting patiently, I know. You've been a perfect little lady all day long, not bothering me while I sewed. No water and no food—what do you live on, you little black shadow? A sip of water every four hours or so? I have some milk for you but you only take a few sips when it is fresh out of the can, and afterwards you don't even look at it."

I sat beside the wheel and sang to the night. It took me about fifty minutes or so to go through my songs, sometimes more. They were songs from everywhere, bits from all corners of the earth; folk songs, too, wrung from the heart of mankind. I sang songs of men lying under shellfire, thinking of home and loved ones, songs of sailors when their ships went down, songs of the exiled. . . . And Meekie slept beside me and the stars were pulling us west across the Pacific.

I drank some coffee and watched the compass to see if I could steady up the raft more by changing the centre-boards. I had started on the home stretch now—from the Marquesas to the Samoas. About two thousand miles of sailing was still to be done with one man handling the raft. I wondered about the wind, wondered whether it would continue strong. That was the big thing—the wind. I didn't care if it blew from the north or north-east, east or south-east or almost south—I could take anything from those quarters and make time.

The Southern Cross had gone down. The other big southern constellations were sprawling across space like timetables of eternity. I thought of Teddy. I had told her that I would most likely follow the twelfth parallel across, sail through the opening between the northern end of the Tuamotus and the Marquesas and continue west to Samoa. which lay approximately on the fourteenth parallel. But I had taken the better route. I had had wind.

I felt like reciting poetry tonight and blazed away for a while. Poetry came next to singing in giving me a lift. I had published a collection of my sea poems after I had decided on my raft voyage, calling it 'Hell, Hail and Hurricanes'. I had thought it my duty to Teddy and myself to leave something in the way of a tombstone behind if I didn't come back. I wondered if Teddy ever read any of them. . . .

An accident in 1922 while loading a ship had started me on poetry again. My first attempt was at the age of twelve, but I had turned away from it, being too busy with my studies, and later going to sea.

For fifteen years I had followed the world's hardest labour when an accident while loading cotton on the Japanese freighter *Yufuku Maru* sent me to a hospital with multiple fractures of the left leg. The verdict was that I would be club-footed for the rest of my life. I was not worried. They had not cut it off as they had first said they would. I went daily to the beach in Galveston, sitting on the sand in salt water and sun. Nights, I drew cartoons, and after midnight I wrote poetry. A year after the accident, with my bones knitted and no club-foot, though the leg had shrunk to the size of a stick, I went on. It was labour and libraries and writing now. . . .

There was still a heavy swell running. This afternoon, looking up from my sewing, I saw the swells break the horizon line like prehistoric whales born with tremendous, bulging backs, three or four in succession, harnessed out of sight beneath the sea and pulling the tides slowly and evenly across watery space.

Sometimes, as tonight, I felt as if I were in a prehuman world, where man had not yet been created—alone in a world of water and stars and suns and roaming winds. I alone had been created and sent out to see the grandeur of the heavens and bear witness to it. . . .

She was rolling a lot tonight. If I had tried to go on sewing I would have punched myself all over with the needle. A few times during the afternoon, when I was tired, I had almost jabbed my face. The stuff didn't sew like canvas and one couldn't control the needle so well. But I would get it done quick enough.

The mast was whipping the sky. It made the stars look as if they hung from a string and were swinging from one end of creation to the other.

Did I doze again? I had been dreaming about New York, sure enough. What were they doing back home? I could turn on my radio but it was consecrated to my time signals and nothing else. I had heard no human voice since I left, only the recorded voice saying, "When the tone begins it is. . . ."

But I know what you are doing, America; almost half a century along your highways, I should know you. My eyes saw the map and somehow settled on Kansas. I had dropped off a cattle train in Kansas City coming from the West. The harvest had been bad and I needed a little money to get back to the farm in Texas. "Try the packing-houses, fellow—always a job there," somebody said. "Plumber's helper this morning, nothing else." "Okay, anything," I said. I walked around all day carrying a wrench and followed the plumber who carried nothing.

Thousands of cattle were being driven up the chutes . . . America needs meat for her labour, to reshape the world to her liking, according to her mathematics and religions and philosophies—her titanic mixture of brains and souls. . . .

I'll just doze a little—let 'er take care of herself. "Meekie, keep away from the compass or I'll put you forward again. You scrawny little beast, you don't weigh as much as a feather. Keep your eyes open and watch the raft for me a while. No, I wouldn't feed you *machica*, don't you worry. I'll catch a shark for you if it comes to the worst and feed you the liver. Trouble is, the bums are so big around here I can't pull them in."

The *Seven Little Sisters* was making her way through the dark sea, through the low moaning of the wind with her masts and her lashings and all her ropes. There was order in the wild-looking waste, in its sounds and in its movements. Everything was at peace in the world and within me, and I could sleep a little. Sleep. . . . The stars were going their ancient way above.

# ★ 25 ★

## IN SQUALL LAND

ONE squall had followed another, for two days already;
it looked as though I had sailed into an area of squalls.
A few were behind me all the time, moving up. Some had
quite a bit of wind. Some looked black and solid, like
walls, swollen with wind and ready to burst with the
pressure, and a number of times I had taken my mainsail
down. I had patched it up in good shape and it seemed to
be as strong as ever. The moment I thought it was safe
I hoisted it again. It was a lot of work, but I wanted to
get out of this section of the sea.

I wondered how long the squalls would keep up. They
were all dry. Most of them looked as if they could barely
travel, being so heavy with rain that their black bellies
trailed in the sea. And then they were right on top of
me, moaning and howling and coming apart, and there
wasn't a drop of rain in them.

This morning the sea around me was brown with
sharks. I had to do some work aloft and from there saw
three fellows a few hundred yards off that were the
largest I had seen so far. There were no dolphins
near.

At noon, while getting ready for my sights, I saw a
churning about half a mile off to the north-west. I didn't
want to lose my noon sight and so didn't get my binoculars
to see what was happening. It appeared as though whales
were fighting with something. I saw bulging black backs
and large fins thrashing the sea. It seemed to be a struggle

of tremendous fury. Spray was thrown up high, in huge masses. Then it grew calm again. I thought that big sharks or some other giant fish had attacked a whale.

Fresh clouds were pushing their heads over the horizon. They would make up into squalls too, picking up wind as they came. Some of them barely moved, taking an hour or so before they caught up with me. Nearly all of them struck me; only occasionally they drifted by to the north. I seemed to be in a pit or a vast amphitheatre watching them make up and approach. Between them they took all the wind from the open spaces and I was becalmed, waiting for the next squall to push me ahead. Sometimes I sped along for five or ten miles, almost flying, until everything stopped again.

There was a cloud bank making up now that looked as though it had a whole hurricane inside it. The clouds had a way of growing, changing entirely within a minute. I would see a few dark columns, not looking at all dangerous, and in a short while there would be a wall of darkness coming my way. When the squalls were above me they tore and scattered over the darkened sea. Neither Eekie nor Meekie paid any attention to them. Eekie just kept munching away. Meekie slept; the most I could get out of her during the day was a stretch and a pair of half-opened eyes. "Don't bother me with that stuff," was her attitude; "aren't we raft sailors?"

This squall looked bad. How much wind did it have? Perhaps I should take the sail down. I would hang on a while longer; I would wait. I got fooled the last time. But I would hate to see my sail tear again. There it came down on me, droning like a hundred planes. It had plenty of wind.

Keep her steady, watch her—watch your steering. Shouldn't have taken a chance with that one. Too late now.

A native chief comes aboard the raft for a visit.

*Courtesy of A. Myron Howell, Samoa*

The raft on land at Samoa. Note the barnacles on logs.

The raft was really foaming along. I didn't doubt but that we were making almost six miles an hour. I had timed her yesterday doing better than five. If that didn't strain her, I didn't know what would. If she were a ship, she would be half under water. The backstays were getting it; as long as the rigging could take it, I'd be O.K. I had to watch my steering when she ran like this. The size of the rudder was just right; it took hold just right—not too much and not too little.

Sailed through it in a little over half an hour. Now I was becalmed once more and watching them make up again all around me. The one that had just passed stood to the north-west, a few miles away, as though anchored, with all the wind gone out of it. It would take an hour to dissolve completely.

They were making up behind me fast, assuming fantastic shapes, taking something from every passing cloud, shaping themselves into black walls with mushroom heads. All this wide, disturbed area was in the throes of spring. Five squalls stood above the hush of the sea, like vast drapes of doom, staring down at me from the brooding distance—executioners sent out for my annihilation. The sea was becoming a dark, steely blue, almost black. Here and there appeared white streaks of foam, gleaming whiter than snow in the strange light.

There she comes now. Hear the howling in the centre? I'll take a chance with the sail again; it takes too much out of me to get it down.

There she is! Compass is safely in the house. I'm steering by the sails; let 'er run with the wind; just keep 'er full. Should have taken the sail down for this one. If this keeps up, I'll just take it down and keep it down till we're out of this stretch.

Right in the squall now; right in the belly of the wind; it's still coming like a storm. The sail stands like a white

OCP/931—H  225

stone against the black sky. Those stitches better hold! Don't let 'er run off or you'd have the mast and sail wrapped around you and the cabin.

This is sailing! Feels like steering a square-rigger with every sail set, scorching the sea, and half of her under water. Fastest time I've made so far. Keep that sail full, Bill.

Suddenly it started to rain. The squall was about half over. Rain, rain—first rain of the trip! The whole sky had become a grey, dark mass. Rain, and I was anchored to the wheel. I couldn't wreck the raft just to get some of the water; I couldn't leave the wheel for a second. Water just poured out of the sky, flattening the sea, smashing down on the raft in a deluge. I was sailing through bubbles.

It kept on raining and blowing, a real solid rain, not a mere wetting of the deck. My eyes were glued on the sail. I was soaked to the skin and almost blown off my feet; the temperature dropped and I felt the cold. The rain was still coming in undiminished masses and the sky was black and howling and gusts of wind drove the rain in sheets, like barely visible sails. My washbasin, standing on deck, was soon half full of rain water. I intended to grab it the first chance I had and drink my fill.

The wind was slackening; the worst was over. The rain kept up. I set up the compass and watched it with the wheel lashed. She was doing all right.

I jumped for my cans and pots and put them down all over the raft to catch the rain. I tied two empty five-gallon water cans to the ends of the mainsail. The rain ran down the big, full-standing sail, along the boltrope and down to each corner, where it spilled into the cans. They were the same ones that had once held my fresh water, but they were watertight now. I had scraped some asphalt from an old can, melted it, and poured it along the rusted seams.

Back to the wheel, then, to steady her. The wind was still strong and the sky dark. Then the rain slackened and within a few minutes only a few wind-driven drops came spattering down. I gathered up my cans and eagerly drank my fill. I had got about seven gallons of water altogether. I was rich. And perhaps I would get more rain.

After my water was secured, I took off my clothes and rubbed myself down to get the chill out of me. Then I put on dry gear. After that I drank coffee made with fresh rain water and ate some *machica*. I had eaten sugar while driving through the big squall.

All the wind was gone again and I was becalmed. But behind me clouds were making up. This was real squall area.

I had bumped my bad hand lashing the cans to the sail and wondered whether I had opened the wound again. I had left the first bandage on for about two weeks without taking it off. Then the whole hand had started to itch and the skin to peel off and I had decided to change the bandage. The wound was healing well, but a few spots were still open. There was no trace of infection. However, the knuckles of both middle fingers appeared permanently injured; they had spread out and thickened. There was proud flesh on the high ridges of the gash, but if I exposed it to the sun, a lot of this tissue would disappear. I was afraid to do this yet, since at any moment I might have to jump to do something with the sails and so hurt the unprotected and still sensitive wound. Before bandaging it again, I had put on penicillin salve.

I felt a touch of air on my face, but I had been fooled so many times I didn't pay any attention to it. Then I realized that the air was really stirring. It became a little breeze. Yes, a little breeze had come, and I thanked the clouds. Everything around me looked bright and hopeful again.

I sailed along for about half an hour, barely moving but always hoping it would pick up more. Then it stopped and everything was still again. Another false alarm; the sails had never stood full. Now it was gone again into nowhere; just as it had come, it had faded off into nothing.

Agonies again. . . . Where was the wind? Come on, wind.

The sails hung straight down. A desolate sight—sails hanging without wind. The blocks groaned, the yard swung from one side to the other. Nothing stood ready and shipshape; everything seemed to be disintegrating.

Was that a stirring in the air? I couldn't see a ripple anywhere on the glassy sea. There it was again. Yes—no! I poked the mizzen behind the wheel, feeling for wind. It was like poking a loose bag. Now there was a little pressure. A little breeze was making up again and the rigging was slowly tightening as the sails filled. For five, ten minutes I hardly breathed, hoping for more wind. But it became calm again. I sat down, waiting and hoping.

Squalls formed behind me while I sat; black columns were approaching. The least puff of wind sent my heartbeat up. But I lay becalmed through the long hours of the day. The sun went down behind black clouds that had passed over an hour before. Behind me squalls were still making up.

It was a dark night, with here and there a break in the cloud masses, revealing bright stars. And there was the moon. The Southern Cross was trying to break through, close to my port bow, with three stars showing pointing towards Australia, its homeland. I felt like taking down the sail and getting a good rest. But I hung on, making the most of every breath of air. I was fighting for inches in this vast space. I did not figure miles, degrees of longitude —only inches.

At last, a steady breeze arose. It was hard to believe. It looked like the old sea again. I had wind once more. I went around the raft, feeling all the ropes. Everything stood hard and solid again. All over, the sky was clearing. The moon was down to the jib-boom, riding it. I started to sing a song learned as a youngster on a British square-rigger:

> *"When we go around the world*
> *From Cape Hope to Sydney Bay,*
> *And 'round the Horn and home again*
> *For that is the sailors' way. . . ."*

I kept on singing, roaring away. The stars looked as if they were saying: "What did you get so excited about? Can't you take a few days of calm? That's part of the game, you know."

The wind continued steady. I hoped that I had sailed out of that patch of squalls and dead calms. But I knew I couldn't hope for a steady wind at this time of the year; I would have more squalls and calms and thunderstorms.

I needed plenty of wind to make time, for the balsa logs were soaking up water—actually the raft was slowly sinking.

## FALL FROM THE LADDER

I HAD had the mainsail down a few times since the big shredding in the storm, to stitch up seams that had again parted from the pressure of the wind or from the sail's beating against the mast and forestay. I noticed the new rent on September 8, just before sundown. I was steering south-west, lying on the port tack. The rays of the setting sun had broken through the clouds, and against the red and gold of the sky I could see the rip in the sail. It was about six inches long and high up near the yard.

I should have taken it down at once to repair it, but I was worn out and for weeks had done only what was absolutely necessary. Every movement was an effort. These states of exhaustion varied, sometimes lasting a week, sometimes only a few days. So I let the damage go until the next day, hoping I wouldn't get a squall during the night and have the sail tear from top to bottom, as had already happened before.

Throughout the night, between staring at the compass and nodding at the wheel, I watched the rent. About three o'clock in the morning, when my eyes had turned to lead, the raft ran into the wind. The sharp, fierce staccato slapping of the sail against the mast brought me to my senses.

The raft lay in the wind and the mainsail was trying to beat itself to pieces. I dropped the mizzen, pulled the wheel over and lashed it, slacked up on the brace beside me and jumped forward, fearing the worst. The rent was down to the first cross seam, a full eight feet. I lowered the yard and secured it and then set the jib and the reefed mizzen. As usual, she steered well that way and, after watching for a while and raising a centreboard, I took a catnap.

As soon as the sea lighted up in the morning, I had my breakfast of barley flour and coffee and went to work on the sail. I had to sit between the legs of the mast with the yard and sail in front of me. The raft was rolling and pitching, taking seas and spray, and I had to take care that my needle didn't jab my face as the wind kept tearing the seams out of my grasp. But I had done a lot of sewing on the voyage under worse conditions, with seas and spray almost blinding me so that I was forced to hang on between stitches to keep from going over the side. I finished about noon and did not bother about a sight, since it had clouded up. The main thing was to get the sail up as soon as possible and get under way.

I was checking the rigging to see that the yard would go up smoothly when I noticed that a topping lift had fouled in a block. Another block didn't look right, either. I took my marlinspike, hung it from a strop over my shoulder so that I could have my hands free, stuck a sheath knife in my belt, and went up the ladder.

The ladder was swinging badly and I had to struggle to get aloft. Finally up, I managed to do the job and started down again, carrying a block and my marlinspike. At about the middle of the ladder I had a hard time hanging on. I finally dropped the block to the deck. The marlinspike over my shoulder was striking me in the fierce whirling from side to side. I hung on with all the strength I had. Never before had I seen the ladder so bad.

My hands began to give out. I hooked my arms and legs around the side ropes of the ladder, thinking I would wait for a let-up and then come down. It grew worse. I thought my arms would come apart at the elbows or my forearms break or my legs snap. I unhooked myself to get down.

I stopped again to hang on, was torn loose, and just managed to clutch the sides. Again I was torn loose and half-slid, half-jumped and fell to the deck, about ten feet below. I tried to clear the hand winch under which Meekie lay asleep. My foot caught on its handle and I pitched forward. In spite of twisting myself to land on my shoulder, I fell badly because of the motion of the raft. My head struck a mangrove plank, a solid three by twelve, originally part of the forward centreboard.

When I regained consciousness it was night. For a long time, or so it seemed, I listened to the roaring of the seas around me, to the crash of the seas against the raft. A symphony of pounding filled my being. Water came over, sometimes striking and drenching me. It felt cold. I was shivering all over. I saw the night sky. The moon was out. I saw the jib pulling.

The back of my head was sore; I wanted to vomit. I was in a daze and felt that I couldn't move. I saw Meekie, tied to her rope, sitting beside me like a shadow, still as a statue with her eyes on the sea. I blacked out again.

I regained my senses somewhat but did not realize what had happened. But I was aware of the raft in the night and heard the sound of the seas around me and underneath, among the logs. I was aware of getting drenched and once had a notion of being on the fore-castle head of a steamer, on the lookout while she was taking seas over the bow. The raft was sailing under the jib—that much I knew.

I awoke with the sun blazing on my head, hurting me. I tried to sink into oblivion again. I wanted to escape from the pain, and to rest. But the pain persisted and I gradually came to. The sun stood in a clear sky. It was afternoon already, for the sun was right on my beam. Now I realized what had happened. My shoulders, neck and head felt as if I had been struck heavily. My body was numb all over.

I was still on my course; I could tell by the sun. Everything was restful and quiet. My yard and mainsail were as I had left them, but the sail was drenched from the seas and some of the folds were full of water, hanging swollen like watertight bags. I sat up. Eekie, watching me from his cage, gave out a little squawk. Meekie was asleep, her leash tangled around the winch, not giving her an inch to move.

I had to get up and go aft. There was no longer any excuse for remaining here. My head felt weighted. I crawled to my water-can beside the cabin, took the dipper from the nail, and drank. I was thinking that I had never before been knocked altogether unconscious.

I crawled aft, knowing that the sail ought to go up. I looked at the compass. Then I sat with my back against the cabin. I almost blacked out again. But the sail had to go up; this was not sailing, with just the jib and mizzen. I wanted to sleep, but the thought of the sail kept nagging me.

What a raft I had! The *Seven Little Sisters* had really become part of me, sailing on its own like that. Again it had taken care of me through the darkness. I wouldn't do anything now, not till morning. Let 'er run as she wanted. I wouldn't do anything. I felt my scalp. There was no blood; the skin was not broken. I might have broken my shoulder, falling that way, but I hadn't. I might have broken my neck. I really should celebrate, getting off as easy as that, without a broken bone, or being washed off the raft.

I dozed off and woke up and kept on dozing and waking again, worrying about the raft and getting the sail up.

Hour after hour went by. The sun had long since gone down.

Suddenly I realized I should have crossed off the day in my *Nautical Almanac*. But I didn't have the strength to get up. "I'll remember, I'll remember," I said to myself. "I'll cross off an extra day tomorrow. . . . No, no, scratch it off now, scratch it off now." After what seemed a long time I crawled into the cabin, groped for my flashlight, and with my pencil scratched out the lost day, September 9.

I recovered during the night, getting in quite a bit of sleep. My head still felt numb and sore in the morning, but I could move about and think clearly. I was worrying most about the weather, for I had been making poor time since passing the Marquesas. There had been one calm after another and never much wind except when I sailed through a squall.

I took a number of sights during the day, even in the forenoon, which I had rarely done during the voyage, and worked out an accurate position. My entry in the logbook for September 10 was: "Noon 21—47—00 GCT; sun's altitude 76° 24'; Lat. 8° 31' South; Long. 146° 31' West."

I was on a general course for Samoa, approximately sixteen hundred miles away. A tiny spot on the chart lay right on my course line—Flint Island. Its position was Lat. 11° 26' South, Long. 151° 48' West, about three hundred miles away. I took my 'Sailing Directions' from the shelf to see what it had to say about Flint. The idea occurred to me: How about making a course for Flint and taking a look, trying for a landing even, and filling all my cans with water? Flint Island had two lagoons of brackish water.

The idea intrigued me. It would depend on the weather —on the wind and the seas breaking on the reef surrounding Flint. I wouldn't take any foolish chances with my raft, of course. If ever I smashed up the raft I would sit on Flint till doomsday eating fish and crabs and singing songs. I had time to think it over; it was still 300 miles away. But my mind had taken hold of the idea.

And then the sun went down and the stars came out and I disassociated myself from the raft and all the realities, and went off into space on my nightly travels.

My head was still sore, but it was nothing to worry about. A few doses of aspirin washed down with coffee had helped. A man who has knocked around and worked as I have, has taken many a beating and quickly forgets them. But it was hard for me to believe that I could be knocked unconscious by any blow that didn't fracture my head. That hurt my vanity. Maybe I wasn't as tough as I used to be.

The last time something like this happened, I recalled, was in the winter of 1950. I was on the S.S. *American Merchant*, a freighter, in the North Atlantic. We had heavy weather off the Grand Banks on the way back to New York from Europe. It was blowing a hurricane. The *Queen Mary* and *America,* both eastbound, were hove to within fifty miles of us. During the night, while we were hove to, the radio broke down and the next morning, being A.B. on the eight-to-twelve watch, I was sent up with another sailor to see what could be done. It was a battle for life getting up on the mast in the wind with the ship rolling. Our clothes were almost ripped from our bodies. A piece of cable with a heavy insulator hanging from it became dislodged aloft and smashed down on my head. I believe I would have blacked out if I hadn't seen the deck beneath and realized that my brains would be scattered all over the ship. I hung on. I finally got down to the deck, blood streaming over my face. It was two months before my head cleared. . . .

The idea of sailing to Flint Island had taken solid hold; I couldn't get it out of my mind. I took my flashlight and went into the cabin to spread out my chart. If I kept on my course, it would take me close to it. In my mind I saw palms nodding in the wind, and a white beach, but I also could see the reef that surrounded it, saw-studded walls rising straight out of the sea. They would smash and tear and shred my raft of soft balsa wood.

I opened my 'Sailing Directions' and read:

"Flint Island is surrounded by a steep, fringing coral reef which dries at low water and extends about a hundred yards off the island except at the northern end of the island, where it extends seaward about nine hundred yards, and at the southern end, where it extends in an east-south-easterly direction for about five hundred yards.

"Flint Island was visited by the U.S. Exploring Expedition under Lieut. Wilkes in 1840.

"The island is uninhabited.

"The possibility of obtaining anchorage at Flint Island depends entirely on the wind and weather, but even under favourable circumstances anchorage is not safe."

It also said that the island was about two and a half miles long and about a thousand yards wide.

Beyond Flint Island the chart showed me a few other dots, specks of palm-thatched sand in space, ringed in by reefs, like the bare ends of ancient anchor ropes still fast to the bottom of the sea although the ship had long since rotted away. I felt sad, fearing that the sense of timelessness and unbroken space might disappear now. But perhaps I would get used to these few dots on the sea. There was still the same sky, and in that I really lived. I looked up: the moon, my golden planet, and a tiny star, as if newborn, stood close together in clearest space— three creations in the firmament, gazing down. It had the beauty of a celestial apparition.

236

"Don't worry about those tiny dots of sand; they are not crowding you," I said to myself.

The sea was alive with large patches of light that flowed endlessly by, flashing up and disappearing. It made me think of monsters of the deep rising and going down again. There were small patches and large ones, ten to twenty feet wide, both roundish and irregular-shaped. Sometimes it looked as though fish were darting through them. Once I thought I saw something like a giant octopus waving flaming tentacles, and jumped for my axe.

All around me, as far as I could see, was this changing pattern of greenish light. Sometimes it flashed brightly, sometimes dully, but was never the same. It was like looking down on strange, submarine streets where creatures hurried through the darkness holding lanterns, flashing them up the sides of buildings to see if they were going in the right direction. In the bow, churned up by the seas and streaming aft along each side of the raft, were beads of clear, bright light, like miniature stars. The raft was sailing over this mass of phosphorescence, through this changing mosaic of light and darkness.

A shark swam through the lazily flaming sea, himself flaming, his outline traced in the weird light. Yesterday afternoon, I had lain down for a little sun bath by the edge of the raft, and the warm sun had put me to sleep. My head was covered against the light with my shirt. The terrific rolling of the raft awakened me. What had happened; had we gone into the wind? I tore the shirt away to look. A big sea stood right above me with the sun shining through it and the brown body of a huge shark inside it, within a few feet of my naked body, seemingly ready to attack. I was still dazed from sleep and thought I had to fight for my life. Then the wave, along with the shark, dropped from view as the raft rolled the other way. I decided to lie a few feet farther from the edge next time.

The fish were nearly all gone, at least the dolphins, bonitos, and flying fish. There were still sharks now and then. Long Tom had left me north of the Marquesas. It looked like a different ocean now, with different winds, mostly squalls. But I had no more rain.

I thought often of shipwrecked men, imagining myself in their position. I knew, of course, that I was not undergoing any real hardships. It was never too hot; I could nearly always get into the shade for a while, and I avoided all unnecessary exertion. Also, my mind was calm. But maybe other trials were ahead of me. I might lose my water and my food. I knew that one squall could wreck me. Mentally I was prepared for any catastrophe.

I think that the sun, fear, and physical exertion are the real killers of shipwrecked men. As for the sun, the danger depends on the latitude, of course. For food, fish may be caught, but there may be no fish or else they may be too big. Plankton I had not seen here and it could not be depended on as a source of food. When the food is gone it just means tightening the belt. A well-nourished man should be able to go without food for two weeks or so, providing, of course, he has no fear of starvation; a lot depends on the mental attitude. When the drinking water is gone, sea water in small doses may keep men alive, once they know it will not harm them. Experiments in going without food and drinking salt water may bring out some interesting facts.

I tested the U.S. Navy Disaster Rations for a week during the early days of my voyage and thought well of them.

In the open spaces between clouds the stars shone bright; they seemed to come right down to the horizon so that, dozing beside the compass and waking up

suddenly, I thought for a moment that I was surrounded
by ships and on the point of being run down. Later, while
I stood in the bow and looked at the stars beneath the
arching sail and at the beads of bright light flung up by
the bow from the phosphorescent sea, the two mingling
in the darkness, it was as if I was sailing among stars.

## ★ 27 ★

### FLINT ISLAND

A BIG cloud came up behind me, moving slowly to my right, spreading out and finally covering half the horizon and darkening the sky. It had only little wind. Another squall came from the left, moving to cross my bow. Then all wind stopped. It became hot and oppressive. The big squall to my right was still moving but thinning out. It was dead calm. The sails hung down slack, then backed up and filled. Then all the wind went out of them and they hung down straight and lifeless.

The raft swung around and headed east and slowly began to move east, I watched it for a while and then dropped the mizzen and brought her around and she went on her course again. Then the atmosphere began to clear a little and it felt fresher. After a while a breeze sprang up. A black cloud had made up behind me and came rather fast. It proved harmless. I went into the cabin for my sextant, for it was time for my noon sight.

It was noon, September 16, at 21—54—25 GCT; the sun's altitude 76° 5.5′; the Latitude was 11° 7′ South. The previous day my position had been Lat. 10° 56′ South; Long. 149° 18′ West.

I was anxious about my position on account of Flint Island, which I figured to be a little over a hundred miles away. I was making a good course for it, and had decided to land if possible.

The wind had died while I was working out my latitude. Clouds stood all around me, straight and still, like

240

beautiful white monuments. There was no slant to them as in the regular trade wind clouds pushed by the wind. They were the beautiful but terrible clouds of the calms.

I had had a lot of this weather. A little wind would come sometimes, just wandering around but enough to keep me on my toes. And in the morning the sun rose like a ball of fire, bringing no wind, not even a morning breeze, and so it went all day with the sails flapping and slapping the mast. Patience was needed here. When I was completely becalmed, and there was only a slight swell, I could walk on deck without hanging on—a new experience.

The afternoon sight put me at 150° 00′ West Long., 108 miles from Flint Island. The rather steady wind had slackened as the sun went down and I was becalmed again. Clouds stood all around me, seemingly holding their breath, waiting for wind. Everything was so still that I felt as if I lay in a pond of eternity. After dark a wind sprang up again but it was fitful, shifting from one quarter to the other. A bright moon made it easier to take. Then it started to blow steady. The raft handled beautifully at once.

The wind lasted through the night. I kept wondering whether it would be wise to go close to Flint Island in such uncertain weather.

I had not had any fish to eat for over a week until yesterday afternoon, when I saw a few dolphins around the raft. I cut a piece of the belly side of my last dolphin that still hung from the canoe and put it on the hook. One dolphin touched it but didn't bite. I took the same strip, soaked it in the water overnight, and in the grey dawn put it back on a hook and started fishing. After about twenty casts, a dolphin struck. It was a young male, small, but it furnished welcome food for Meekie and me for a day. Eekie got a taste of it too.

Meekie had been getting little food but she accepted her fate calmly and was happy. All she asked for was a little petting, kind words, and her contact with me, nights, as we sailed along through space and there was nothing but peace in the universe. I think she had not drunk as much as a cup of water during the last month. Eekie consumed quite a bit, being on a dry starch diet. If he had had mangoes, oranges and bananas he would not look at water. Both my little companions were in excellent health. Eekie was on top of the mast again today, taking his bearings. He squawked a bit and asked me which way Peru lay and if we would ever get back, or if I had gone crazy and intended to keep on sailing for ever. He watched a flock of birds fishing to the south, their white wings shining in the sun as they circled and dived and rose again.

They were the first birds I had seen since clearing the Marquesas. They must have come from Flint Island, which should be a paradise for birds, since they had it all to themselves. I longed to go ashore there, to walk among them where they sit on their nests or rest from the sea—all the different kinds of sea birds, and to talk to them. It might be somewhat like visiting a sailors' home:

"Hello, fellows, who do you think I am? Bet you ain't seen me before! And where have you been keeping yourselves all your lives? Raising a family out here, is that it? . . . And you—where's your old man? Let *him* hold down the eggs for a change while you fly around and cool off. Don't be scared of him; the world has changed.

"You're a pretty little girl; bet you can fly like a dream. How is the weather around here? No rent problem here, I hope. This looks like an apartment house with all the roofs off, even in the bathroom. You got some tough-looking neighbours. Look at those frigate birds; they are hard hombres, aren't they? Look at those beaks! And who

242

is that gazooney over there?—bet that's a battler. You are just a fluff of white spray and cloud, aren't you? The sand is hot and the wind half asleep and the clouds are dozing too, and the lazy surf is booming on the reef; yes, a thousand years are like a day. You picked a good spot— all of you; I'm going on. . . ."

There she comes—there's the old moan! Look what's been cooking up behind me! All right, let's see what you've got in you. There come the whitecaps. Looks solid black. Take down that sail!

It was late in the afternoon. The yard was halfway down when it started to swing. One end caught behind the port leg of the mast, then the sail ripped, beaten against the ladder. Two bad rips—one crosswise. I finally cleared the yard and got it down and lashed it. There was quite a lot of wind in the squall but by the time everything was secured and I had set the jib and mizzen it slacked up again. The sky looked as if it had been through a hurricane with fragments of fierce-looking clouds standing around or drifting. Another squall was beginning to make up about south-south-east. And then the sun went down in ugly red and purple and black.

It was September 17 and my logbook figures were: Noon, 21—58—10 GCT, alt. 76° 38.5′; Lat. 10° 57′ West; Long. 151° 13′ South.

I had changed my plans regarding Flint Island; the weather was too uncertain. I decided to keep clear. I had intended to pass to the south of it but the wind had shifted and then almost died down. At nine o'clock that night I was under jib and mizzen, a little worried about the course. I finally dropped my sails to stop all headway so that I could pass Flint Island in daylight. I was still about thirty-two miles away, if my navigation was correct, but I thought it best to play safe. I knew I would not drift more than a few miles during the night. It was the first time during the voyage that I had voluntarily lowered my sails.

I mixed myself some coffee, got out my sewing gear, and went forward. I took my compass lantern, the only good lantern I had left, and hung it up beside the torn sail. It did not give enough light, however, and I took my flashlight and held it under my right armpit. Since I sewed with my right hand, this restricted my movements but I could do nothing else. The flashlight kept slipping down and pointed everywhere but at the seam, and I had to keep putting it back in position. There was a swell, and now and then, when too engrossed in my task, I was thrown from my box.

I sewed steadily, though on account of the bad light I didn't get along very fast. Twice a little rain pattered down and wet the deck. With no sails to steady the raft, she rolled quite a bit. Now and then a furtive sea came over and drenched my legs and the sail. Hours passed. There was little or no wind. Occasionally the moon came out from among the clouds and looked down at me. I finally got dizzy trying to keep my eyes on the seam while the flashlight was for ever slipping from under my armpit. The raft was rolling badly now, lying like a dead weight in the sea. The result was that I sewed my pants to the sail, besides jabbing the needle into my fingers several times; a couple of times I barely missed my face. I was forced to stop often, just hanging on and gazing into the night. I purposely used short threads so I wouldn't have to raise my right arm so high, but it was difficult anyway. Twice I made myself coffee. Meekie was sleeping on the box beside Eekie's cage.

At last I finished the job. It was near morning. I rested till it was light enough to see and then hoisted the sail. A little wind sprang up at sunrise and I set a course that would take me north of Flint. It seemed to be a steady wind. I was glad I had worked all night and now had my sail up and pulling, and could manoeuvre the raft.

I picked up Flint Island a little before ten o'clock in the morning. A small white bird flying fast and straight across my bow towards the south caused me to climb up on the mast with my binoculars.

Flint bore just a little off my port bow, and after descending to the deck I swung off a point at once to give it more clearance. The wind was southerly and allowed me to pass the island to the north. I thought that an approach might be possible. I climbed aloft again to have another look. It was a hazy day with limited visibility. I could see a tiny, wooded piece of land. Trees covered it in an even, unbroken mass, rising from a strip of white sand.

I got my anchor ready, coiling up the line in long bights on deck for easy running. The first land since Callao had dropped behind me, almost three months ago, lay ahead. I had sailed 5,500 miles. It looked unreal, this great film. The clouds and the sea in which the island lay seemed to have more substance; those I knew, they had been my daily companions. Could that still-lying, cloud-coloured mass be really earth? It was more than just earth, it was the Earth; I heard it say quietly: I am the Earth, I am the real master on this planet.

I swung back in a little. If conditions were favourable I would sail close and perhaps land. Perhaps. I could afford no mistake with the reef, the iron wall that surrounded it.

I was in the lee and would take a chance. I sailed closer and closer, scanning the sea with my glasses while steering. I could see the reef plainly, it ran out north-north-west, a long and dangerous, partly submerged spur with high breakers. I would have to get on the other side of it to anchor.

245

I sailed closer and closer and finally could hear the sound of the surf. I saw the churning water in the shallows beyond the reef. On the farther side of the spur it also looked bad. And there might be a current setting in towards the reef. I didn't have too much wind, I had better be careful. The weather was hazy. "Don't get reckless, Bill, don't try it. . . . Hold off, you're too close already! You've drunk your fill, your eyes just about devoured it. Yes, that's land but forget it—you're bound for Samoa."

The siren song of land was sounding through my blood. *Swing off more, Bill—westward and clear it. Clear it!*

Goodbye, Flint Island, lonely as the mass grave of a forgotten race. I looked back a few times. It started to sink into the haze of the approaching night. Was that a cry for help—the earth crying for help? Its loneliness was appalling; it affected me, who wanted to be alone, who had lived in ecstatic happiness for eighty-eight days, in solitude. Once more I stepped down into the stern, bent under the boom, and looked back. Goodbye, Flint Island. I waved, just as if someone were standing on the shore watching me sail away.

I sailed through the night. The wind had become stronger. I sat there dreaming. I had now forgotten Flint Island. I had long swung back to the south-west, on my course. The next land would be Samoa, about eleven hundred miles away.

## MONTEREY—1925

THE raft rolled in the swells, the mainsail flapping against the mast and trying to tear its seams again. I had been becalmed for hours.

I wondered how Teddy must feel knowing that my voyage would soon be over. She must know that I was nearing my goal. She must feel it. It was already September 25 and I was within 600 miles of Samoa.

It was night and we were sailing through space flanked by our bodyguard of stars. Bill, you are as happy as you can be on this earth—as you have the right to be. All your dreams have come true on this voyage; your spirit went out into space and found many answers. You sailed with life on one side of your raft and death on the other, and your eyes were fixed beyond. You had never dreamed of asking for more.

It was a clear, beautiful night and made me think of Monterey, California, around 1925-26. I had known many such nights there. I had travelled over a good part of California looking for an ideal place to write a long poem on the life of Christ. I had found it in Monterey.

"Where are you going?" my mother had asked when I packed my little knapsack in San Francisco.

"I don't know yet," I had replied, "but I'll find the right spot."

Roaming over California, looking for an ideal place. . . . I found it in a clean stable in Monterey. It was built against the wooden fence surrounding the Mission of

Monterey, famous from the early days of California, the Royal Presidio Chapel.

For fifteen months I lived within sound of the tolling of the Mission bells. I heard them in my sleep and when I was out walking. While I wrote I heard nothing. I knew no one except a handful of Portuguese, Italian and Yugoslav fishermen. I wrote after midnight when the world was asleep and all the stars stood over California.

I worked about a week of each month to make the money I needed for my rent. My wants were few; I spent about twenty-five cents a day. There was plenty of food: fresh mackerel caught every night by the sardine fishermen in their big nets. These had no market value and could be had for the asking. For over a year I lived in my little stable, walking on the earth but hardly a part of it, writing my 2,700-line-long poem about the life of Christ. . . .

My mainsail had taken a severe beating throughout the voyage; it had been shredded so often that I had to be especially careful with it. I didn't know what winds were still ahead of me and decided to run south as quickly as possible while the sail was still good, and if it should become useless I would make the last stretch on the jib and mizzen.

I was having trouble with my eyes again though I wore sun-glasses during the day. Teddy had brought down six pairs from New York and bought others in Lima. I bathed my eyes in salt water several times during the day, which helped considerably, but the pain persisted.

I checked my lashings today to see how they had stood up under the long submersion. Even the manufacturer in New York thought that six months of life was about all I could reasonably expect from the rope. I had been in the water almost that long now but could notice no sign of disintegration; the lashings were as solid as iron bands and the square knots could not come apart unless deliberately cut. The parts directly in the water were thicker since they were more saturated. If any of the lashings had been weak they would long ago have given way; other parts would have become involved and the raft have come apart by now. I checked carefully from bow to stern and found everything as solid as on the day it was built. And in case something should happen I always had my canoe.

I was telling myself that I might go on to Australia or New Guinea, mentally trying to prepare myself for any possible misfortune. I knew my mainsail was my weak spot, but other things could happen to force me to drift for a long time. I had been thinking along these lines since the beginning and now felt that if I reached Samoa it would be too early an ending of my voyage. I was fully prepared to go on for six months, though I was fighting for every inch to get to Samoa. I had said to Teddy time and again, even before leaving New York:

"Don't worry if you don't hear from me for six months. Don't let anyone talk fear into you or start looking for me before that time."

I was prepared to finish strong. My whole life had prepared me for it. I did not want to reach Samoa merely with the last ounce that was left in me, break the tape and keel over—that was not my way of doing things; I wanted to do this thing and go quietly on to the next day's work.

# ★ 29 ★

## BLIND

I WAS becalmed. The last steady wind I had had was on September 26 when I made a day's run of sixty-five miles. The previous day, September 25, I had sailed seventy-four miles, and the day before that, sixty-seven miles. That was about a week ago and I had been averaging only about thirty-five miles per day. Yesterday, October 2, my logbook entry was: Noon at 22—44—5 GCT, sun's zenith 80° 5'; Lat. 13° 30' South; Long. 163° West. That was only a few miles away from tiny, uninhabited Suvarow Island whose geographical position is 13° 15' South and 163° 05' West.

After clearing Suvarow yesterday my eyes gave out. I lowered my sails, tied them up and went into the cabin and lay down. The door was closed to shut out all light. A few days of this should straighten me up again, a few days or a week at the most. I was not worried since there were no other islands ahead of me.

On deck everything was secured. Now and then I dipped a towel into the basin beside me and put it on my eyes and forehead. I was glad to be out of the sun, for at this time of the year it was high and burning straight down on the sea. Yesterday its altitude was over eighty degrees.

There was some wind on and off all day but I paid no attention to it, I just lay there in the dark with my eyes closed. It felt strange not to make use of the wind and I felt better when it stopped. I was really praying for it to be calm. If a real breeze came up it would be a struggle not to go out and set the sails. But that would mean steering and watching the compass. The compass light stabbed my eyes like a hot iron; I had felt it ever since leaving Callao; it was the glare on the glass. It was not a strong light, either, and sometimes I had to stare hard to get the heading.

This last stretch had been the worst of the voyage, lying becalmed with the sails slapping day and night, impatiently begging for wind, threatening to tear if they didn't get it. I always felt as if I was being whipped, hearing it. I had been over every seam of the mainsail with my needle by this time, but thought it would hold up; it would take me to Samoa or beyond if I were blown off my course. Then I would most likely try the Tonga Islands or the Fijis, about six or seven hundred miles farther on to the south and south-west. Seven hundred miles meant nothing out here. The only worry I would have in such a case would be to get the news of my landing to Teddy, for many of those atolls and islands were uninhabited or far from communications.

Again I thought of my logs that were settling lower and lower. . . .

Eekie had been on the sick list for two days already, thus two of us were out of commission. Two nights ago there had been a terrific squawking forward and when I got to the scene Meekie was half inside Eekie's cage and trying to take him apart. The cat had managed to get loose from her rope. Eekie suffered a dislocated leg and several scratches and bites, and he lost some feathers. The next day I found him in his cage with his beak hooked high up around one of the bars, hanging on tight so as to take some of the weight off his leg. The injured member hung limp, swinging like a rag to the motion of the raft. He looked like an acrobat in green tights hanging by his teeth. Later in the day I opened the cage to give him more freedom and perhaps make him feel better. When I went forward again I found him squatting on deck like a whip-poor-will in a meadow. The next time I came forward he was gone. I looked all over but saw no Eekie. Suicide maybe? Or maybe—Meekie. . . .

Meekie was asleep beneath the winch, or seemed to be. I woke her up.

"No," she said, "not me, I didn't eat him. That bird's too tough for me; he's as hard as a piece of wood." I opened her mouth, all the way to the back teeth, but saw no evidence of Eekie.

I finally considered little Eekie gone. Then I saw him sitting way forward on the weather side, gazing upon the sea. I crawled along on the outside of the logs to head him off in case he should try to fly the Pacific, caught him, and put him back in his cage. A few minutes later he was calmly hanging by his beak again.

It felt strange to be sitting in the tiny cabin, doing nothing. It seemed all creation was outside wondering what I was up to, what was wrong with me, hiding from the clouds and squalls and dead patches. "I'll be out there again," I said; "just make up a lot of wind for me."

I was not worried about my eyes; I almost had to expect it after putting them under such strain. I refused to be alarmed, telling myself that even if blinded I would eventually drift to some beach. I was reminded of the doctor in New York who had examined me after my accident on the *American Merchant* when I was struck by the wireless insulator. "Possible blindness in both eyes," he had said. He was a serious, pessimistic sort of man. O.K., I thought, taking the shock as best I could; then it's goodbye to the sight of the world that is so beautiful. I'll concentrate on hearing and on the touch. A thousand songs are sung around me all the time, asking to be heard; I'll wake up to a new sort of life. There is more in life than I dreamed of. I've been lying fallow. "You seem pretty cheerful about it," the doctor had said. "Yes, Doc," I replied, "I'll just try to see without eyes!" . . .

With a steady wind on my face my eyes would feel better. My whole brain was burning now—the area around the eyes and all the way back. Yes, all I wanted was wind. How I begged for wind! Wind, wind, where are you? Come on, wind, ruffle the sea for me just a little! Show me you're on the way! Fill the sails a little, just full enough to keep them from flapping. Come on, clouds, where is the wind? There must have been a trail of prayers behind me across the Pacific—from the Marquesas down, anyway; and a trail of hard words. . . .

Begging for wind reminded me of a native sailor I once had on my sloop in the Caribbean while sailing off Santo Domingo, somewhere along the mountainous south coast near the Dominican and Haitian border. Teddy was with me. We were becalmed and drifting slowly towards the beach where the native thought we would be massacred. I could not talk him out of his fear. He came from Virgin Gorda, in the British Virgin Islands. How that man prayed! He knelt down, his forehead touching the deck, making strange signs on his body, mumbling in a strange African tongue. How he prayed! His eyes were enormous as they stared into space, into the terrors he saw. "Oh, Lord, give us a little wind. Please, Lord, just a little wind!" He remained on his knees, praying fervently. About an hour later, just after sundown, when we were only about four hundred yards from the beach that had a reef and no bottom to anchor to, we got the wind he had prayed for and we headed out to sea.

I recalled other calms—one in the Gulf of Mexico, homeward bound on a schooner with a full load of red snappers from the Campeche Banks. The wind had failed and we were becalmed till the ice melted and we had to dump all the fish over the side.

Calms, and heat . . . I had had my share of these in Texas, along its coasts and on land. The Galveston docks were as hot as any Red Sea port. But I didn't mind. I went wild with my strength in those days; I could have pulled out trees with my bare hands.

And Houston, too—hotter even than Galveston. Someone had a dream in Houston, which was fifty miles from salt water, of making it into a deep-sea port. I went in with the others, with the big dredges into the muck and slime, the alligators and mosquitoes and the fever, digging a channel to Houston from the sea, Scandinavians and Finns and the tough breeds from the sea, digging and dying. At last we had a world port, lined with ships and barges, tugs and piers—lined for miles with the world's biggest refineries and plants.

Another dream was Texas City, seven miles across the Bay from Galveston. It was not even a fishing village, just a settlement through which cattle roamed, with no paved street, no streets even—just the mosquito-ridden prairie. We built the first pier and the boom was on.

When Houston was down on the map as a port and Texas City was no longer wild and woolly and the Galveston docks were slack, I went into the oil fields. Texas was crying for brawn. I worked as rig builder at fantastic wages, but a piece of bread cost a dollar—when it could be bought. I made the booms of Burkburnett, Ranger and Breckenridge. Texas had gone wild standing around her black gushers, blanching when a hole came in dry.

I could imagine being in Texas now, as I lay here in my

cabin in the heat and darkness. Those were the days! ...

Passed the 163rd meridian already—it was getting towards the end of my voyage. Tau, the first of the Samoan Islands, lay at 169° 28′ West or about four hundred miles away. But anything could happen yet. Right now I was just a blind man drifting on the endless sea.

# ★ 30 ★

## DEAD AHEAD

ANOTHER squall was making up and my eyes wanted to close. Speed up, come on, let's see what you have inside you! It was night and I was almost worn out from two days and nights of fighting the shifting winds and squalls. I had made only thirty-five miles in the last twenty-four hours. But I was getting there, perhaps it would be over soon. I was heading straight for Tau, the first of the Samoan Islands. It was October 10 and my day's observation was Noon 23-00-00 GCT; sun's zenith 82° 49′; Lat. 13° 41′ South; Long. 168° 26′ West.

I sent a message to Samoa at 6.15 p.m. Eastern Standard Time over the 6384 and 500 frequencies, giving my position and asking to have a boat stand by to show me the way over the reef when I approached.

With a little steady wind tonight I might sight Tau the next day. It felt strange, knowing I was getting there. It really shouldn't be over yet, having to leave all this. It had not been an easy voyage—I couldn't say that. I had gone through all the agonies; I had not been spared anything. But at the end of each day I always had to say: "The skies and seas poured their good-will out upon me."

It looked as if the sky was putting on a show for me, taking all the black curtains it had gathered from a hundred miles around and hanging them up around me. What a spectacle! How I revelled in it! Those were the sights I had dreamed of while still in the cradle—the sky ripped and torn and the fragments running wild, winds and

256

*Courtesy of A. Myron Howell, Samoa*

Preparing to lift the raft from the water at Pago Pago.

The derricks begin to hoist the raft ashore.

*Courtesy of
A. Myron Howell, Samoa*

Native ceremony at which the author is given an honorary title.

Future site of the museum and final resting place of the *Seven Little Sisters*.

clouds in a titanic struggle. It was spring here now and the equatorial vapours from the north and trade winds from the south-east were fighting it out. They would go at it fiercer and fiercer, trying to produce a hurricane.

I stood at the wheel and sailed through the squall. Yes, everything was forgotten, everything but the good. I had left Callao only yesterday . . . no, I had left it a hundred years ago! I had been sailing ever since I was born, since the beginning of time, since the first man saw the earth and lifted his eyes to the stars and saw that they were for-ever beyond reach—and then saw the sea and heard a voice saying: "This is for you; you can get pretty far on that."

Man, man—a thousand times accursed and a thousand times lifted up again, don't turn your eyes away from the stars. What do you seek: a short cut to eternal life by means of trickery? Your dreams of being god-like, of being all-feeling and all-knowing, are the soundest traits you have. But even though you conquer death you are no-where, you are still as in the beginning; the road has no ending, man, not on the earth and not in the sky. . . .

"Yes, Meekie, it looks like we are getting there. What do you think of it? What are you dreaming of in the line of grub, my little black beast?"

I had been thinking of apples and grapes for a few weeks now. I'll send a cable to Teddy telling her to load up the ice-box with fruit. She'll do that, of course, cable or not. I'll get there right in the apple season and just the time for the grapes too; timed it just right this time! I used to get sore every time I was at sea when the fruit was at its best— the peaches especially, since they don't keep. I used to think I would some day buy myself an orchard in Georgia. . . .

"So what are you hankering for, little Meekie, tell me? Come on, you little snuggler, is it just a lot of *filet* of dolphin? We can't get that in New York. Can't buy dolphin anywhere, for that matter; fishermen eat it themselves if they are lucky enough to catch any. You'll get cod or mackerel, or halibut from Seattle. Yes, I'm going down to the Fulton Fish Market to get you anything you want. You're about down to the last notch of your little belt, aren't you? You say you ain't got no belt? That's right, I forgot—you have no belt, just a rope around your little neck. But you are in good shape, Meekie, fur just glistening and your yellow eyes shining, and happy all day long even when you are asleep. Hope you're not sorry you left Callao. Do you remember your ma and brothers and sisters sometimes? The sailors at the Base in Callao thought I would eat you when I ran out of grub. I wouldn't eat my little shipmate, would I? . . . And you lay off Eekie, too; he's just getting so that he can stand on that leg again."

Meekie was in a bit of trouble the other day. Maybe Eekie wished her bad luck for having tried to eat him. It was a cloudy day and I was just having a good wind. I had not been able to get the sun at the zenith and was working out what navigators call an ex-meridian sight when I heard Meekie give out an agonized miaow. It was the first time she had ever made a sound since the voyage began, and it was plainly a call for help. I was out of the cabin in a flash, my books and charts flying. And there was Meekie in the sea!

She had been washed overboard, forward, and was drifting aft, about four feet from the raft. Since the time I had fallen overboard I had a line trailing from the stern and another one aft, from a bamboo boom that stuck out to starboard. I had used this boom during the early part of the voyage for running my jib from it to the top of the mainmast, as a sort of topmast stay-sail; I had had steady wind then and could risk it. So there was Meekie looking at me, yowling for help, and drifting past the raft. With one eye on her and the other on the bight of the line hanging from the bamboo boom I went over the side, grasped Meekie and the rope at almost the same moment. Meekie got on top of my head and dug her claws deep into my scalp. I felt she wouldn't come loose unless my head came off too. Then I had hold of the raft and the turning buckle of the mainmast stay, and climbed on deck. In a few seconds it was all over. Meekie was shaking the sea water out of her fur while I changed clothes. "Boy, you was slow coming! What was the matter with you?" Meekie said over her shoulder. She stalked off to her favourite spot under the winch, where she stayed the rest of the day. . . .

I was sailing under a full moon. Big white clouds stood around it, like tremendous castles with strange-shaped turrets and trailing pennants. Why was I sad? Perhaps because I would soon have to part from all this. How happy I had been when the tug *San Martin* turned me loose and I was on my own and heard the heavens singing, "Here's your space, all of it—the whole world with nobody in it but you—now do your stuff!" There was sadness now, deep-gripping sadness. Soon I must say goodbye to you, too, my golden planet, you who lighted my way across the whole Pacific and did not go down till the night was far advanced and you knew that all was well with me. . . .

Samoa lay just ahead.

Wind was holding up. If I stayed steady I could lie down a bit and close my eyes. My eyes were all right again after three days' stay in my cabin, but at noon today it was no fun taking about twenty sights, with the sun almost vertical above me and blazing down.

I had no channel fever, as sailors call the excitement

that grips them a day or two from port. Sadness there was but nothing else. I was heading for Tau but also set for the Fijis, or the Tongas if need be.

I had drawn a sketch of the Samoan Islands from the description in "Sailing Directions" and stuck it up inside the cabin. There are four islands in the American Samoas, beginning with Tau. Tutuila is the last one, lying farthest west. It was just like me not to have got a special chart of the Samoa group while buying my other charts at the Hydrographic Office in New York.

Pago Pago, the capital of American Samoa, lies on the southern coast of Tutuila Island. That meant I could not steer for it unless the wind shifted considerably, for I had to keep on the northern side to avoid getting trapped on a lee shore. After sailing 6,500 miles or more I certainly did not want to pile up on a reef.

I had to try to pick a bay where there was no reef. Perhaps natives would be out in canoes and guide me in or show me an anchorage. The American islands were described as "steep to" and "rocky" which means rising in straight cliffs—on the northern coast. They were also small. A lot depended on the weather and if I could approach at daytime. If I could not land I would go on to British Samoa, a little farther to the west and much larger. Its northern coast was ideal for landing, with a few hundred miles of coastline lying in a north-westerly direction and so in line with the wind. It also had many deep bays and places where there was no reef. If I could not land in American Samoa, I would not miss the British Islands, of which there were two.

Just stay steady, wind, and I'll sleep a little. I don't know what is ahead, and I want to get all the rest I can. Tomorrow may be an easy day, plain sailing; but after that I'll have to fight the reefs, for I'll try to get in on the first island, Tau. I will send a message tomorrow

260

again, maybe somebody will pick it up. The transmitter might work out here; the sun conditions were bad in the eastern and central part of the Pacific, I had been told in New York.

I sat there and dreamed. I had tried to sing, earlier, but it did not come off so well—something inside of me couldn't tune in right. *This is the end, Bill, you're going back among people.* . . . I was sad and glad at the same time.

I dozed and steered, and dozed and steered again, and finally the night was over and the sea lighted up. The wind continued steady all morning and I kept on my course for Tau. At noon I took the sun: Noon 23—3—0 GCT; alt. 83° 17'; Lat. 13° 36' South. I thought it might be the last noon sight of the voyage.

At 4 p.m. local time (11th Time Zone west of Greenwich) I worked out four different sights for a position line and picked what I thought was the best. It put me at Lat. 13° 41' South; Long. 169° 02' West, about fifty miles from Tau. I thought I might see it around six o'clock in the evening.

The sun dropped towards the horizon. Great masses of clouds stood in the south-west, ahead of me, shielding Tau from my eyes. I thought of going up the ladder and looking from the masthead but didn't consider it worth the effort. I was bound to see it in the morning as soon as the sun came up; it wouldn't run away. The main thing was to know my position so I wouldn't run up on it during the night. But it was no tiny atoll like Flint Island. It was a mass of rocks rising over three thousand feet out of the sea. And the moon would be out.

At six o'clock the clouds had blown away and I sighted Tau straight ahead standing on the horizon at the end of my bowsprit. I figured it to be about fifty miles away and bearing 200 degrees on my magnetic compass. It looked blue among the bluish clouds lying on the horizon and was dome-shaped, with a flattened-out top.

At 6.15 p.m. local time, during the silent period when all ships and shore stations are requested to stand by for ship disaster signals, I sent a message over 8364 kc and 500 kc to Samoa giving my position and asking for a boat to stand by to show me the way over the reef. As on the previous day, I added that all was well.

Tau was still in sight when I had finished transmitting but shortly afterwards disappeared among the clouds. I got my gear ready for running in case I would have to lower my sails. And then darkness set in with the swiftness of the tropics.

# 31

## SAMOA AHOY!

THE night was squally but the wind fairly steady and strong. There was quite a sea. I was steering about south-west. Now and then I dozed off. The moon came out occasionally but was mostly behind clouds. The clouds hung low, and new masses came up continuously. After midnight it became quite blustery and the wind increased considerably, howling in the darkness. Rain followed. I filled all my cans with water, hanging two from the main-sail as I had done north of the Marquesas.

Meekie was lying beside the compass. "Meekie," I said, "wake up, we are heading for land." Meekie opened one eye a little and then the other, and finally got both wide open. Then she yawned, showing all her white teeth, unhurriedly stretched herself and ended up with the back stretch, her speciality. After that she ignored me.

The wind had hauled around a little during the rain but now swung back and I could lie on my course again. The sky had cleared quite a bit. I had a lot of lightning but it disappeared with the rain. I had had lightning for weeks.

The day broke grey amid large cloud masses. With the first streak of light I took my binoculars and went to the bow. I could see nothing. But about half an hour later, while steering, Tau came out of the clouds and I could see it clearly without glasses. It was straight ahead and looked as if it was hanging from my jib-boom. A little to my right I saw another blue, mountainous mass of land, the saddle-ridged, double islands of Olosega and Ofu.

At 7.45 a.m. local time, and again during the International silent period, I sent the following message into the ether, both over the 8364 and 500 frequencies:

7HTAS (my call letters) RAFT 25 MILES FROM TAU NEED HELP TO LAND ALLS WELL WILLIS

I tapped out the message twice, as on the previous day. I was too busy with steering to repeat oftener, or to listen for an answer; besides, I did not have enough training to pick up code at average speed.

It was October 12—Columbus Day, I remembered, and a fit day to try for a landing. I was 112 days out from Callao. At about eleven o'clock I was within half a mile of the northern coasts of Tau, steering straight for the mountainous mass covered evenly with dense green vegetation. I was driven by a strong wind. The sky was clear and the sun bright but a low, heavy cloud lay over the top of Tau. Another cloud bank sprawled over the twin islands of Olosega and Ofu, about six miles to the north-west.

I broke out my flags and hoisted them. The Stars and Stripes went up at the stern. Flying from the main were the flag of Peru, the country from which I had sailed; the Ecuadorian flag, representing the country where the raft was built; and then the British, in honour of Sir George Nelson who had given me the transmitter.

I was heading a little to the left of the centre of the northern shore of Tau and watching closely, not knowing the wind and current below the steep mountain slopes. My "Sailing Directions" said that this part of the coast was lined with a reef, and that an anchorage ground was off the north-western tip of the island in fifteen fathoms but was considered dangerous. I saw no point in trying to anchor; besides, I did not have enough dependable rope left for such depth, which required about forty fathoms. There was a small village, it said also, on this same northern coast but at the extreme eastern end and so to my left.

I stood in closer and closer, watching the shores through my glasses for a sign of life. The coast was steep and dangerous with a heavy sea breaking on a formidable red reef. I saw no bay, no opening, and swung off to starboard and began to follow the coastline beneath the steep, green mountains, four or five hundred yards from the reef.

I finally came to the end of the island which was six miles long from east to west, and from there made a course for Olosega and Ofu to see if I could find more favourable conditions for landing.

It was already past noon when I approached. The sun was still bright and the wind had held. Olosega rose almost perpendicular from the sea, facing north. It was 2,100 feet high and from east to west only a little over a mile long before it dropped down, as if cut with a knife, to a narrow channel from which rose, on the other side, its twin island, Ofu, about three miles long. Both islands were perpendicular on the northern shore and, like Tua, covered with dense vegetation. A reef surrounded both islands.

I knew there were two villages on the islands, one on each side of the narrow dividing channel, but on the southern coast and so out of sight. It was well along in the afternoon before I was fully abeam of Olosega. Since my approach to Tau I had steered carefully, sailing as close as possible to the reefs, to be ready for any opening that might show itself. I went much closer now than at Tau, trying to be in position to run into the gap between the two islands if it looked feasible.

Again I saw no canoes or any other sign of life on the sand or on the rocky shore. I sailed very close. The channel seemed to be blocked by reefs coming out like jetties. The sea was breaking all along. In some places I saw a double shelf of reefs. I realized that it was useless trying to get into the gap.

I sailed past the winding entrance hidden among the steep-rising, thickly wooded mountains. The sea was choppy and breaking around the raft. There seemed to be cross-currents, and now and then the raft went almost out of control. Seas came on deck. I kept sailing closer, my eyes glued to the yard-arm for the slightest flutter, to hold off if I came too close to the wind. Twice the sail went aback and the raft drifted towards the reef on the current. I managed to get it around again, but the last time it was close.

A dolphin jumped near me out of the sunlit sea. High up on Ofu I saw two wreaths of blue smoke drifting down the mountain slope. I thought they might be coming from charcoal burners near the summit. If they had looked towards the sea they would have seen my raft drifting towards the reef with sails aback, and, if they had good eyes also, would have seen me rushing about and getting her under control again at the last minute.

I realized that landing was impossible on this steep and open coast but decided to sail along the island and keep on looking, and then head out to sea for Tutuila, about fifty miles away to the west-north-west.

*Watch out, Bill! Watch that sucking, treacherous surf —she's pulling you in! Keep her off, man, off—off!* That back-slapping wind from the mountains is trying to turn you around and set you up for the kill. You haven't even got your outrigger on your canoe and you'd have a hard time saving your own skin, never mind the rest. It would be like falling into a mass of knives and shears, striking that reef. . . .

I had steered for hours, not having the time even to take a drink of water. No, I wouldn't take any more chances with my raft, I would rather sail on for another month or more. I wanted the open sea if this was the best they had here. At six o'clock in the evening I cleared the north-west end of Ofu and headed back to sea, setting a course for Tutuila, the main island of American Samoa, about fifty miles away.

From time to time I looked back. Tremendous clouds had gathered over the three mountainous islands, looking as if they were ready to demolish them and give the space back to the sea. The clouds settled lower and lower and, together with the oncoming darkness, soon blotted out the islands. Ahead of me the sun was setting in a stormy, red-streaked sky. No harbour for us, yet, my *Seven Little Sisters*, my little ocean-home. We'll try Tutuila. . . .

# 32

# PAGO PAGO

I DID not know the extent of the current between Ofu and Tutuila. I knew only that Tutuila was seventeen miles long and that I did not want to run the risk of finding it on my starboard bow in the morning and therefore be on a lee shore. I held off a little towards the north.

The night commenced squally and blustery with quite a heavy sea. The moon came up about eleven o'clock. I watched my course closely and finally had my centreboards just right. The raft was rolling and pitching along.

The howling of the wind awoke me. I had dozed off. I jumped up and grasped the wheel. A black cloud stretched across the whole sky, coming up full of wind. For half an hour we raced along, then it calmed down somewhat. The wind had shifted a little and I wondered where I would pick up Tutuila in the morning. I made myself a cup of strong coffee. Then I went forward, remembering that Eekie had squawked loudly during the squall at a moment when I could not leave the wheel.

A glance told me that something was wrong.

The cage lay on its side. The piece of cardboard at the opening, put there after the door was broken some time before by a dolphin, was gone—and the cat was inside the cage. She had got away from her rope and had killed Eekie.

The cardboard had become soaked by the spray and had fallen off; that's how Meekie had got in. I took a piece of tin and fastened it over the opening of the cage. Then I tied up Meekie and went back to the wheel. It had become a bad and blustery night and I had to be on my watch. . . .

When the sun had cleared the horizon I went forward to Eekie's cage and wrapped him up in a piece of canvas. With a few stitches, I sewed him up, as should be done with a shipmate. Then I put him back in the cage with a heavy shackle for a weight and wrapped a line firmly around to keep the door shut, so that he wouldn't float out and the sharks get him. Then I took the cage to the side of the raft and let it go. It went straight down in the stormy sea between the islands of Ofu and Tutuila.

The day before, he had squawked with joy as we sailed close to the green slopes; he had seen land and trees again after the long voyage from Peru. He hadn't quite made it, the little comedian with his hooked nose and green coat who had helped so much to make the journey pleasant. Good-bye, Eekie!

Meekie sat nearby, not even looking. . . .

It was October 13. At about 9 a.m. local time I sighted Tutuila in the haze, approximately twenty miles off my port bow, bearing about south-south-west. I had made a northerly course during the night. I rigged up my transmitter and at 9.15 a.m., during the silent period, sent out the following message:

7HTAS RAFT 20 MILES FROM TUTUILA NEED HELP TO LAND WILLIS

As on the previous days I sent it over the 8364 and 500 frequencies and repeated just once.

I was now heading for Tutuila, a mountainous island similar to the other three Samoan islands I had passed. The wind was south-west. I had one squall after another and a moderately heavy sea. I was steering for the eastern end of the island and intended to follow its northern shore as close as possible in search of a landing place.

The wind became more steady and together with the sea pushed me to the north. I was steering as close as I could to the wind, hour after hour, never taking my eyes off the sail or off the haze-shrouded, mountainous coast. I had hoisted all my flags again.

About three o'clock in the afternoon I was close to the shore. Visibility was bad, for the air was full of spray. I saw a high sea breaking on the reef. No landing was possible there but I hoped that farther down the coast the mountains would somewhat break the wind and the seas and give me a chance to get in somewhere. I steered with one hand while looking through my glasses for an opening on the beach. I knew the whole island was about seventeen miles long and that I did not have much time.

It seemed only a little while later that I noticed with dismay that the sun was dropping. Then I saw a spot that looked good and tried hard to get in, to sail right up on a little stretch of sand; but the wind and sea pushed me off. I had to keep on wiping my binoculars on account of the flying spray. The mountains came down in folds, making little headlands and bays, but I could never see what lay behind till I was full abeam or had passed already. I skirted the shore about five hundred yards away, the closest I could get. I saw no canoe or other signs of life.

It darkened quickly. A little while later, lights appeared strung out along the shore at the foot of the mountains. They looked like kerosene lamps in open native huts. I took out my flashlight and signalled, waving it back and forth.

Some lights were waved in answer but no canoe bearing

a light came out. Probably there was too much sea for a canoe.

Then I saw what looked like a flat bay. I had seen it from the distance before it grew dark and thought it was the best prospect I had had so far. I tried to get in but again the wind and seas prevented me. During the struggle I went three times too close to the wind and the sail went aback, and before the raft took hold again I had lost fifty yards or so.

This bay had been my final hope along this section of the coast. A little farther to the west, rising straight from the shore, stood a formation of tall, almost spire-like rocks towards which the wind was pushing me. There was an opening between the rocks, wide as a gate and perhaps large enough to let my raft through; but as I did not know what was behind I could not take a chance. I had no time to lose and held off to clear the rocks and then to try again to get in at the farther side, where the coast continued in a more southerly direction.

I passed the rocks within a few hundred yards and was approaching the reef-lined coast again. The night had now become quite dark. I had been watching the sun all afternoon, over every inch of the course across the sky, wondering if I would be able to land while it was still light or if I would have to risk it at night.

I began skirting the shore in utter darkness. The moon wouldn't be up for a long time, and besides, would remain hidden for hours behind the mountains. There was only a little sea on this side and the wind was light, since I was almost in the lee of the island. Again I tried to get in close; if I saw an opening in the reef or in a bay, I would sail in.

I steered for inches, calculating just how much I could let the sail flutter without having to go aback and lose ground. Yard by yard I sailed through the darkness along

271

the reef, along the breaking, booming surf, watching its whiteness to judge its force. Sometimes I seemed to be able almost to touch the mountain sides that reverberated to the doleful boom of the sea.

I was hoping for a shift of wind or a wayward current, to get in closer. It seemed impossible. The wind would take me off again or some giant hand seemed to get hold of my bottom and turn it away. Two hundred yards off, sometimes even one hundred and fifty—but I could get no closer. I was sailing down the breadth of the island following every single inch of her shoreline, tracing it like an etcher making a chart, sliding along beneath the mountains, one after the other, all black with gloom and giving off a strange scent. Smoke drifted down and obscured my view again and again. Sometimes I was lost in a white fog. Gusts of fierce winds came down from the peaks, almost tearing my sail, and there were quick showers of rain. Above me stood dark clouds to match the dismal gloom of the shore.

Without a sound I glided along in the measured boom of the breakers. I saw a few scattered lights along the shore and began waving my flashlight. There was one answering signal, no more. I felt certain that among the bays I had passed there had been at least one spot where my little raft might have got in. . . .

The night wore on. The moon was already climbing into the sky on the other side of the island; I could tell by the diffused light above the peaks. The sky looked like a nightmare of torn clouds and raging winds. I was still in utter darkness. The raft steered like a yacht and still went only so far towards the shore and no farther. I could plainly see the seas washing over the reef, sometimes rising high and white in the darkness and then lying in boiling masses in the narrow strip of shallows beyond, at the foot of the mountains. Time after time I tried to get into what appeared to be a good spot, a little bay without a reef, but was pulled aside. Wind and current were against me.

At last I believed I could make it, sure that I was getting into the shore; for there, all at once, was a mountain to the right of me. I must have sailed into a bay. I could not miss this time. I was getting into a bay right ahead—in fact, was inside the bay already, by the looks of it. I came in like a ghost. It was black as a pit within the bay; there was no sound. Even the boom of the surf had ceased.

"Bill, you'll hit the reef if you've made a mistake; your masts will come down and your raft will be cut to slivers. In the morning they won't even find a rag from your body." But I told myself: "I'll take a chance. My main centreboard is on a tackle—I can pull it up quick, let the others break off. I'm going in. . . ."

I couldn't miss now, I thought, for I was almost on the shore. Then my bow swung off and all at once there was nothing to my right but the open sea, lighted up beyond the shadows of the mountains by the still invisible moon.

Helpless, I looked up at the sky, trying to understand. The clouds were hurrying past. Some had been caught by the wooded mountain tops and had torn themselves loose in black, wild streamers. I looked up at the silent peaks, dark with gloomy forests.

Dense smoke rolled down from the slopes, blotting out the landscape. I was gliding along again, watching with halted breath the flutter of the sail, holding it the most important thing in the world. A sudden blast of wind came down from the slopes, almost blowing the sail out of the bolt-rope, and I had to hold off.

"Bill, you put your unreasoning head on the line that time—sailing straight into the darkness, and still you could not get in."

No use. The coast ahead, now lying partly in the moonlight, was swinging to the left . . . no use. The shore was flattening out towards the south and east. "Don't lose your head, Bill. Don't pile her up."

It was two o'clock in the morning.

"You can't make it; you tried it but you can't make it. That's all you can do. There's the open sea—head for British Samoa. Get away from here before you get wrecked. That reef will saw you to shreds."

I let the sail come full, holding her off a little so she wouldn't get it in her head to make a sudden dive for the reef that was throwing up seas like waterfalls. I was still undecided whether to go on or not.

"Forget it, Bill," the voice said; "this shore is not for you; you've had plenty of chance to see that. Get back into the open sea where you belong. You tried it and couldn't make it. Back to sea with you. You were lucky you didn't wreck the raft, man—don't you see that? You tempted your fate if ever a man did!"

Twelve hours fighting with my bow almost on the reef—twelve long hours with my eyes every second on the reef and the sail, with every pulse beat set for a showdown. I felt sure that if it had been daytime I would have made it. I threw out a line with a piece of lead fastened to the end but found no bottom. No use. I had made soundings before.

I sailed out of the shadows of the coast into the light of the moon, heading into the sea. At first there was little wind, and a weak current took me south; I had to go from one tack to the other, but then the wind increased and became steady. After about an hour I was well on my way.

I ate and drank and eased up a little after the long strain. Then I looked at my chart for a general check of my position. I decided to land in British Samoa during daylight. I would also get my canoe ready for landing.

As soon as it was light enough to see I took out my "Sailing Directions" and made a sketch of the northern coast of the two large British Samoan islands, the first being Upolu and the other Savaii. Upolu, thirty-six miles west-north-west of Tutuila, was about forty miles long, east and west, and thirteen miles wide. Like Tutuila it was mountainous and of volcanic origin. I calculated that I had about two hundred miles of shore on both the islands where I might try a landing. There were numerous places without reefs and of these I took particular notice.

Looking behind I could still see American Samoa lying among clouds. I could even see the tower-like rocks around which I had sailed after sundown and the gate-like opening between them, set off against the eastern sky. Ahead of me to the north-west lay a tremendous mass of dark clouds towards which squalls were continuously drifting; I knew they were hiding the high mountain-tops of Upolu and Savaii. Upolu was 4,000 feet and Savaii over 8,000 feet high.

The day was windy and there was a moderate sea. I got my canoe ready for landing and put in a supply of flour and water, I decided to use a plank held against the side of the canoe instead of an outrigger if it was necessary to put it in the water, the way I had seen Indians do. My cameras and films, ship's papers and passport were already wrapped in watertight bags.

The clouds ahead were pushed aside by the wind, and British Samoa appeared some twenty miles away. I had been on the right course, had made no drift during the night. I was heading straight for Cape Tapaga, the eastern end of Upolu. It clouded up again almost immediately and for the next two hours I had only glimpses of the islands. Finally it cleared and they remained in sight.

I had to approach the island from the northern coast as I had done with Tutuila, to avoid a lee shore. Fortunately

Appia, the capital and main port of Opolu, and most of its bays and anchorages lay on this side of the island. The wind was fair and steady and I could reasonably expect to get ashore today or tomorrow. I decided against sending a message, believing that the transmitter did not work, for no ship or plane had come out from American Samoa looking for me. I would not transmit again unless I landed on some uninhabited part of Upolu or Savaii.

I had plenty of water from the rain the night before approaching Tau and thought I had better spruce up a little for the British, knowing that they are greater sticklers for form than we. I lashed the wheel, got out my shaving gear, and did the best I could. I also cut off some of my Buffalo Bill locks. While I shaved, British Samoa became clearer and clearer.

Meekie hung around me, looking as if she did not approve at all. "You ain't your old self, Bill, with that haircut," she seemed to be saying.

"Can't be helped, Meekie, it's my duty. We're going to shake hands with the British governor today or tomorrow. And that means you too, yes; no backing out; he's not going to hurt you, you little scaredy cat."

I was through shaving and cleaning up when I turned my head for a last look at American Samoa just disappearing amid the clouds, and saw a ship behind me about three miles away. I looked at it through my binoculars. Yes, it was a ship, definitely a ship, right behind me. It had a white hull and buff-coloured masts, booms and stack— Coast Guard colours. And it was on the same course as I, heading for British Samoa, probably for Appia. I thought it must be a British inter-island trader. I at once hoisted the Stars and Stripes to the mizzen masthead.

She was right on my course. If she came close to see who I was, I would ask her to notify Appia to send out a boat to guide me in. I picked up my glasses for another look and saw the Stars and Stripes standing straight out in the wind. An American ship! It flashed through my mind that she was coming for me. One of my messages might have been picked up.

There she was, ploughing into the foam, coming up fast behind me—only a few hundred yards away now. The upper deck and bridge were lined with men holding cameras on my raft. Now she was abeam, less than a hundred yards away. I could make out faces. What was all the excitement about with all those cameras? I wondered. It might be a Hollywood studio ship; maybe a movie company was shooting a film in Samoa and had come after me for some fun.

A voice from the bridge rang out over the water: "How does it feel to see human beings again?"

"Fine." What else could I say?

"How does it feel to hear human voices again?" the same voice asked.

"Fine."

"Will you let us tow you back to Pago Pago?"

"Okay."

Three powerful Samoans jumped overboard from the *Manuatele* and swam towards the raft. Meekie took one look at them and ducked into a spot too small for a squirrel. The Samoans climbed aboard and helped lower the sails, then caught a heaving line that was thrown over and pulled in a towline and made it fast. It was about 11 a.m., local time. Presently, two Americans swam over also. We swung around and headed for Pago Pago, approximately sixty miles away.

I now heard the news that I had been considered lost for 113 days. Not a single message had got through except the very last one, only the day before, October 13, telling of my approach to Tutuila. Doug Cunnold, a British radio operator on Raratonga, in the Cook Islands about seven hundred miles away, had picked it up and notified Pago Pago. The *Manuatele* had at once put to sea to look for me but had not been able to find me because of heavy weather and bad visibility, and had returned to Pago Pago for the night. She had set out again the next morning. Her radio man had first spotted my sail in the grey sea, more than two hours before I sighted the ship.

It was a long pull to Pago Pago. The *Seven Little Sisters* did not want to be towed—it wanted to be on its own, fighting the wind and the seas as it had fought them for close to seven thousand miles. Three times it broke the heavy towline to get away. . . .

The day had long since faded into dusk and then into night and we were still far from Pago Pago. Seas and spray came over continuously. One of the Samoans was at the wheel all the time.

Not till an hour after midnight, flying all my flags, did we enter the harbour, which is formed by the high walls of an extinct volcano whose one side has fallen away into the sea. A small launch came alongside to push me the last few yards through the darkness to the dock.

It was very still between the sheer, rising walls. I seemed to be moving through the pit of a blacked-out, vast amphitheatre. I was all alone on the raft, on my *Seven Little Sisters*. Not a sound came from the shore. A small pier and a few low sheds were lighted up by floodlights. I saw people bedecked with flowers. Many stood beneath the lights but the crowds had overflowed into the darkness. I saw hundreds of Samoans.

As we drew up about twenty feet from the little wooden landing, something welled up within me. I gazed at the Samoans, in the great hush of silence, standing straight and still and expectant. Few moments in my life had so moved me. This seemed to be a moment of holiness for the people waiting for my raft to touch their earth—the

278

first land after crossing the sea from faraway South America. At the time, I did not understand the religious significance with which they regarded my voyage, but I, too, felt the sacredness of the occasion. And it welled up more and more within me and it seemed as if I stood in the centre as all around me the hearts of the Samoans were lifting up like slow wings, moving higher and higher, mingling with the dark mountains, and enfolding me. I stood speechless, overcome in the unbroken silence. I bowed my head in humility, accepting their greeting. My raft was moving inch by inch into the light. At last it touched the pier.

I tied her up, shipshape with four good lines, and stepped ashore. My legs were steady. On the dock waiting for me stood the Governor of Samoa, Mr. Lowe, with his wife. Graciously Mrs. Lowe put a *lei* of flowers around my neck. I spoke into a microphone. Then I was introduced to the Samoan chiefs and their people.

After that I went back to the raft to find Meekie. "Come, Meekie," I said, "we're in Samoa—we're going ashore."

I landed at 1.30 a.m. on October 15, completing my 115-days' voyage of 6,400 to 6,700 miles across the Pacific. Two days later, at a solemn Kava meeting, the traditional greeting ceremony of Polynesia, attended by all the chiefs and dignitaries of the island, I was given the honorary title of *Tautai O Le Vasa Laolao,* meaning "Captain of the High Seas".

My raft, the *Seven Little Sisters,* will remain in Tutuila, a gift to the people of American Samoa to be placed in a museum and preserved for their own and future generations.

After I had spent a few days in beautiful and friendly Tutuila the Australian Consolidated Press flew in a plane from Suva, Fiji Islands, with its ace reporter and feature writer, Tom Farrell, and a photographer. I left with them, five days after landing in Pago Pago. I took Meekie with me. In Suva we boarded an American plane, roared across the Pacific to Canton Island, Honolulu, and from there to San Francisco. After a short stop in Texas, my old home, the DC-7 set its grounding sights for Idlewild Airport, New York.

Everything had been wisely arranged. When all the passengers were off and I was alone in the cabin, Teddy came up the gangway.

After the first greeting was over she said, still sobbing: "Bill, the next time I'll come along. It was terrible, waiting. . . ."

"Did you think I was lost?"

"No, you told me not to worry. But everybody else thought so."

Then we went down the gangway together, Teddy, I, and Meekie.

The photographers and the Press had their day. Meekie almost broke her leash trying to get back to the raft and away from it all.

# ENVOY

It is night and all the stars are out. Deep below lies the ocean over which the winds roam. I see no ship in the great darkness where my little raft sailed alone, guided only by my frail hand. But though my flesh was weak my spirit soared, for this was a voyage of the spirit beneath your eternal gaze.

# APPENDIX

## Instruments

2 Sextants
2 Compasses
1 Chronometer
1 Good Watch
1 Cheap Watch
1 Clock
1 Alarm Clock
1 Pair of Binoculars (6x30)
1 16 mm Movie Camera
1 Still Camera
Film, colour and black-and-white

## Charts (United States Hydrographic Office)

South Pacific Ocean
Sheet I—No. 0823
Sheet II—No. 0824
Sheet III—No. 0825
Pilot Chart of the South Pacific Ocean, June, July, August, 1954—No. 2601

## Books and Tables

Bowditch, *American Navigator*
2 copies of the *American Nautical Almanac* (1954)
H.O. No. 214, Tables of Computed Altitude and Azimuth
    Latitudes 0° to 9° Vol. 1
    Latitudes 10° to 19° Vol 2

Latitudes 20° to 29° Vol. 3
*Sailing Directions*, The Pacific Islands, Volume III

## Food

50 lbs. of *cañihua* (roasted and ground)
70 lbs. of barley flour (roasted and ground)—(*máchica*)
70 lbs. of unrefined sugar with its molasses content—(*chancaca*, or *raspadura*)
50 small cans of lemon juice
2 lbs. of tea
25 1 lb. cans of vegetable shortening
24 12 oz. cans of evaporated milk for Meekie
50 cans of cat food
10 lbs. of corn on cob for Eekie
15 lbs. of shelled corn for Eekie
15 lbs. of rice for Eekie
120 gallons of drinking water
50 small cans of instant coffee
U.S. Navy Abandon Ship Rations

Emergency rations

## Other Supplies

15 gal. of petrol
20 gal. of kerosene
1 gal. of lubricating oil

1 radio receiver
1 motor and generator to operate radio

1 emergency transmitter—Marconi Salvita III

200 feet—1½-inch rope
400 feet—1-inch rope
400 feet—¾-inch rope
400 feet—½-inch rope

Shackles, turning-buckles, cable-clamps
100 feet of ⅜-inch chain
50 feet of ⅜-inch steel cable

1 70 lb. anchor

3 lanterns (kerosene)
3 flashlights and batteries
1 searchlight and batteries

Bolts and nuts
Small wire
Nails
Full assortment of tools, including axe, hatchet, hammer and crowbar, drills and augurs, marlinspikes and sailmakers' palms, canvas for patching sails, sailing twine and needles

12 blocks, single and double sheaved, for ¾- and ½-inch rope

## Clothing

2 Storm suits—U.S. Navy
1 Heavy cold-weather jacket
4 Pairs of dungarees
4 Pairs of khaki pants

8 Suits of underwear
6 Shirts
3 Flannel shirts
3 Wool sweaters
3 Sweatshirts
6 Pairs of woollen socks
3 Pairs of sneakers
1 Pair of sea boots
2 Pairs of leather shoes
2 Watch caps
1 Heavy cap
4 Light caps
8 Pairs of sunglasses
3 Blankets
1 Mattress
Tarpaulins
Ponchos

## Miscellaneous Supplies

2 Kerosene pressure stoves
Saucepans and frying-pans
Plates and cups
Knives, forks and spoons
2 Buckets
4 Large knives

Assorted fish hooks
Wire leaders
Fishing lines
Sinkers, lures

Airtight containers
Watertight bags and wraps

1 seagoing canoe fully rigged
Bamboos for canoe outrigger and emergency rigging-masts and yard

Medical supplies and first-aid kit

# REPUBLICA DEL PERU

CAPITANIA DEL PUERTO DE _Callao_

### LICENCIA DE SALIDA No. _843_

Por cuanto: Don _Willian Willis_ Capitán del buque _Balsa "7 hermanitas"_ de ___ 12 ___

toneladas de Registro, y con capacidad para _____ pasajeros

que navega con una tripulación de hombres ___ 1 ___ ha comprobado

no tener ningún impedimento para salir de este Puerto.

Por tanto: Le otorgo la Licencia que solicita, a fin de que

pueda dirigirse a _Samoa_ con escalas en _____

_Callao_ 22 _Junio_ de 195 4

EL CAPITAN DE NAVIO
CAPITAN DE PUERTO

Capitán del Puerto

17 JUN 1954

OFFICIAL DOCUMENT CLEARING THE *SEVEN LITTLE SISTERS* FROM
CALLAO, PERU, FOR SAMOA

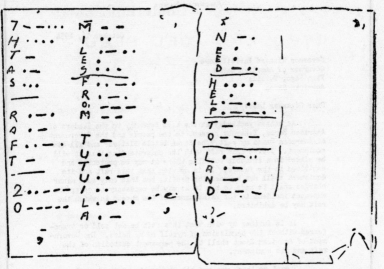

**THIS LAST MESSAGE SENT FROM THE RAFT WAS PICKED UP 700 MILES AWAY IN RARATONGA, COOK ISLANDS**

GOVERNMENT HOUSE
AMERICAN SAMOA

October 16, 1954

Governor Richard Barrett Lowe
Governor of American Samoa
Pago Pago, Tutuila
American Samoa

Dear Governor Lowe:

As stated yesterday at the Kava Ceremony to the leaders of
American Samoa, I hereby present to the people and the Government
of American Samoa my raft "The Seven Little Sisters" and all its
equipment. I give this raft with the understanding that it will
be placed in a suitable building where it may be protected and
exhibited in the future. It is my wish that this raft and its
equipment shall not be used for profit, but that only such minor
charges shall be made to see it as may be necessary to cover the
expenses incident to the maintenance of the museum in which the
raft may be exhibited.

It is further my wish that this raft be not sold or transferred without the permission of myself or my heirs. The Government of American Samoa shall be the permanent custodian of the
raft and its equipment.

I want to thank you and all the people of American Samoa
for making the search for me and for the hospitality extended to
me upon my arrival on your shores.

Very Sincerely,

WILLIAM WILLIS (SEAL)

WW/ki

LETTER GIVING THE RAFT TO THE PEOPLE OF AMERICAN SAMOA

THE GOVERNMENT OF AMERICAN SAMOA
OFFICE OF THE GOVERNOR
PAGO PAGO, AMERICAN SAMOA

October 16, 1954

Mr. William Willis
Pago Pago, Tutuila
American Samoa

Dear Mr. Willis:

On behalf of the people and the Government of American Samoa I am most happy to accept the gift of your raft "The Seven Little Sisters", and to assure you that the terms of the gift will be upheld in conformity with the wishes expressed in your letter of this date.

The gift of this historic vessel is a most gracious act on your part and one which is sincerely appreciated by the people of American Samoa and the Government.

We feel deeply honored that your raft will remain on Tutuila where present and future generations may see it. A suitable bronze plaque will be cast which will commemorate your historic voyage and indicate your presentation of "The Seven Little Sisters" and its equipment to our people.

I want to congratulate you on the successful completion of your historic voyage and to commend you for the indomitable courage which led you to our shores. It has been a pleasure to have you here as our guest.

Sincerely yours,

RICHARD BARRETT LOWE
Governor

RBL/ki

ACCEPTANCE OF GIFT BY GOVERNMENT OF AMERICAN SAMOA

287